Reviewing Biology

THE LIVING ENVIRONMENT

With Sample Examinations

FOURTH EDITION

Carl M. Raab

Former Director of Academic Initiatives for the
Office of School Programs and Support Services
New York City Board of Education, New York

Former Assistant Principal, Supervision Science
Fort Hamilton High School, Brooklyn, New York

Revised by

Michael F. Renna

Adjunct Professor/Student Teaching Field Supervisor
Department of Secondary Education
Queens College, CUNY, Queens, New York

Former Principal, Preparatory Academy
for Writers MS/HS, Queens, New York

Former Assistant Principal, Supervision Science
Hillcrest High School, Queens, New York

Amsco School Publications, Inc.,
a division of Perfection Learning®

The publisher wishes to acknowledge the helpful contributions of the following reviewers:

Rochelle Battersby
Science Department Chair
Sanford H. Calhoun High School
Merrick, New York

Morein Gordon
Science Teacher
New Rochelle High School
New Rochelle, New York

Susan Clay
Biology Teacher, Retired
Maple Heights High School
Maple Heights, Ohio

Text Design: Brad Walrod

Cover Design: Michael A. Aspengren
Composition: Kenoza Type, Inc.
Artwork: Hadel Studio
Cover Photo: Thinkstock Photo

Readings in Science, Engineering, Technology, and Society: Carol Davidson Hagarty

Note to the Teacher

This fourth edition of *Reviewing Biology: The Living Environment* comprehensively reviews the National Science Standards-based Core Curriculum for NYS. The specific core ideas covered in each chapter are listed in the table of contents. The book is readily correlated with the standard textbooks for high-school-level biology. The books of this series are specifically geared to meet the needs of students who want to review the material in preparation for final exams.

The material in *Reviewing Biology: The Living Environment* is divided into ten chapters, each of which is subdivided into major topic sections. The book is abundantly illustrated with clearly labeled drawings and diagrams that illuminate and reinforce the subject matter. Important core science terms are **boldfaced** and defined in the text. Other important science terms that may be unfamiliar to students are *italicized* for emphasis. In addition, the large work-text format and open design make *Reviewing Biology: The Living Environment* easy for students to read.

Within each chapter are several sets of Part A, Part B-1, Part B-2, and Part C questions that test the students' knowledge and reasoning while provoking thought. These Regents and Regents-type questions include multiple-choice, short-answer (constructed response), diagram-analysis, and essay (extended constructed-response) formats. Topical reading comprehension passages with question sets appear at the end of Chapters 1–9, giving students further opportunity to refine their science reading and writing skills. Tables, graphs, and diagrams that aid in interpreting, reviewing, and testing the material often accompany the questions. The nearly 900 questions found in the text can be used for topic review throughout the year, as well as for exams and homework assignments. The sample examinations at the back of the book can be used as final exams or practice for the final exam.

Chapter 10: Laboratory Skills and Part D Labs reviews the scientific skills and methods that all students should master in the course of completing one year of biology instruction at this level. *Reviewing Biology: The Living Environment* also contains a full Glossary in which students can find concise definitions of all boldfaced scientific terms. Students can use the extensive Index to locate the text discussions of these and other important biological terms and concepts.

The Appendix is comprised of Part D Sample Lab Questions. Also included in *Reviewing Biology: The Living Environment* are nine completely new readings in Science, Engineering, Technology, and Society that explore current controversial issues in biology. Several constructed-response questions are presented at the end of each reading to test comprehension and to encourage students to evaluate the issues and make their own decisions about the impact of biological science, engineering, and technology on society, the environment, and their lives.

Contents

1 Ecology

Ecology is the study of the relationships between organisms and between organisms and their physical environment. No organism exists in nature as an entity apart from its environment.

ECOLOGICAL ORGANIZATION

In ecology, the relationships between organisms and the environment may be considered at various levels. The smallest, least inclusive level in terms of ecological organization is the population; the largest and most inclusive level is the biosphere.

Levels of Organization

All members of a species living in a given location make up a **population**. For example, all the water lilies in a pond make up a population, and all the goldfish in a pond make up a population. Together, all the interacting populations in a given area make up a **community**. For example, all the plants, animals, and microorganisms in a pond make up the pond community.

An **ecosystem** includes all the members of a community along with the physical environment in which they live. The living and nonliving parts of an ecosystem function together as an interdependent and relatively stable **system**. The *biosphere* is the portion of Earth in which all living things exist. The biosphere, which is composed of numerous complex ecosystems, includes the water, soil, and air.

QUESTIONS
Part A

1. All the different species within an ecosystem are collectively referred to as the (1) niche (2) community (3) consumers (4) population

2. Which term includes the three terms that follow it? (1) population: community, ecosystem, organism (2) community: ecosystem, organism, population (3) ecosystem: organism, population, community (4) organism: ecosystem, community, population

3. Which sequence shows increasing complexity of levels of ecological organization? (1) biosphere, ecosystem, community (2) biosphere, community, ecosystem (3) community, ecosystem, biosphere (4) ecosystem, biosphere, community

4. The members of the mouse species *Microtus pennsylvanicus* living in a certain location make up a (1) community (2) succession (3) population (4) phylum

5. Which term includes all the regions (on land and in water) in which life exists? (1) marine biome (2) climax community (3) biosphere (4) tundra

Part B-2

6. Define each of the following ecological levels: *ecosystem, population, community, biosphere.*

7. List the four ecological levels of organization in their order of increasing complexity.

CHARACTERISTICS OF ECOSYSTEMS

Ecosystems are the structural and functional units studied in ecology.

Requirements of Ecosystems

An ecosystem involves interactions between its living factors and nonliving factors. It is a self-sustaining unit when the following two conditions are met.

First, there must be a constant flow of energy into the ecosystem, and there must be organisms within the ecosystem that can use this energy for the synthesis of organic compounds. The primary source of energy for most ecosystems on Earth is sunlight; the organisms that can use this energy for the synthesis of organic compounds are green plants, algae, and other photosynthetic autotrophs. Second, there must be a recycling of materials between the living organisms and the physical, nonliving parts of the ecosystem.

Until recently, it was thought that all life-forms depend, either directly or indirectly, on **solar energy** (the main source of Earth's energy) to carry out their life activities. However, this is not true. There are some organisms that survive in the deepest parts of the ocean, where no light penetrates. They live around hot-water vents on the seafloor and rely on bacteria that use chemicals—hydrogen sulfide and carbon dioxide—in the seawater to produce energy-rich sugars. These bacteria, which function as the food producers in this ecosystem, carry out *chemosynthesis* rather than photosynthesis. They use the energy of chemical reactions, rather than the energy of the sun, to produce carbohydrates. Survival of the other organisms in that ecosystem, such as worms, clams, shrimp, crabs, and octopuses, depends on the food energy that the bacteria produce.

Abiotic Factors of Ecosystems

The components of an ecosystem include nonliving, or **abiotic**, factors, and living, or **biotic**, factors. The abiotic factors of the environment are physical factors that sustain the lives and reproductive cycles of organisms. These factors are intensity of light; temperature range; amount of water; type of soil; availability of minerals and other inorganic substances; supply of gases, including oxygen, carbon dioxide, and nitrogen; the pH (acidity or alkalinity) of the soil or water, and the amount of space.

Abiotic factors vary from one environmental area to another. The abiotic conditions in any particular environment determine the types of plants and animals that can exist there. Thus, abiotic factors are *limiting factors*. For example, the small amount of available water in a desert limits the kinds of plants and animals that can live in that environment.

Biotic Factors of Ecosystems

The biotic factors of an ecosystem are all the living things that directly or indirectly affect the environment. The organisms of an ecosystem interact in many ways. These interactions include nutritional and symbiotic relationships.

Nutritional Relationships. Nutritional relationships involve the transfer of nutrients from one organism to another within the ecosystem.

Autotrophs are organisms that can use energy from the environment to synthesize their own food from inorganic compounds. Most autotrophs are photosynthetic, using energy from sunlight along with carbon dioxide and water from the environment to synthesize organic compounds.

Heterotrophs cannot synthesize their own food and must obtain nutrients from other organisms. Depending on their source of food, heterotrophs are classified as saprophytes, herbivores, carnivores, or omnivores.

Saprophytes are organisms that obtain nutrients from the remains of dead organisms. Types of saprophytes include bacteria and fungi. Animals that feed exclusively on plants are called **herbivores**. Animals that consume other animals are called **carnivores**. The carnivores include **predators**, which kill and eat their **prey**, and **scavengers**, which feed on the remains of animals that they have not killed. **Omnivores** are animals that consume both plant and animal matter.

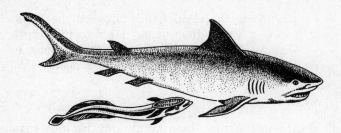

FIGURE 1-1 The shark and remora have a type of symbiosis known as commensalism.

Symbiotic Relationships. Different kinds of organisms sometimes live together in a close association. Such a close relationship, or **symbiosis**, may or may not be beneficial to the organisms involved.

A type of symbiotic relationship in which one organism benefits while the other is neither helped nor harmed is called *commensalism*. Barnacles living on whales, remora (a type of fish) living on sharks, and orchids living on large, tropical trees all obtain favorable places to live without doing any noticeable harm to the other organism (Figure 1-1). Barnacles are transported to new environments by the whale, which is not harmed by the barnacles. The remora obtain food scraps that fall from the shark's mouth without the shark being harmed. Orchids obtain air and rainwater by living high in the branches of trees while the trees are not harmed by the orchids.

A symbiotic relationship in which both organisms benefit is called *mutualism*. For example, certain protozoans (unicellular organisms) live within the digestive tracts of termites. Wood eaten by the termites is digested by the protozoans, and both organisms benefit from the nutrients that are released. Another example of mutualism is found in lichens, which are made up of both algal and fungal cells. The algal cells

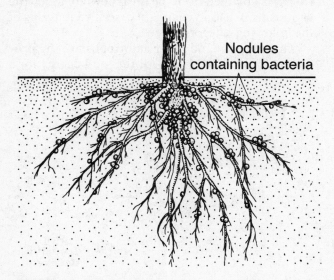

Nodules containing bacteria

FIGURE 1-2 Nitrogen-fixing bacteria live in the roots of legumes in a type of symbiosis known as mutualism.

carry on photosynthesis, which provides food for the lichen, while the fungal cells provide moisture and minerals and anchor the lichen to a surface.

Nitrogen-fixing bacteria live in the roots of legumes (such as the peanut plant). The relationship between these organisms is mutualistic because the bacteria provide nitrogen compounds for the plant, while the plant provides the bacteria with nutrients and a favorable place to live (Figure 1-2).

A symbiotic relationship in which one organism, the **parasite**, benefits while the other, the **host**, is harmed is called *parasitism*. Examples include the athlete's foot fungus that can live on humans, and tapeworms and heartworms that can live in dogs.

QUESTIONS
Part A

8. Different species of animals in a community would most likely be similar in their (1) physical structure (2) size (3) abiotic requirements (4) number of offspring produced

9. All the living things that affect each other and their environment are considered (1) biotic factors (2) inorganic substances (3) physical conditions (4) chemical factors

10. A study was made over a period of years in a certain part of the country. It showed that the area had a low amount of rainfall, a wide seasonal variation in temperature, and short periods of daylight. These environmental factors are (1) abiotic factors of little importance to living things (2) abiotic factors that limit the type of organisms that live in the area (3) biotic factors important to living things in the area (4) biotic factors that are affected by the abiotic factors

11. The presence of nitrogen-fixing bacteria in nodules on the roots of legumes (such as the peanut plant) illustrates an association known as (1) commensalism (2) mutualism (3) parasitism (4) environmentalism

12. At times, hyenas will feed on the remains of animals that they have not killed themselves. At other times, they will kill other animals for food. Based on their feeding habits, hyenas are best described as both (1) herbivores and parasites (2) herbivores and predators (3) scavengers and parasites (4) scavengers and predators

13. Which is an abiotic factor in the environment? (1) water (2) earthworm (3) fungus (4) human

14. The organisms that prevent Earth from becoming covered with the remains of dead organisms are known as (1) herbivores (2) parasites (3) autotrophs (4) saprophytes

15. A particular species of fish has a very narrow range of tolerance for changes in water temperature and dissolved oxygen content. For this fish, the temperature and oxygen content represent (1) autotrophic conditions (2) a community (3) limiting factors (4) symbiosis

16. An example of a parasitic relationship is (1) tapeworms living in the intestines of a dog (2) algal and fungal cells living together as a lichen (3) barnacles living on a whale (4) wood-digesting protozoa living in the gut of a termite

17. Parasitism is a type of nutritional relationship in which (1) both organisms benefit (2) both organisms are harmed (3) neither organism benefits (4) one organism benefits and the other is harmed

18. A stable ecosystem is characterized by having (1) predators that outnumber their prey (2) a continual input of energy (3) limited autotrophic nutrition (4) no competition between species

19. Heterotrophs include (1) autotrophs, saprophytes, and herbivores (2) omnivores, carnivores, and autotrophs (3) saprophytes, herbivores, and carnivores (4) herbivores, autotrophs, and omnivores

20. The primary source of energy for most ecosystems is (1) radioactivity (2) sunlight (3) animal proteins (4) carbon dioxide

21. An ecosystem that does *not* depend on sunlight for its energy source is found (1) at the tops of mountains (2) on tropical islands (3) in hot deserts (4) near deep-ocean vents

22. A partial food web is represented in the diagram below. Letter *X* most likely represents (1) autotrophs (2) carnivores (3) decomposers (4) parasites

23. A particular species of unicellular organisms inhabit the intestines of termites, where they can live protected from predators. The unicellular organisms digest wood that has been ingested by the termites, thus providing nutrients to the

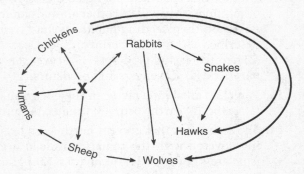

termites. The relationship between these two species can be described as (1) harmful to both species (2) harmful to the host (3) beneficial to both species (4) beneficial to the parasite only

24. Identify the two main conditions that must exist for an ecosystem to be self-sustaining.

25. Explain why abiotic factors are considered to be limiting factors; give an example of one.

26. In his biology class, a student claims that all living things depend on the sun for survival, either directly or indirectly. Provide one example that shows why this student's claim is incorrect.

Energy Flow Relationships

For an ecosystem to be self-sustaining, there must be a flow of energy between organisms. The pathways of chemical energy from food through the organisms of an ecosystem are represented by food chains and food webs.

Food Chains

The transfer of energy from green plants through a series of organisms with repeated stages of eating and being eaten is described as a **food chain** (Figure 1-3). Green plants obtain energy for their life processes from the radiant energy of sunlight (that is, solar energy), which they convert to usable chemical energy (glucose) through the process of photosynthesis. For all other organisms in the food chain, energy is obtained from the breakdown of food. The organisms in a food chain are described in terms of the following categories.

Green plants and other autotrophs are the **producers** in the food chain. All the food energy for a

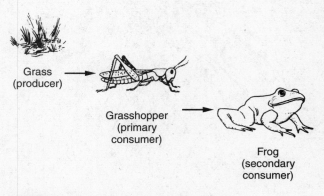

FIGURE 1-3 A food chain (not drawn to scale).

community is derived from the organic compounds synthesized by the producers (for example, grass in a savannah, algae in the sea, or chemosynthetic bacteria near a deep-ocean vent).

All the heterotrophic organisms in a community are **consumers**. They must obtain energy from the food they eat. Animals that feed on green plants and algae are called *primary consumers,* or herbivores. Animals that feed on primary consumers are called *secondary consumers,* or carnivores. Omnivores may be either primary or secondary consumers; that is, omnivores may feed on plants and/or animals. Humans are a good example of an omnivore, since we eat both plant and animal foods.

Saprophytes are **decomposers**, the organisms that break down the remains of dead organisms and organic wastes. Decomposers return substances in the remains and wastes of plants and animals to the environment, where other living organisms can use them again. Most decomposers are either bacteria or fungi. This recycling of materials is critical to the survival of an ecosystem; it ensures that the limited supply of materials can be used over and over again. In addition, the remains, or **residue**, of dead organisms do not accumulate in the ecosystem, since they are broken down to simpler compounds.

Food Webs. In a natural community, most organisms eat more than one species and may be eaten, in turn, by more than one species. Thus, the various food chains in a community are interconnected, forming a **food web** (Figure 1-4). Food webs have the same levels of organisms (producers, consumers, and

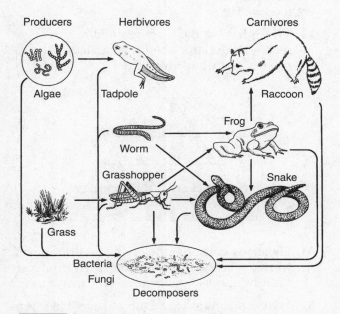

FIGURE 1-4 A food web (not drawn to scale).

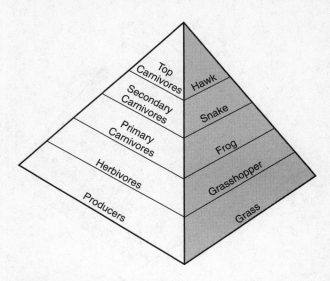

FIGURE 1-5 A pyramid of energy.

decomposers) as food chains, but the flow of energy and materials is much more complex.

Pyramid of Energy. The greatest amount of energy in a community is present in the organisms that make up the producer level. Only a small portion of this energy is passed on to primary consumers; only a small portion of that energy in the primary consumers is passed on to secondary consumers; and so on. An **energy pyramid** illustrates the loss of usable energy at each feeding, or *trophic,* level (Figure 1-5).

At each consumer level in an energy pyramid, only about 10 percent of the ingested nutrients are used to synthesize new tissues, which represent the food available for the next feeding level. The remaining energy is used by the consumers for their life functions and is eventually converted into heat, which is lost from the ecosystem. Thus, an ecosystem cannot sustain itself without the constant input of energy from an external source. In most ecosystems, this energy source is the sun.

Pyramid of Biomass. In general, the decrease in available energy at each higher feeding level means that less organic matter, or *biomass,* can be supported at each higher level. Thus, the total mass of producers in an ecosystem is greater than the total mass of primary consumers; the total mass of primary consumers is greater than the total mass of secondary consumers; and so on. A *biomass pyramid* illustrates this decrease in biomass at each higher feeding level (Figure 1-6 on page 6).

If, for some reason, biomass becomes greater at a higher trophic level than at a lower level, the

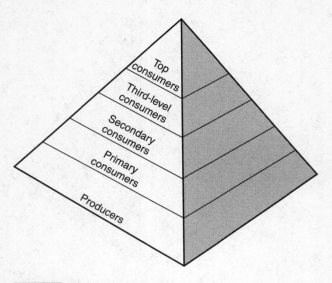

FIGURE 1-6 A pyramid of biomass.

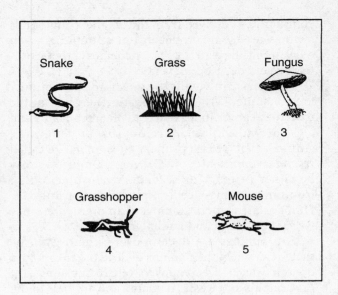

ecosystem will become unbalanced and unsustainable. The consumers at the higher trophic level will have exceeded the capacity of the ecosystem to support them. Eventually, they will begin to die off as their food supply runs out, and the ecosystem will return to a state of balance.

QUESTIONS
Part A

27. Which occurs within self-sustaining ecosystems? (1) The producers have a limited source of energy. (2) Consumers eventually outnumber producers. (3) Carnivores usually outnumber herbivores. (4) Organisms recycle materials with each other and the environment.

28. Which food chain relationship illustrates the nutritional pattern of a primary consumer? (1) seeds eaten by a mouse (2) an earthworm eaten by a mole (3) a mosquito eaten by a bat (4) a fungus growing on a dead tree

29. Which term describes both the bird and the cat in the following food chain?

    sun → grass → grasshopper → bird → cat

    (1) herbivores (2) saprophytes (3) predators (4) omnivores

30. Organisms from a particular ecosystem are shown in the next column. Which statement concerning an organism in this ecosystem is correct? (1) Organism 2 is heterotrophic. (2) Organism 3 helps recycle materials. (3) Organism 4 obtains all of its nutrients from an abiotic source. (4) Organism 5 must obtain its energy from Organism 1.

31. The elements stored in living cells of organisms in a community will eventually be returned to the soil for use by other living organisms. The organisms that carry out this process are the (1) producers (2) herbivores (3) carnivores (4) decomposers

32. One season, there was a shortage of producers in a food web. As a result, the number of deer and wolves decreased. The reason that both the deer and the wolf populations declined is that (1) producers are not as important as consumers in a food web (2) more consumers than producers are needed to support the food web (3) organisms in this food web are interdependent (4) populations tend to stay constant in a food web

33. Which level of the food pyramid shown below represents the largest biomass? (1) bass (2) minnows (3) copepods (4) algae

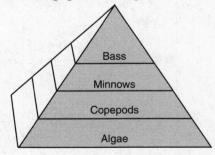

34. Fly larvae consume the body of a dead rabbit. In this process, they function as (1) producers (2) scavengers (3) herbivores (4) parasites

35. Which diagram on the top of page 7 best represents the usual relationships of biomass in a stable community? (1) 1 (2) 2 (3) 3 (4) 4

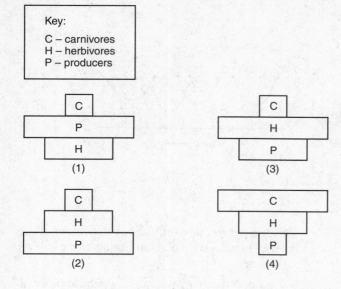

Key:
C – carnivores
H – herbivores
P – producers

(1)

(3)

(2)

(4)

36. Which level in an energy pyramid has the highest amount of available energy? (1) highest level consumers (2) secondary consumers (3) primary consumers (4) producers

Part B-1

Base your answers to questions 37 through 40 on the diagram below and on your knowledge of biology. The diagram represents different species of organisms that may interact with each other in and around a pond environment.

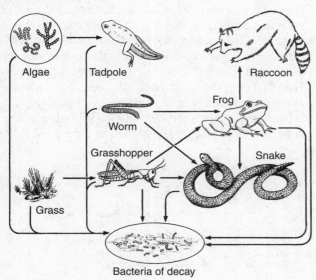

Bacteria of decay

37. The adult frog represents a type of consumer known as a (1) producer (2) carnivore (3) saprophyte (4) parasite

38. Which organisms are classified as herbivores? (1) algae, tadpole, raccoon (2) worm, snake, bacteria (3) tadpole, worm, grasshopper (4) grasshopper, bacteria, frog

39. Which statement about the algae and grass is true? (1) They are classified as omnivores. (2) They are parasites in the animals that eat them. (3) They contain the greatest amount of stored energy. (4) They decompose nutrients from dead organisms.

40. The interactions among organisms shown in this diagram illustrate (1) a food web (2) geographic isolation (3) abiotic factors (4) organic evolution

Base your answers to questions 41 through 43 on the following food chain and on your knowledge of biology.

rosebush → aphid → ladybird beetle
→ spider → toad → snake

41. Which organism in the food chain can transform light energy into chemical energy? (1) spider (2) ladybird beetle (3) rosebush (4) snake

42. At which stage in the food chain will the population with the smallest number of animals probably be found? (1) spider (2) aphid (3) ladybird beetle (4) snake

43. Which organism in this food chain is a primary consumer? (1) rosebush (2) aphid (3) ladybird beetle (4) toad

Base your answers to questions 44 through 47 on the diagram below, which represents four possible pathways for the transfer of energy stored by green plants.

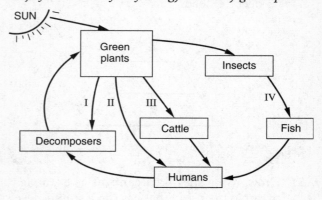

44. Pathway IV represents (1) a food chain (2) a population (3) an ecosystem (4) an abiotic factor

45. Through which pathway would the sun's energy be most directly available to humans? (1) I (2) II (3) III (4) IV

46. In this diagram, humans are shown to be (1) herbivores only (2) carnivores only (3) omnivores (4) parasites

47. The cattle in the diagram represent (1) primary consumers (2) secondary consumers (3) producers (4) autotrophs

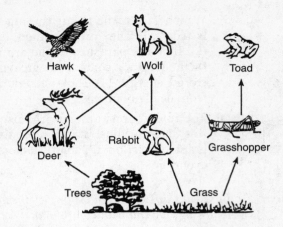

Hawk   Wolf   Toad

Deer   Rabbit   Grasshopper

Trees   Grass

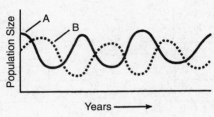

Base your answers to questions 48 through 50 on the food web and graph above and on your knowledge of biology. The graph represents the interaction of two different populations, A and B, in the food web.

48. Population *A* is made up of living animals. The members of population *B* feed on these living animals. The members of population *B* are most likely (1) scavengers (2) autotrophs (3) predators (4) parasites

49. Identify one specific heterotroph from the food web that could be a member of population *A*.

50. An energy pyramid is shown below. Which organism shown in the food web would mostly likely be found at level *X*? (1) wolf (2) grass (3) deer (4) toad

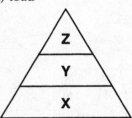

Z

Y

X

Part C

51. Draw, using specific organisms as examples, a pyramid of energy that has three trophic levels.

52. Distinguish between a pyramid of energy and a pyramid of biomass.

53. Explain why there is a "loss" of energy as one goes step-by-step up an energy pyramid. Discuss where the seemingly "lost" energy actually goes.

54. Explain why an ecosystem could not sustain itself without the constant input of energy from an outside source.

55. Consider the following food pyramid: corn → mice → snakes → hawks. If the total amount of energy captured by the corn is 1,000,000 calories per day and only about 10 percent of this energy is passed on at each higher trophic level, calculate:

• how much energy (in calories) would be available per day at each higher level (for mice, snakes, and hawks)

• how many hawks this ecosystem could support if the hawk population needs 500 calories per bird per day

Carrying Capacity

In every ecosystem on Earth, there are limited amounts of available resources. These resources include food, water, energy, minerals, and space (territory). Even though some of these resources may be recycled through the actions of bacteria and fungi, the pace of recycling may not keep up with the demand for these materials. The amount of resources available limits the number of organisms that an ecosystem can support. The maximum number of organisms of a particular type that can be supported in an area is known as the **carrying capacity**. In a stable ecosystem, a population of organisms will fluctuate slightly (due to seasonal and other factors), as shown in Figure 1-7. If the

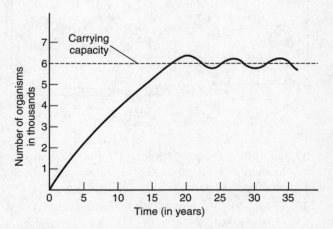

FIGURE 1-7 The carrying capacity for a population of organisms will fluctuate slightly in a stable ecosystem.

population increases significantly above its carrying capacity, many individuals will die because there are insufficient resources available to support them.

Competition

Different species living in the same environment, or **habitat**, may require some of the same resources for their survival. Since resources (such as food, water, space, light, and minerals) are usually limited, **competition** occurs among the various species. Competition is the struggle between different organisms for the same limited resources.

The more similar the needs of the species, the more intense the competition. For example, lions, leopards, and hyenas may compete to consume the same type of antelope. In addition, because their requirements are most similar, the strongest competition for resources often occurs among members of the same species. For example, competition for antelope prey (or water, mates, territory, and so on) may be more intense between neighboring prides of lions than between lions and other nearby large predators.

Each species occupies a particular ecological niche in a community. A **niche** is the role that the species fills in its habitat. A species' niche includes the type of food, or nutrients, it requires; where and how it lives; where and how it reproduces; and its relationships with other species in the area. When two species compete for the same niche, the one that is more successful at utilizing the available resources will outcompete the other, thereby maintaining just one species per niche in the community.

56. Carrying capacity is best thought of as the amount of (1) abiotic factors present in an ecosystem (2) light available for photosynthesis (3) organisms the ecosystem can support (4) producers compared to consumers in the ecosystem

57. A stable ecosystem is characterized by (1) a greater number of consumers than producers (2) population sizes at or near the carrying capacity (3) a greater need for energy than is available (4) a lack of decomposers to recycle materials

58. In a freshwater pond community, a carp (a type of fish) eats decaying matter from around the bases of underwater plants, while a snail scrapes algae from the leaves and stems of the same plant. They can survive at the same time in the same pond because they occupy (1) the same niche but different habitats (2) the same habitat but different niches (3) the same habitat and the same niche (4) different habitats and different niches

59. Limited resources contribute to evolutionary change in animals by increasing (1) the genetic variation within the population (2) competition between members of the species (3) the carrying capacity for the species (4) the rate of photosynthesis in the population

60. When two different species live in the same environment and use the same limited resources, which interaction will usually occur? (1) competition (2) cooperation (3) commensalism (4) mutualism

61. The size of a frog population in a pond remains fairly constant over a period of several years because of (1) decreasing competition (2) environmental carrying capacity (3) excessive dissolved oxygen (4) the depth of the water

Base your answer to the following question on the information and diagram below.

A population of chipmunks migrated to an environment where they had little competition. Their population quickly increased but eventually stabilized, as shown in the graph below.

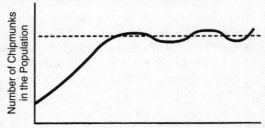

62. Which statement best explains why the population stabilized? (1) Interbreeding between members of the population increased the mutation rate. (2) The population size became limited due to factors such as availability of food. (3) An increase in the chipmunk population caused an increase in the producer population. (4) A predator species came to the area and occupied the same niche as the chipmunks.

63. An earthworm lives and reproduces in the soil. It aerates the soil and adds organic material to it. The earthworm is a source of food for other organisms. All of these statements together best describe (1) an ecological niche (2) a habitat (3) autotrophic nutrition (4) competition for resources

64. Purple loosestrife plants are replacing cattail plants in freshwater swamps in New York State.

The two species have very similar environmental requirements. This observation best illustrates (1) variations within a species (2) dynamic equilibrium (3) random recombination (4) competition between species

Part B-2

65. Some bacteria can reproduce once every 20 minutes. As a result, their populations can double several times an hour. Even at this phenomenal rate of reproduction, bacteria do not overrun the planet. Give a brief, valid explanation for this fact.

66. Explain why competition between individuals of the same species is often more intense than competition between members of different species.

Cycles of Materials

In a self-sustaining ecosystem, various materials are recycled between the organisms and the abiotic environment. The recycling process allows materials to be used over and over again by living things.

Carbon-Hydrogen-Oxygen Cycle. The elements carbon, hydrogen, and oxygen are recycled through the environment by the processes of respiration and photosynthesis (Figure 1-8). During aerobic cellular respiration, plants and animals use oxygen (O_2) from the air and release carbon dioxide (CO_2) and water (H_2O) via the breakdown of glucose. During photosynthesis, plants use carbon dioxide (CO_2) from the air and water (H_2O) from the environment in the synthesis of glucose ($C_6H_{12}O_6$), and oxygen (O_2) is given off as a by-product.

Water Cycle. In the water cycle, water moves between Earth's surface and the atmosphere (Figure 1-9). The

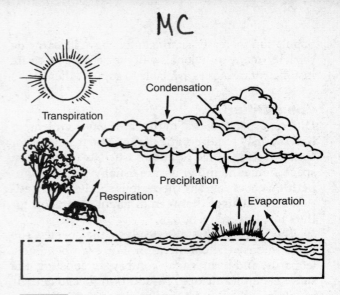

FIGURE 1-9 The water cycle.

main processes involved in this cycle are *evaporation* and *condensation*. Liquid water on Earth's surface changes to a gas by the process of evaporation and enters the atmosphere in the form of water vapor. As a result of condensation, water vapor is returned to the liquid state (precipitation) and falls to Earth. Some water vapor is added to the atmosphere by aerobic respiration in plants and animals, and by transpiration in plants. Water is also an essential nutrient for all living things, allowing them to carry out essential life processes and chemical reactions.

Nitrogen Cycle. The element nitrogen is needed by all living things because it is part of the structure of amino acids and proteins. The nitrogen cycle, when compared to other materials' cycles, is much more complex and involves the interaction of several types of organisms. Nitrogen exists freely in nature as N_2 but it is *not* available to organisms in that form. It must first be converted to compounds containing nitrogen to make it usable. Plants absorb nitrogen-containing compounds from the soil; animals obtain nitrogen in the form of proteins in the foods they eat. These proteins are broken down by digestion to amino acids, which are then used in the synthesis of animal proteins.

The nitrogen cycle involves decomposers and other soil bacteria. Figure 1-10 shows the various components of the nitrogen cycle, which are described below.

Nitrogen-fixing bacteria, which live in nodules inside the roots of some plants (refer to Figure 1-2), convert free nitrogen (N_2) from the air into nitrogen-containing compounds called nitrates (NO_3). *Nitrates* are absorbed from the soil by plants and used in protein synthesis. Animals that eat plants convert the nitrogen-containing plant proteins into animal

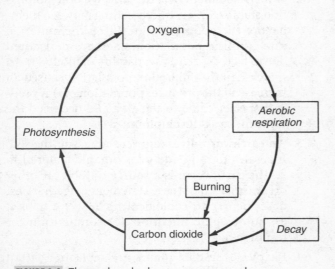

FIGURE 1-8 The carbon-hydrogen-oxygen cycle.

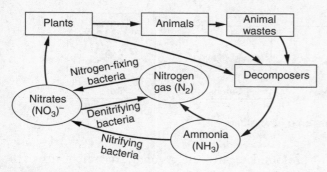

FIGURE 1-10 The nitrogen cycle.

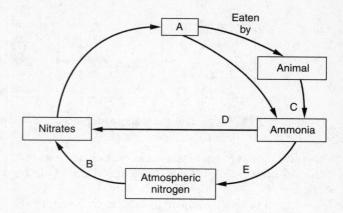

proteins. The nitrogenous wastes of living animals and the nitrogen compounds in the remains of dead plants and animals are broken down by decomposers and converted to ammonia (NH_3). *Nitrifying bacteria* in the soil convert ammonia into nitrates, which can be used again by plants. *Denitrifying bacteria* break down some nitrates into free nitrogen (N_2), which is released into the atmosphere as a gas.

QUESTIONS
Part A

67. Carbon dioxide is added to the atmosphere by (1) photosynthesis in plants (2) evaporation of water (3) respiration in animals only (4) respiration in plants and animals

68. Oxygen (O_2) is added to the atmosphere by (1) evaporation and photosynthesis (2) respiration in plants (3) photosynthesis only (4) denitrifying bacteria

69. Which process is *not* involved in the water cycle? (1) condensation (2) nitrification (3) evaporation (4) transpiration

70. The processes involved in the recycling of carbon, hydrogen, and oxygen are (1) evaporation and condensation (2) photosynthesis and respiration (3) nitrification and denitrification (4) respiration and transpiration

71. Nitrogen is both removed from the atmosphere and returned to the atmosphere by the activities of (1) plants only (2) animals only (3) plants and animals (4) bacteria

72. Animals obtain their nitrogen from (1) proteins in their food (2) nitrates in the soil (3) gas in the atmosphere (4) bacteria in their intestines

Part B-1

Base your answers to questions 73 through 75 on the following diagram, above right, which represents a cycle in nature, and on your knowledge of biology.

73. The cycle represented by the diagram is the (1) nitrogen cycle (2) carbon cycle (3) water cycle (4) oxygen cycle

74. Nitrifying bacteria in the soil are represented by the letter (1) A (2) E (3) C (4) D

75. The letter *B* most likely represents (1) bacteria of decay (2) denitrifying bacteria (3) a legume (peanut plant) (4) nitrogen-fixing bacteria

Part B-2

76. Describe how carbon dioxide and oxygen are recycled by the processes of respiration and photosynthesis.

77. Explain why both nitrogen-fixing bacteria and nitrifying bacteria are important for the survival of plants.

ECOSYSTEM FORMATION

Ecosystems tend to change over a long period of time until a stable one is formed. Both the living (biotic) and nonliving (abiotic) parts of the ecosystem change.

Succession

The replacement of one kind of community by another in an ecosystem is called ecological, or biological, **succession**. *Ecological succession* is usually a long-term process, happening over the course of many years (and many generations of different plants and animals). The kind of stable ecosystem that eventually develops in a particular geographical area depends on the region's climate.

Pioneer Organisms. Depending on climate and other abiotic environmental factors, succession on land can begin in an area that has no living things and end with a forest. Succession begins with *pioneer organisms*, which are the first plants, or plantlike organisms, to populate an area. Lichens and algae are

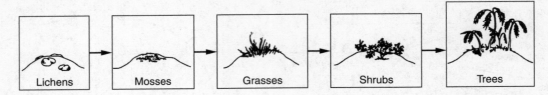

FIGURE 1-11 Ecological succession occurs, over time, on a new island.

Lichens → Mosses → Grasses → Shrubs → Trees

typical pioneer organisms on bare rock, such as that found on a newly emerged volcanic island (Figure 1-11).

Starting with pioneer plants, each community modifies the environment, often making it less favorable for itself and more favorable for other kinds of communities. One sequence of plant succession in New York State might be lichens → grasses → shrubs → conifers (pine trees) → deciduous (beech and maple) woodlands.

Since plants are the basic source of food for a community, the types of plants present in a community determine the types of animals that can live in the community. As the plant populations change, the animal populations also change.

Climax Communities. Succession ends with the development of a *climax community* in which populations of plants and animals exist in balance with each other and with the environment. In New York State, for example, the oak-hickory and hemlock-beech-maple associations represent two climax communities. In the Midwest, where there is less rain, grasslands are the typical climax community.

The climax community remains stable until a catastrophic change, such as a volcanic eruption or forest fire, alters or destroys it. Thereafter, succession begins again, leading to the development of a new climax community. This new community may be of the same type as the previous one or, if the catastrophe has changed the environment in some important way, it may be of another kind.

Biodiversity

In addition to the factors mentioned above, a stable community or stable ecosystem requires **biodiversity**. This term refers to the presence of a wide range of different species of organisms living and interacting with each other and with their nonliving environment. These organisms play a variety of roles that contribute to the overall stability of an ecosystem. For example, green plants and algae act as producers; fungi and bacteria act as decomposers, recycling vital materials; and animals act as consumers. Some roles are readily apparent while others may not be so obvious. Nevertheless, the removal of any one species from its natural environment may have

profound negative effects on the overall health of the ecosystem.

Biodiversity also increases the probability that at least some organisms would be able to survive a catastrophic environmental event, such as climate change or a volcanic eruption. In time, the surviving organisms could reestablish a healthy community.

In addition, stable ecosystems that are rich in species, such as tropical rain forests, contain a wealth of genetic material that may have beneficial uses in medicine, agriculture, or other areas. Today, tropical forests, wetlands, coral reefs, and other ecosystems that are rich in biodiversity are being destroyed at an alarming rate, mainly due to human activities. Once species are lost to extinction, they can never be recovered. Careful protection of diverse habitats and their living resources is critical to preserving the biodiversity of Earth, not only for the needs of humans or individual ecosystems but also for the health and stability of the entire planet.

QUESTIONS
Part A

78. The natural replacement of one community by another until a climax stage is reached is known as (1) ecological balance (2) organic evolution (3) dynamic equilibrium (4) ecological succession

79. In an ecological succession in New York State, lichens growing on bare rock are considered to be (1) climax species (2) pioneer organisms (3) primary consumers (4) decomposers

80. One of the first organisms to become established in an ecological succession leading to a pond community is (1) grasses (2) algae (3) minnows (4) deciduous trees

81. Ecological succession ends with the development of (1) a climax community (2) a pioneer community (3) an ecological niche (4) an abiotic community

82. Which two groups of organisms are most likely to be pioneer organisms? (1) songbirds and squirrels (2) lichens and algae (3) deer and black bears (4) oak and hickory trees

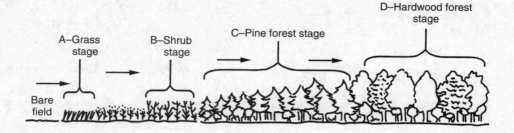

A–Grass stage B–Shrub stage C–Pine forest stage D–Hardwood forest stage

Bare field

83. Stage *D* in the diagram above is located on land that was once a bare field. The sequence of stages leading from bare field to stage *D* best illustrates the process known as (1) replication (2) recycling (3) feedback (4) succession

84. Biodiversity in an ecosystem is important because it (1) allows one species to dominate the others in its habitat (2) slows the pace at which species evolve (3) provides stability to the ecosystem (4) limits the amount of variation among organisms

85. Stable ecosystems are characterized by (1) only two major species interacting with each other (2) an infinite amount of available resources (3) a variety of different species interacting with one another (4) very little recycling of materials between the biotic and abiotic components

86. After a major forest fire occurs, an area that was once wooded is converted to barren soil. Which sequence describes the most likely series of changes in vegetation after the fire?
(1) shrubs → maples → pines → grasses
(2) maples → pines → grasses → shrubs
(3) pines → shrubs → maples → grasses
(4) grasses → shrubs → pines → maples

87. Deforestation of areas considered to be rich sources of genetic material could limit future agricultural and medical advances due to

(1) the improved quality of the atmosphere
(2) the maintenance of dynamic equilibrium
(3) an increase in the rate of evolutionary change
(4) the loss of biodiversity

Part B-2

88. List the stages that precede a beech-maple forest in New York State. Identify the pioneer organism and the climax community in this succession.

Part C

89. Compare a natural meadow with a cornfield in terms of biodiversity. In your answer, be sure to address the

- comparative number of species that live in each habitat,

- comparative number of interactions among species that occur in each habitat,

- and the relative ability of each habitat to survive a natural disaster that might occur.

Base your answers to questions 90 through 92 on page 14 on the diagram below, which represents the changes in an ecosystem over a period of 100 years, and on your knowledge of biology.

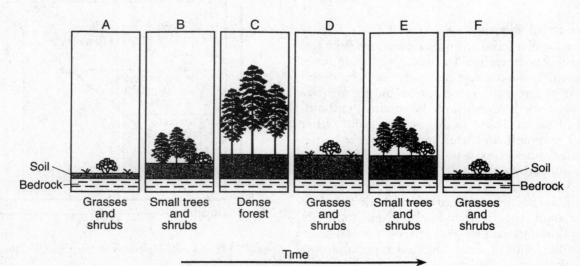

A — Grasses and shrubs
B — Small trees and shrubs
C — Dense forest
D — Grasses and shrubs
E — Small trees and shrubs
F — Grasses and shrubs

Soil
Bedrock

Time

TABLE 1-1

Major Terrestrial Biomes on Earth

Biome	Characteristics	Plants	Animals
Tundra	Permanently frozen subsoil	Lichens, mosses, grasses	Snowy owl, caribou
Taiga	Long, severe winters; summers with thawing subsoil	Conifers	Moose, black bear
Temperate forest	Moderate precipitation; cold winters; warm summers	Deciduous trees (maple, oak, beech)	Fox, deer, gray squirrel
Tropical forest	Heavy rainfall; constant warmth	Many broad-leaved plant species	Snake, monkey, leopard
Grassland	Variability in rainfall and temperature; strong winds	Grasses	Antelope, bison, prairie dog
Desert	Sparse rainfall; extreme daily temperature fluctuations	Drought-resistant plants and succulents	Lizard, tortoise, kangaroo rat

90. State one biological explanation for the changes in types of vegetation observed from *A* through *C*.

91. Identify one human activity that could be responsible for the change from *C* to *D*.

92. Predict what would happen to the soil *and* vegetation of this ecosystem after stage *F*, assuming no natural disaster or human interference.

BIOMES

Earth can be divided into broad geographic regions by climate. The kind of climax ecosystem that develops in these large climatic areas is called a **biome**. Biomes may be terrestrial (land biomes) or aquatic (water biomes). The stretch of tropical rain forests around the equator is a land biome. The ocean is an aquatic biome.

Terrestrial Biomes

The major plant and animal associations (biomes) on land are determined by the large climate zones of Earth. These climate zones are, in turn, determined by geographic factors, including *latitude* (distance north or south of the equator) and *altitude* (distance above or below sea level). Other major geographic features, including large bodies of water, mountains, and deserts, modify the climate of nearby regions.

Climate includes the temperature range and the amounts of precipitation and solar radiation received by a region. The presence or absence of water is a major limiting factor for terrestrial biomes and determines the kinds of plant and animal communities that can be established.

Kinds of Terrestrial Biomes. Land biomes are described in terms of, and sometimes named for, the dominant kind of climax vegetation found there. Table 1-1 lists the major land biomes, their characteristics, dominant plant life, and some representative animals.

Effects of Latitude and Altitude. At the equator, the temperature and amount of rainfall remain relatively constant throughout the year. With increasing distance from the equator, temperature and rainfall show more variation during the year.

Increasing altitude may have the same effect on climate as increasing latitude. Thus, the temperature and kind of climax vegetation found at the top of a high mountain near the equator may be very much like that of a sea-level region far north of the equator. This relationship is shown in Figure 1-12.

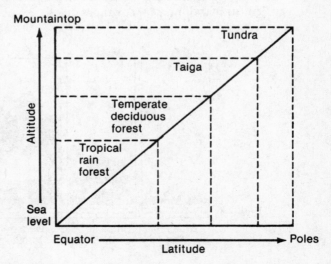

FIGURE 1-12 Relationship between latitude and altitude and terrestrial biomes.

Aquatic Biomes

Aquatic biomes make up the largest ecosystem on Earth. More than 70 percent of Earth's surface is covered by water; the majority of living things on Earth are water dwellers.

Aquatic biomes are more stable than terrestrial biomes; they show less variation in temperature because water has a greater capacity to absorb and hold heat. The kinds and numbers of organisms present in an aquatic biome are affected by various abiotic factors, such as the water temperature, amounts of dissolved oxygen and carbon dioxide, intensity of light, and the kinds and amounts of dissolved minerals and suspended particles in the water (Figure 1-13).

Aquatic organisms are well adapted for the removal of dissolved oxygen from water. They also have adaptations for maintaining a proper water balance in their cells. (Water balance is affected by the concentration of salts in the water.)

In aquatic biomes, most photosynthesis takes place near the surface of the water, since light intensity is strongest there. At greater depths, where sunlight does not penetrate, there is no photosynthesis. However, as discussed earlier in this chapter, another type of food-making reaction takes place on parts of the ocean floor; chemosynthesis supports entire communities of organisms very different from those found elsewhere in the ocean or on land.

Marine Biome. The marine, or saltwater, biome includes all the oceans of Earth, which actually make up one continuous body of water. Most of the water on Earth is contained within the saltwater biome (Figure 1-14). The most important characteristics of

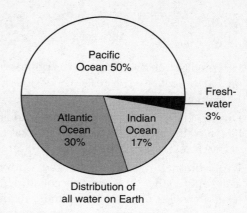

Distribution of all water on Earth

FIGURE 1-14 Most of Earth's water is contained within the marine biome.

the marine biome are that it: (a) is the most stable environment on Earth; (b) absorbs and holds large quantities of solar heat, thereby stabilizing Earth's temperature; (c) contains a relatively constant supply of nutrients and dissolved salts; (d) serves as a habitat for a large number and wide variety of organisms; and (e) includes the area in which most of the photosynthesis on Earth occurs (in coastal waters, along the edges of landmasses).

Freshwater Biomes. The freshwater biome includes ponds, lakes, and rivers. Because these are separate bodies of water, they vary widely in size, temperature, oxygen and carbon dioxide concentrations, amounts of suspended particles, current velocity, and rate of succession.

Ponds and lakes tend to fill in over time. Dead plant material and sediment accumulate on the bottom and around the banks, gradually making the body of water shallower and smaller (Figure 1-15). Thus, in all but the largest lakes, there is a gradual succession from a freshwater to a terrestrial climax community.

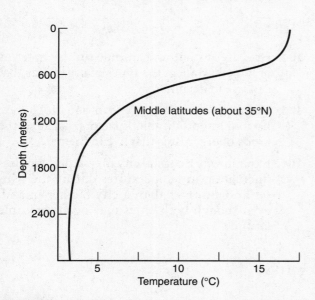

FIGURE 1-13 The relationship between ocean depth and water temperature: These factors, among others, have an effect on the types of organisms found in a marine biome.

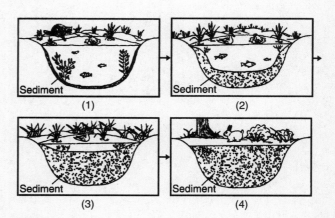

FIGURE 1-15 Over time, ponds tend to fill in as natural materials accumulate on the sides and bottom.

93. In which biome does most of the photosynthesis on Earth occur? (1) forests (2) oceans (3) deserts (4) grasslands

94. Drastic changes in air temperature would be *least* likely to affect which biome? (1) tundra (2) temperate forest (3) marine (4) tropical forest

95. Land biomes are characterized and named according to the (1) secondary consumers in the food webs (2) primary consumers in the food webs (3) climax vegetation in the region (4) pioneer vegetation in the region

96. The largest and most stable ecosystems are the (1) aquatic biomes (2) terrestrial biomes (3) high-altitude biomes (4) high-latitude biomes

97. Which is the most common sequence of major land biomes encountered when going from the equator to the polar region? (1) tundra, taiga, temperate forest, tropical forest (2) tropical forest, temperate forest, taiga, tundra (3) temperate forest, tropical forest, taiga, tundra (4) tropical forest, temperate forest, tundra, taiga

98. Which biome is characterized by its ability to absorb and hold large quantities of solar heat, which helps to regulate Earth's temperature? (1) desert (2) marine (3) grassland (4) taiga

99. Generally, an increase in altitude has the same effect on the habitat of organisms as an increase in (1) latitude (2) moisture (3) available light (4) longitude

For each description given in questions 100 through 103, select the biome from the list below that most closely matches that description.

(A) desert
(B) grassland
(C) taiga
(D) temperate deciduous forest
(E) tundra

100. This area has a short growing season and low precipitation, mostly in the form of snow. The soil is permanently frozen and the vegetation includes lichens and mosses. (1) A (2) B (3) C (4) D (5) E

101. This area has 25 to 50 centimeters of rainfall annually. The growing season does not produce trees, but the soil is rich and well suited for growing crops such as wheat and corn. Grazing animals are found here. (1) A (2) B (3) C (4) D (5) E

102. There are many lakes in this area and the vegetation is coniferous forest composed mainly of spruce and fir. There are many large animals, such as bear and deer. (1) A (2) B (3) C (4) D (5) E

103. This area has broad-leaved trees, which shed their leaves in the fall. Winters are fairly cold, and the summers are warm with well-distributed rainfall. (1) A (2) B (3) C (4) D (5) E

104. How are latitude and altitude similar in terms of how they affect the types of organisms that can live in a biome?

105. Describe the two main types of aquatic biomes; list four important abiotic factors that affect the kinds of organisms that live in them.

106. Explain why a coastal city may experience less fluctuation in temperatures during the winter and summer than a city farther inland, even though both cities may be at the same latitude.

Base your answers to questions 107 through 110 on the information below and on your knowledge of biology. Source: Science News (May 7, 2011): vol. 179, no. 10, p. 16. Reprinted with permission of Science News.

Borneo Orangs Fish for Their Dinner: Behavior Suggests Early Human Ancestors Were Piscivores

Orangutans swim just about as well as they fly, but research on three Indonesian islands shows that these long-limbed apes nonetheless catch and eat fish.

Orangutans living in Borneo scavenge fish that wash up along the shore and scoop catfish out of small ponds for fresh meals, Anne Russon of York University in Toronto reported on April 14. Over two years, Russon saw several animals on parts of the forested island learn on their own to jab at catfish with sticks, so that the panicked prey would flop out of ponds and into a red ape's waiting hands.

"If orangutans can do this, then early hominids could also have practiced tool-assisted fishing," Russon said.

Observations of fishing by orangutans raise the likelihood that hominids ate meat, including fish, before the emergence of the *Homo* genus around 2.5 million years ago, said anthropologist David Braun of the University of Cape Town in South Africa. Anthropologists have traditionally held that meat-eating first assumed prominence among early *Homo* species and fueled brain expansion.

Fish, even more than red meat, contains fatty acids essential for human brain growth. Good archaeological evidence of fish-eating goes back no further than about 2 million years in members of the *Homo* genus, which includes modern humans.

Russon and her colleagues monitored daily behavior among orangutans in Borneo from 2004 to 2006. In 2007, the researchers stocked a small pond with catfish and videotaped orangutan visits to the pond over the course of one day.

Seventeen times orangutans scavenged for fish or grabbed fish out of ponds—several times from the prestocked pond—and immediately ate their prey. Apes used sticks to jab at catfish in the prestocked pond and in other ponds as well.

Orangutans' determined fishing efforts underscore the nutritional importance of aquatic foods for apes in general, not just people, Russon said. Individual orangutans in Borneo may have discovered by accident that they could grab fish along the shore and in ponds. These animals then adapted sticks to the task of catching elusive pond catfish.

107. How do orangutans use tools to catch fish? What implications does this observation have for early hominids?

108. Why are fish particularly healthy for humans to eat?

109. How do scientists think this fishing behavior developed in orangutans?

110. Briefly describe the research that Anne Russon and her colleagues conducted to learn about fishing behavior in orangutans.

2 Cellular Processes of Living Things

CONCEPT OF LIFE

Scientists have not yet agreed on a single definition of life. Thus, life is often defined in terms of certain activities, or life functions, that are performed by all living things. These essential life functions are regulation, nutrition, excretion, transport, respiration, growth, synthesis, and reproduction.

Life Functions

All living things, or **organisms**, carry on several basic life functions. First of all, *regulation* involves the control and **coordination** of the life functions. The process of **nutrition** provides all the substances that are used by an organism for the growth and repair of its **tissues**. Nutrition among heterotrophs (organisms that must obtain nutrients from other organisms) includes the activities involved in *ingestion* (obtaining food from the environment), **digestion** (processing food for use by the organism), and *egestion* (removal of solid wastes). *Transport* includes the absorption of materials through cell membranes and the **circulation**, or distribution, of materials to all the cells of the organism. After the materials are delivered to the cells, the process of **respiration** can occur. Respiration includes the chemical activities that release energy from organic molecules for use by the cells. During respiration, the chemical bonds of **glucose** are broken down, and the energy released is stored in the compound **ATP (adenosine triphosphate)**. An organism uses the energy in ATP to perform its life functions. ATP functions much like a rechargeable battery—when it gets "run down," it is recharged by the breakdown of glucose.

Other chemical reactions are involved in building, rather than breaking down, **molecules**. During **synthesis** reactions, small molecules combine to form larger ones. *Growth* is an increase in size brought about by increases in cell size and cell number. The products of synthesis are the raw materials that are used for growth. The process of **excretion** includes all those activities that are involved in the removal of cellular waste products from the organism. These wastes include **carbon dioxide**, water, salts, and nitrogen-containing compounds. The life function of **reproduction** results in the production of new individuals. However, since each organism has a limited life span, reproduction is necessary more for the survival of each **species** (a group of like organisms) than for the individual organism itself.

Metabolism. All the chemical activities that an organism must carry on to sustain life are its *metabolism,*

18

or **metabolic** activities. The breaking apart of glucose molecules to release their energy and the growth and repair of tissues to maintain a functioning body are both examples of metabolic activities.

Homeostasis. The external conditions in an organism's environment are subject to frequent changes. Sometimes, there are changes that occur in an organism's internal environment as well. The maintenance of a stable internal environment in spite of changes, or **deviations**, in the external environment is known as **homeostasis**. All body systems are involved in the regulation of homeostasis. An example of homeostasis is the maintenance of a constant body temperature in spite of temperature fluctuations in the external environment. The ability to maintain homeostasis is critical to survival. If maintenance of homeostasis fails, the organism becomes ill and, in some cases, may die.

1. The tendency of an organism to maintain a stable internal environment is called (1) homeostasis (2) nutrition (3) reproduction (4) synthesis

2. The energy available for use by the cell is obtained from the life function of (1) reproduction (2) respiration (3) transport (4) synthesis

3. The chemical process by which complex molecules of protein are made from simple molecules is called (1) regulation (2) respiration (3) synthesis (4) excretion

4. Which life function includes the absorption and circulation of essential substances throughout an organism? (1) transport (2) excretion (3) ingestion (4) nutrition

5. Which term includes all the chemical activities carried on by an organism? (1) regulation (2) metabolism (3) digestion (4) respiration

6. Which life activity is *not* required for the survival of an individual organism? (1) nutrition (2) respiration (3) reproduction (4) synthesis

7. In an ameba, materials are taken from its environment and then moved throughout its cytoplasm. These processes are known as (1) absorption and circulation (2) food processing and energy release (3) energy release and synthesis (4) coordination and regulation

8. In an organism, the coordination of the activities that maintain homeostasis in a constantly changing environment is a process known as (1) digestion (2) regulation (3) synthesis (4) respiration

Part B-2

9. Identify a life function that provides the substances an organism uses for its growth and for repair of its tissues.

10. Why are such different things as single-celled amebas and multicelled humans both considered to be organisms?

Part C

11. You are working as a biologist in a laboratory. An unknown specimen is brought in for analysis. Describe the steps you would take to determine if the specimen is a living organism or simply a collection of nonliving molecules.

CELLULAR STRUCTURE OF LIVING THINGS

Virtually all living things are composed of one or more discrete units called **cells**. Some organisms consist of only one cell, while others may consist of billions of cells. The processes that are essential for the survival of an organism are performed by its cells. Most of the cells in a multicellular organism are capable of performing all the life functions independently, as well as with the other cells of the body.

The Cell Theory

The *cell theory*, which is one of the major theories of biology, can be stated as follows: (a) Every organism is made up of one or more cells; (b) the cell is the basic unit of structure and function in all living things (for example, cells make, or synthesize, proteins and release energy); and (c) all cells come only from preexisting cells (that is, new cells are formed when previously existing cells divide). In living things, the level of complexity follows this general pattern, going from simplest to most complex: cells → tissues → organs → systems → organisms.

Development of the Cell Theory. During the last four centuries, improvements in the microscope and the development of other techniques have made it possible for biologists to observe and study cells. The cell theory was developed from the work of a number of scientists. First, *Anton van Leeuwenhoek* (1632–1723) made powerful simple microscopes (magnifying glasses) that he used to study living cells; he was the first person to observe sperm cells, bacteria, and protozoa. Then, *Robert Hooke* (1635–1703) made compound microscopes (microscopes with two or more lenses) that he used to observe thin slices of cork; he used the term "cells" to describe the small compartments that make up cork tissue. In 1831, *Robert Brown* concluded from his studies that all plant cells contain a nucleus. Later, in 1838, *Matthias Schleiden* concluded that all plants are made up of cells and, in 1839, *Theodor Schwann* concluded that all animals are made up of cells. Finally, in 1855, *Rudolf Virchow* concluded that all cells arise only from preexisting cells. These last three ideas formed the basis of the cell theory.

Exceptions to the Cell Theory. Recent discoveries have led scientists to identify several exceptions to the cell theory. For example, mitochondria and chloroplasts, which are cell organelles, contain genetic material (DNA) and can duplicate themselves within living cells. It is thought that both mitochondria and chloroplasts were originally independent, free-living simple organisms that were captured by larger cells and then became incorporated into them.

Another exception to the cell theory is the **virus**, which is not a living cell. It consists of an outer coat of protein surrounding a core of DNA or RNA. A virus can reproduce only while it is inside a living host cell; but outside the host organism, it shows no sign of life. As such, viruses are not included in any of the six **kingdoms** of living things. Recently, scientists have discovered tiny particles known as *viroids* and *prions,* which also are not living cells. However, like viruses, these infectious particles have the ability to reproduce themselves and cause diseases when they enter a living host organism.

There are exceptions to the cell theory among multicellular organisms as well. For example, some tissues in multicellular plants and animals do not appear to be made up of clearly identifiable cells. In humans, skeletal muscle tissue does not show distinct boundaries between the cells. In plants, some tissues found in seeds are also not clearly cellular. A group of protists known as *slime molds* have tissues that do not appear to be made up of individual cells, either. Finally, the very first living cells on Earth must have developed from non-cellular matter (that is, not from preexisting cells).

Cell Structure. Cells contain a variety of small structures, called **organelles**, which perform specific functions (Figure 2-1).

The **cell membrane,** or *plasma membrane,* surrounds and protects the cell and separates the cell contents from the environment. The membrane consists of a double lipid layer in which large protein molecules float. The cell membrane is *selectively permeable*; this means that some substances can pass through it, while others cannot. In this way, the **membrane** regulates the passage of materials into

and out of the cell and controls the cell's chemical makeup.

The **cytoplasm** is the fluidlike material that fills the space between the cell membrane and the nucleus. Many metabolic reactions occur in the cytoplasm, which consists mainly of water. The organelles are suspended in the cytoplasm.

The **nucleus** is the control center of the cell. It is surrounded by a nuclear membrane and contains the genetic material, which is found in the **chromosomes**. The chromosomes are made of **DNA (deoxyribonucleic acid)** and protein.

The **ribosomes** are tiny organelles that are suspended in the cytoplasm and attached to the membranes of the endoplasmic reticulum. Protein synthesis takes place at the ribosomes.

The **mitochondria** are the sites of most reactions of aerobic **cellular respiration**, the process by which energy is released from nutrient molecules (such as

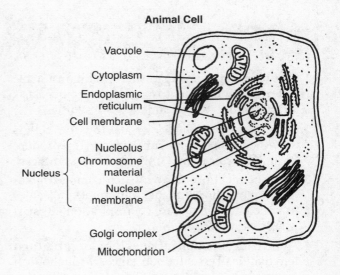

Animal Cell

Vacuole
Cytoplasm
Endoplasmic reticulum
Cell membrane
Nucleolus
Chromosome material
Nucleus
Nuclear membrane
Golgi complex
Mitochondrion

Plant Cell

Nucleolus
Nuclear membrane
Nucleus
Chromosome material
Chloroplast
Endoplasmic reticulum
Golgi complex
Vacuole
Cytoplasm
Mitochondrion
Cell membrane
Cell wall

FIGURE 2-1 Typical cell organelles.

glucose). Most of the ATP produced by aerobic respiration is synthesized in the mitochondria.

The **vacuoles** are fluid-filled organelles surrounded by membranes. In single-celled organisms, digestion occurs in food vacuoles and excess water collects in contractile vacuoles, which pump it out of the cell. Plant cells contain very large vacuoles that may fill much of the cell's interior. In animal cells, there are relatively few vacuoles, and they are small.

The **chloroplasts** are small pigment-containing organelles found in the cytoplasm of plants, algae, and some protists. Photosynthesis takes place in the chloroplasts.

The *cell wall* is a nonliving structure found outside the cell membrane of plant, algal, and fungal cells. It provides strength and rigidity but does not interfere with the passage of materials into or out of the cell.

QUESTIONS
Part A

12. The unit of structure and function of all living things is (1) an organ (2) an atom (3) a cell (4) a nucleolus

13. According to the cell theory, which statement is correct? (1) Viruses are true living cells. (2) All cells are basically different in structure. (3) Mitochondria are found only in plant cells. (4) All cells come from preexisting cells.

14. Which structures carry out life functions within cells? (1) tissues (2) organ systems (3) organelles (4) organs

15. Which statement best describes the term "theory" as used, for example, in the "cell theory"? (1) A theory is never revised as new scientific evidence is presented. (2) A theory is an assumption made by scientists and implies a lack of certainty. (3) A theory refers to a scientific explanation that is strongly supported by a variety of experimental data. (4) A theory is a hypothesis that has been supported by one experiment performed by two or more scientists.

16. The term "selectively permeable" is used in reference to the (1) nucleus (2) cell wall (3) cytoplasm (4) cell membrane

17. The part of a cell that is in most direct contact with the environment is the (1) nucleus (2) cell membrane (3) mitochondrion (4) vacuole

18. Plant cell organelles that contain photosynthetic pigments are (1) chloroplasts (2) ribosomes (3) chromosomes (4) cell walls

19. An observable difference between an onion's epidermal (skin) cells and a human's cheek cells is that the onion's cells have a (1) cell membrane (2) nucleus (3) vacuole (4) cell wall

20. What is the main function of a vacuole in a cell? (1) storage (2) coordination (3) synthesis of molecules (4) release of energy

21. The watery environment in which most life activities of a cell take place is the (1) cell membrane (2) chloroplast (3) cytoplasm (4) vacuole

22. Transport of materials into and out of a cell is most closely associated with the (1) nucleus (2) cell wall (3) ribosome (4) cell membrane

23. Which organelle contains genetic material and controls most cell activities? (1) nucleus (2) cell membrane (3) vacuole (4) endoplasmic reticulum

24. The cell organelles that are the sites of aerobic cellular respiration in both plant and animal cells are the (1) mitochondria (2) vacuoles (3) chloroplasts (4) nuclei

25. An increase in the concentration of ATP in a muscle cell is a direct result of which life function? (1) cellular respiration (2) reproduction (3) digestion (4) excretion

26. A nonliving cell structure is a (1) cell membrane (2) nucleus (3) cell wall (4) mitochondrion

27. Which cell structure is correctly paired with its primary function? (1) nucleus—storage of nutrients (2) mitochondrion—movement (3) vacuole—cell division (4) ribosome—protein synthesis

Part B-1

28. The arrows in the diagram below indicate the movement of materials into and out of a single-celled organism. The movements indicated by these arrows are directly involved in (1) the maintenance of homeostasis (2) photosynthesis only (3) excretion only (4) the digestion of minerals

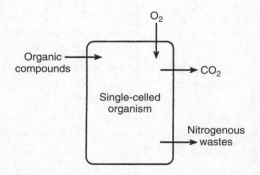

29. In the diagram of a single-celled organism shown below, the arrows indicate various activities taking place. Which systems perform these same activities in humans? (1) digestive, circulatory, and immune (2) excretory, respiratory, and reproductive (3) respiratory, excretory, and digestive (4) respiratory, nervous, and endocrine

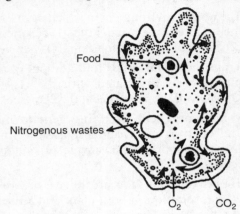

Food

Nitrogenous wastes

O_2 CO_2

Part C

30. Explain why scientists have difficulty including viruses in any category of living organisms.

TOOLS AND METHODS OF CELL STUDY

There are various scientific tools and methods that enable the up-close study of cell structures and functions. These different techniques and types of equipment are used to study cells and cell parts at varying levels of magnification and in different conditions. For example, some tools are used for the study of live cells, while others can be used only for the examination of preserved (dead) cells. Some of these tools and techniques are described below.

Compound Light Microscope

A microscope that uses two lenses or sets of lenses to form an enlarged image is called a *compound light microscope.* Light passes through the specimen, the objective lens, and the ocular lens, or *eyepiece,* before reaching the eye. The objective lens produces a magnified image that is further enlarged by the ocular lens. The main parts of a compound light microscope are shown in Figure 2-2. The functions of these parts are listed in Table 2-1. The amount of enlargement of an image produced by the lenses of a microscope is its *magnifying power.* For a compound microscope, magnifying power is found by multiplying the magnifying power of the objective lens by the magnifying power of the ocular lens. For example, if the magnifying power of the objective is 40× (40 times) and that of the ocular is 10× (10 times), the total magnification is $40 \times 10 = 400\times$ (400 times). The greater the magnification of a specimen, the smaller the field of vision, or observable area. The *resolution,* or resolving power, is the capacity of the microscope to show, as separate, two points that are close together.

Other Types of Microscopes

A microscope that has an ocular lens and an objective lens for each eye is called a binocular or *dissecting microscope.* Dissecting microscopes, which produce

TABLE 2-1

Parts of the Compound Light Microscope and Their Functions

Part	Function
Base	Supports the microscope
Arm	Used to carry microscope; attaches to the base, stage, and body tube
Body tube	Holds the objective lens and eyepiece
Stage	Platform on which the glass slide with the specimen is placed (over the hole in the stage through which light passes)
Clips	Hold the slide in position on the stage
Nosepiece	Holds the objective lenses; rotates so that the different objective lenses can be moved in line with the specimen and eyepiece
Coarse adjustment	Larger knob used for rough-focusing with the low-power objective
Fine adjustment	Smaller knob used for focusing with the high-power objective and for final focusing with the low-power objective
Mirror or lamp	Directs light to the specimen (on the stage)
Diaphragm	Controls the amount of light reaching the specimen
Objective lenses	Lenses mounted on the nosepiece
Ocular lens	Lens at the top of the body tube; commonly called the *eyepiece*

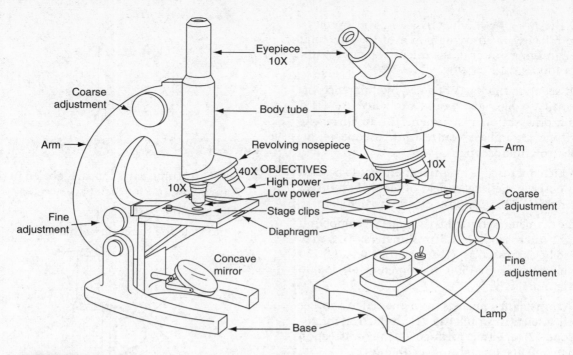

FIGURE 2-2 Main parts of the compound light microscope.

a three-dimensional image, have relatively low magnifying power and are used for viewing fairly large, opaque specimens. For more magnifying power and the ability to observe unstained, living cells, a *phase-contrast microscope* is used; it makes visible parts that cannot be seen with an ordinary light microscope. The most powerful kind of microscope is the *electron microscope,* which can magnify an object more than 400,000×. Unlike other microscopes, the electron microscope uses an electron beam focused by electromagnets, instead of light and lenses. One disadvantage of the electron microscope is that only dead specimens can be viewed with it.

Techniques of Cell Study

Tiny instruments that can be used, with the aid of a microscope, to remove or transfer the parts of a cell are *microdissection* instruments. For example, with the use of microdissection instruments, a nucleus can be transferred from one cell to another. The laboratory instrument that is used to separate small particles or materials on the basis of density is the *ultracentrifuge.* In fact, various cell organelles can be isolated by the process of ultracentrifugation. The ultracentrifuge spins the sample in a test tube at very high speeds so that particles of different densities settle to the bottom of the test tube in layers. In addition, cell structures can be made clearly visible by the use of various *staining* techniques. Depending on its specific chemical makeup, a particular stain will be absorbed only by certain parts of the cell. For example, methylene blue and iodine are stains that are absorbed by the nucleus. Other parts of the cell can be made visible with other stains.

The unit used in measuring structures that can be viewed with a compound light microscope is the *micrometer* (μm). One micrometer equals 0.001 millimeter (mm); 1000 micrometers equal 1 millimeter. The diameter of the low-power field of a compound light microscope is commonly about 1500 μm. A paramecium is about 250 μm (0.25 mm) long. (Measurement with a microscope is discussed in greater detail in Chapter 10.)

31. Which plant cell structure could *not* be seen when using the 10× objective of a compound microscope? (1) nucleus (2) cell wall (3) cytoplasm (4) endoplasmic reticulum

32. A microscope reveals 100 similar cells arranged end-to-end in a space of 1 millimeter. The average length of each cell must be (1) 0.1 micrometer (2) 10 micrometers (3) 100 micrometers (4) 1000 micrometers

33. Which instrument would provide the most detailed information about the internal structure of a chloroplast? (1) compound light microscope (2) phase-contrast microscope (3) electron microscope (4) ultracentrifuge

34. If the low-power objective and the eyepiece both have a magnifying power of 10×, the total magnifying power of the microscope is (1) 10× (2) 100× (3) 1× (4) 20×

35. To separate the parts of a cell by differences in density, a biologist would probably use (1) a microdissection instrument (2) an ultracentrifuge (3) a phase-contrast microscope (4) an electron microscope

36. Which microscope magnification should be used to observe the largest field of view of an insect wing? (1) 20× (2) 100× (3) 400× (4) 900×

37. The diameter of the field of vision of a compound light microscope is 1.5 millimeters. This may also be expressed as (1) 15 micrometers (2) 150 micrometers (3) 1500 micrometers (4) 15,000 micrometers

38. To transplant a nucleus from one cell to another cell, a scientist would use (1) an electron microscope (2) an ultracentrifuge (3) microdissection instruments (4) staining techniques

39. A student used a compound microscope to measure the diameters of several red blood cells and found that the average length was 0.008 millimeter. What was the average length of a single red blood cell in micrometers? (1) 0.8 (2) 8 (3) 80 (4) 800

40. A student using a compound microscope estimated the diameter of a cheek cell to be about 50 micrometers. What is the diameter of this cheek cell in millimeters? (1) 0.050 (2) 0.500 (3) 5.00 (4) 50.0

41. A student has a microscope with a 10× eyepiece and 10× and 40× objectives. She observed 40 onion epidermal cells across the diameter of the low-power field. How many cells would she observe under high power? (1) 1 (2) 40 (3) 10 (4) 4

42. After examining cells from an onion root tip under high power, a student switches to the low-power objective without moving the slide. He would most likely see (1) more cells and less detail (2) more cells and more detail (3) fewer cells and less detail (4) fewer cells and more detail

Part B-1

43. The following diagram, above right, represents the field of vision of a microscope. What is the approximate diameter in micrometers of the cell shown in the field? (1) 50 (2) 500 (3) 1000 (4) 2000

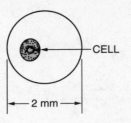

Part B-2

44. Select any three parts that are labeled in the diagram below and for each part selected
- identify the part
- and state the function of that part.

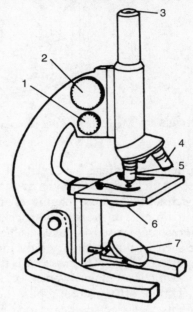

45. Explain how a biology student can calculate the magnification of a specimen when the powers of the eyepiece lens and the objective lens are known.

Part C

Answer question 46 based on the following information and data table.

Eyepiece Lens	Objective Lens	Magnification of Image
10×		100×
	40×	400×
15×	90×	
10×		150×
		900×

46. A lab microscope has two interchangeable eyepieces and four objective lenses. The table above shows various combinations of the eyepiece and objective lenses and the apparent magnification of the specimen image produced. Use the information provided in the table to complete the missing data.

47. Briefly describe how the development of the compound microscope and other magnifying instruments greatly advanced the science of biology.

BIOCHEMISTRY

The chemical reactions necessary to sustain life take place in the cells. The study of the chemical reactions of living things is called *biochemistry*.

Elements
A substance that cannot be broken down into simpler substances is called an *element*. Examples of elements include hydrogen, oxygen, sodium, and potassium. The most abundant elements in living things are **carbon**, **hydrogen**, **oxygen**, and **nitrogen**. Elements found in lesser amounts in living things include sulfur, phosphorus, magnesium, iodine, iron, calcium, chlorine, potassium, and others.

Atoms
All elements are made up of particles called **atoms**. Each element has a different kind of atom. The atoms of the various elements differ in the numbers of protons, neutrons, and electrons they contain. A *compound* is formed when two or more elements combine chemically. For example, water (H_2O) is formed by the chemical combination of two hydrogen atoms and one oxygen atom.

Chemical Bonding
The formation of compounds involves either the transfer or the sharing of electrons between atoms, resulting in the formation of chemical bonds. When atoms lose or gain electrons, they become electrically charged particles called ions, and an *ionic bond* is formed. When atoms share electrons, a *covalent bond* is formed. When a compound forms, it has properties that are different from those of the elements that make it up.

Inorganic and Organic Compounds
There are two basic classes of chemical compounds: inorganic compounds and organic compounds. Both types are found in living things.

Compounds that do not contain both carbon and hydrogen atoms are **inorganic** compounds. Inorganic compounds found in cells include water, salts, carbon dioxide, and inorganic acids such as hydrochloric acid (HCl).

Compounds that contain both carbon and hydrogen atoms are **organic** compounds. Because carbon atoms can form four covalent bonds with other atoms, organic compounds are often large and complex. The major categories of organic compounds found in living things are carbohydrates, proteins, lipids, and nucleic acids.

Carbohydrates
Sugars and starches, which are used primarily as sources of energy and as food-storage compounds, are *carbohydrates*. These substances are made up of carbon, hydrogen, and oxygen, and the ratio of hydrogen to oxygen is always 2 to 1. The simplest carbohydrates are the *monosaccharides*, or **simple sugars**. Glucose, galactose, and fructose, each with the formula $C_6H_{12}O_6$, are simple sugars.

Some carbohydrates, such as maltose and sucrose (both $C_{12}H_{22}O_{11}$) are known as *disaccharides*, sugars whose molecules are made up of two monosaccharide molecules bonded together. For example, a maltose molecule is formed from two glucose molecules that are bonded together.

The complex carbohydrates that are made up of chains of monosaccharides are called *polysaccharides*. Starch, cellulose, and glycogen are polysaccharides that are made up of chains of glucose molecules. In plants, **starch** is a food storage compound and cellulose makes up the cell walls. In animals, glycogen is the food-storage compound.

Proteins
Enzymes, hormones, and various structural parts of organisms are **proteins**. Proteins are made up of smaller **subunits** called **amino acids**.

Structure of Amino Acids. Amino acids contain the elements carbon, hydrogen, oxygen, and nitrogen. Some also contain sulfur. Figure 2-3 shows the generalized structure of an amino acid.

The $-NH_2$ is an amino group; the $-COOH$ is a carboxyl, or acid, group; and the *R* represents a

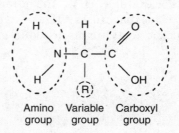

Amino   Variable   Carboxyl
group   group   group

FIGURE 2-3 Generalized structure of an amino acid.

variable group. The *R* group is the part of the amino acid structure that differs from one amino acid to another. Twenty different amino acids are found in the cells of living things.

Like carbohydrates, amino acids combine chemically to form more complex molecules. When two amino acids combine, they form a *dipeptide*. The bond that holds the amino acids together is called a *peptide bond*. More amino acids may combine with a dipeptide to form a *polypeptide*. A protein is made up of one or more polypeptide chains. There are a great many types of protein molecules in living things. These molecules differ in the number, kinds, and sequences of amino acids they contain.

Lipids

Fats, oils, and waxes belong to a class of organic compounds called **lipids**. They serve mainly as sources of energy and as components of structures such as cell membranes. Lipids that are solid at room temperature are *fats*; those that are liquid are *oils*. Lipids contain carbon, hydrogen, and oxygen. The ratio of hydrogen atoms to oxygen atoms is greater than 2 to 1 and varies from one lipid to another. The building blocks of lipids are fatty acids and glycerol.

Nucleic Acids

DNA and RNA are two very important classes of organic molecules; they are both involved in the passing on of genetic information from one generation to the next. DNA (deoxyribonucleic acid) is located in the nucleus, mitochondria, and chloroplasts of cells, where it stores vital information for the cell. DNA molecules are capable of duplicating, or *replicating*, themselves. In addition to transmitting traits, DNA is responsible for the synthesis (production) of proteins, which all cells need to survive. **RNA (ribonucleic acid)** is similar to DNA in that both molecules are *polymers*; this means they are composed of thousands of smaller chemical units that are repeated over and over again, thus forming giant molecules. RNA assists in carrying out the vital information (such as the instructions for protein synthesis) stored in the DNA molecules. In some viruses, RNA, rather than DNA, is the genetic material that allows the virus to function. For example, HIV—the human immunodeficiency virus that causes AIDS—is a type of RNA virus. (Nucleic acids are discussed in greater detail in Chapter 7.)

QUESTIONS
Part A

48. What is the principal inorganic solvent in cells? (1) salt (2) water (3) alcohol (4) carbon dioxide

49. Fats that are stored in human tissue contain molecules of (1) glycerol and fatty acids (2) amino acids (3) monosaccharides and disaccharides (4) nucleotides

50. The shape of a protein is most directly determined by the (1) amount of energy available for synthesis (2) kind and sequence of amino acids in the protein (3) type and number of DNA molecules in a cell (4) mistakes made when the DNA is copied

51. Which formula represents an organic compound? (1) NH_3 (2) H_2O (3) $NaCl$ (4) $C_{12}H_{22}O_{11}$

52. Starch is classified as a (1) disaccharide (2) polypeptide (3) nucleotide (4) polysaccharide

53. Which organic compound is correctly matched with the subunit that composes it? (1) maltose—amino acid (2) starch—glucose (3) protein—fatty acid (4) lipid—sucrose

Part B-2

54. There are only 20 different amino acids found in living things, yet there are thousands of different proteins. Explain why this is possible.

55. Explain why starch molecules and protein molecules are both called polymers.

56. Examine each of the four molecular structures shown below. Identify each molecule as organic or inorganic and explain your classification.

(1)   (2)

(3)   (4)

Part C

Base your answer to question 57 on the following information and data table.

Unknown Sample	Elements Contained	Molecular Characteristics
A	C, H, O, and N	Polymer, high molecular mass
B	C, H, and O	Very little oxygen, much hydrogen
C	C, H, and O	Twice as much hydrogen as oxygen

57. A lab was set up for students to analyze three unknown samples of organic molecules—a lipid, a carbohydrate, and a protein. The results of their lab tests are shown in the table. Based on these results, identify each sample as a protein, carbohydrate, or lipid, and then state the reason for your identification of each molecule.

58. There are four major types of organic molecules that are important in living things: carbohydrates, lipids, proteins, and nucleic acids. Select any two molecules and for each one chosen

- describe or sketch and label the structure of the molecule
- and state two ways that the molecule is useful to living organisms.

ENZYMES

Role of Enzymes

Chemical reactions occur continuously in living things. Each reaction requires the presence of a special protein called an **enzyme**, which regulates the rate of the reaction. In general, enzymes speed up the rate of a reaction. Enzymes are biological **catalysts**, substances that change the rate of a chemical reaction but are themselves unchanged by the reaction.

Enzymes are named after their *substrates*, the substances they act on. The name of an enzyme generally ends in *ase*. For example, a lipase acts on lipids, a protease acts on proteins, and maltase acts on the sugar maltose.

Enzyme Structure

An enzyme is a large, complex protein that consists of one or more polypeptide chains. In addition to the protein, some enzymes contain a nonprotein component called a *coenzyme*; if the coenzyme part is missing, the enzyme will not function. *Vitamins* often function as coenzymes. Although most enzymes are made up of proteins, some enzymes are composed of another type of organic molecule, that is, RNA. This type of enzyme is sometimes called a *ribozyme*.

The polypeptide chains that make up an enzyme are folded in a highly specific way (based on bonding between the amino acids), forming pockets on the enzyme surface into which the substrate molecule or molecules fit. The specific part of the enzyme where the substrate fits is called the *active site*.

Models of Enzyme Action

Different models can be used to describe the mechanism of enzyme action. According to the *lock-and-key model*, the active site on an enzyme has a unique three-dimensional shape that can form a complex

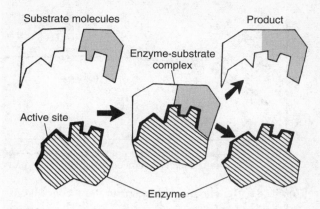

FIGURE 2-4 The lock-and-key model of enzyme action.

with only one type of substrate. The substrate fits an active site just as a key fits a lock (Figure 2-4). However, it is important to note that the enzyme molecule is not rigid. Rather, according to the *induced fit model* of enzyme action, when it binds to a substrate at the active site, the enzyme molecule bends somewhat to cause, or induce, a closer fit between itself and the substrate. This enhanced fit allows the enzyme to function in a more effective manner.

For an enzyme to affect the rate of a chemical reaction, the substrate must become attached to the active site of the enzyme, forming an *enzyme-substrate complex*. The enzyme's action occurs while the enzyme and substrate are bound together. At this time, bonds of the substrate may be weakened, causing it to break apart, or bonds may form between substrate molecules, joining them together. After the reaction is complete, the enzyme and product(s) separate, and the enzyme molecule becomes available to act on other substrate molecules.

Factors Influencing Enzyme Action

The rate of enzyme action is affected by temperature, concentrations of enzyme and substrate, and pH.

Temperature. The rate of enzyme action varies with temperature. Up to a point, the rate increases with

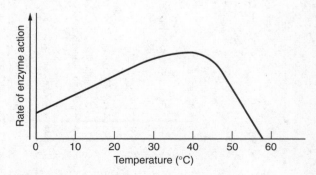

FIGURE 2-5 The effect of changing temperature on the rate of enzyme action.

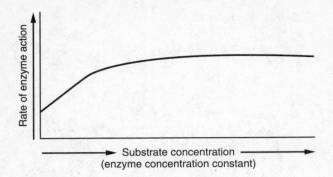

FIGURE 2-6 The effect of changing substrate concentration on the rate of enzyme action.

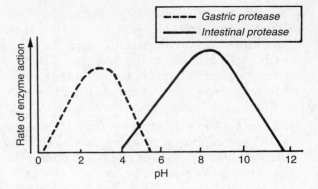

FIGURE 2-8 The effect of pH on the rate of enzyme action.

increasing temperature (Figure 2-5). The temperature at which the enzyme functions most efficiently is called the *optimum temperature.* If the temperature is raised above the optimum, the rate of enzyme action begins to decrease. The decrease in enzyme action occurs because the higher temperature destroys the three-dimensional shape of the enzyme protein. In this process, known as *denaturation,* the shape of the enzyme's active site is altered so that it no longer fits the substrate. In humans, the normal body temperature of about 37°C is also the optimum temperature for most human enzymes. Denaturation of these enzymes begins at about 40°C, upsetting the body's homeostasis.

Enzyme and Substrate Concentrations. The rate of enzyme action varies with the amount of available substrate. With a high concentration of enzyme and a low concentration of substrate, the rate of enzyme action increases as the substrate concentration increases (Figure 2-6). At the point where all enzyme molecules are reacting, the rate levels off—addition of more substrate has no further effect.

pH. The rate of enzyme action varies with the pH of the environment. The **pH** scale is a measure of the hydrogen ion (H+) concentration of a solution. Solutions with a pH of 7 are neutral. Those with a

pH below 7 are acids, while those with a pH above 7 are bases (Figure 2-7).

Each enzyme has a particular pH at which it functions most efficiently. For example, most enzymes in human blood function best in neutral solutions. However, pepsin, an enzyme in the stomach, works best at a pH of 2 (a very high **acidity** level), and trypsin, an enzyme in the small intestine, works best at a pH of 8 (Figure 2-8).

QUESTIONS
Part A

59. Which is characteristic of an enzyme? (1) It is an inorganic catalyst. (2) It is destroyed after each chemical reaction. (3) It provides energy for any chemical reaction. (4) It regulates the rate of a specific chemical reaction.

60. The lock-and-key model of enzyme action illustrates that a particular enzyme molecule will (1) form a permanent enzyme-substrate complex (2) be destroyed and resynthesized several times (3) interact with a specific type of substrate molecule (4) react at identical rates under all conditions

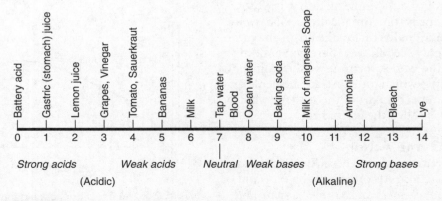

FIGURE 2-7 The pH scale ranges from acidic to basic.

61. An enzyme-substrate complex may result from the interaction of molecules of (1) glucose and lipase (2) fat and amylase (3) sucrose and maltase (4) protein and protease

62. The part of the enzyme molecule into which the substrate fits is called the (1) active site (2) coenzyme (3) polypeptide (4) protease

63. A nonprotein molecule necessary for the functioning of a particular enzyme is called a (1) catalyst (2) polypeptide (3) coenzyme (4) substrate

64. Which variable has the *least* direct effect on the rate of an enzyme-regulated reaction? (1) temperature (2) pH (3) carbon dioxide concentration (4) substrate concentration

65. The diagram below represents a beaker containing a solution of various molecules involved in digestion. Which structures represent products of digestion? (1) *A* and *D* (2) *B* and *C* (3) *B* and *E* (4) *D* and *E*

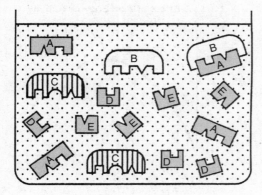

66. Enzymes have an optimum temperature at which they work best. Temperatures above and below this optimum will decrease enzyme activity. Which graph best illustrates the effect of temperature on enzyme activity?

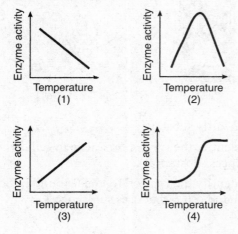

67. A word equation is shown below. This reaction is most directly involved in the process of (1) reproduction (2) protein synthesis (3) replication (4) heterotrophic nutrition

starch molecules + biological catalyst
= simple sugars

68. The change in shape of enzyme molecules that occurs at high temperatures is known as (1) synthesis (2) specificity (3) replication (4) denaturation

Part B-1

Base your answers to questions 69 through 71 on the following graph and on your knowledge of biology. The graph represents the rate of enzyme action when different concentrations of enzyme are added to a system with a fixed amount of substrate.

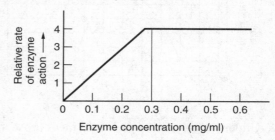

69. At which enzyme concentration does all of the available substrate react with the enzyme? (1) 0.1 mg/mL (2) 0.2 mg/mL (3) 0.3 mg/mL (4) 0.5 mg/mL

70. When the enzyme concentration is increased from 0.5 mg/mL to 0.6 mg/mL, the rate of enzyme action (1) decreases (2) increases (3) remains the same

71. If more substrate is added to the system at an enzyme concentration of 0.4 mg/mL, the rate of the reaction would most likely (1) decrease (2) increase (3) remain the same

Base your answers to questions 72 and 73 on page 30 on the following graphs. Graph I shows the relationship between temperature and the relative rates of activity of enzymes A and B. Graph II shows the relationship between pH and the relative rates of activity of enzymes A and B.

Graph I

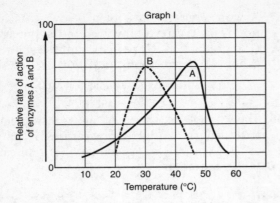

Graph II

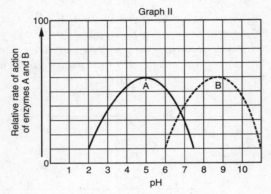

72. Under which conditions is enzyme *A* most effective? (1) at 40°C and a pH of 5 (2) at 45°C and a pH of 5 (3) at 45°C and a pH of 9 (4) at 50°C and a pH of 9

73. The optimum environment for enzyme *B* is (1) a basic medium (2) an acidic medium (3) either an acidic or a basic medium (4) a neutral medium

Use your knowledge of enzymes and biology to answer questions 74 and 75.

74. Fresh pineapple contains an enzyme that digests proteins. Adding fresh pineapple to gelatin (a protein) prevents it from setting or jelling. Adding cooked or canned pineapple does not have this effect and the gelatin can set normally. Explain why these different effects occur.

75. When an apple is cut open, the inside soon turns brown. This is because enzymes that are released from the cut cells react with certain molecules in the apple. Rubbing lemon juice (which contains citric acid) on the cut apple prevents it from browning. Explain why this is so.

76. The human stomach contains an enzyme called pepsin, which actively breaks down (digests) protein molecules found in food. Based on your knowledge of biology, answer the following:

    • At what temperature would you expect pepsin to work best? Give a reason for your answer.

    • Why would drinking very cold beverages have a negative effect on digestion of food in the stomach?

77. Draw a diagram in which you show how the enzyme maltase combines with two glucose molecules to form maltose. Label the enzyme, substrate, enzyme-substrate complex, and end product.

78. An incomplete graph is shown below. What label could appropriately be used to replace letter *Z* on the horizontal axis?

Effect of Z on Enzyme Activity

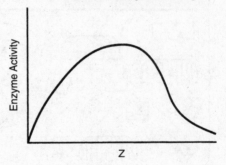

Base your answers to questions 79 through 81 on the two different cells shown below. Only cell A produces substance X. Both cells A and B use substance X.

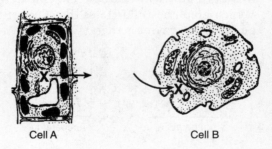

Cell A   Cell B

79. Identify substance *X*.

80. Identify the type of organelle in cell *A* that produces substance *X*.

81. Identify the type of organelle found in both cell *A* and cell *B* that uses substance *X*.

82. The enzyme catalase is found in almost all living tissues. This enzyme catalyzes the breakdown of harmful hydrogen peroxide in the body. Liver tissue is particularly rich in catalase. Like all enzymes, catalase is affected by temperature fluctuations. Design and describe an experiment in which a person can study the activity of catalase over a range of temperatures, from 0°C to 80°C. Be sure to include an appropriate control and a data table in your experimental design.

LITERACY SKILL: READING FOR COMPREHENSION

Base your answers to questions 83 through 85 on the information below and on your knowledge of biology. Source: Science News *(January 15, 2011): vol. 179, no. 2, p. 14. Reprinted with permission of* Science News.

Blood Test Can Spot Heart Risk: Cardiac Troponin T Could Be Added to Existing Indicators

A new blood test might reveal heart damage that puts some people at a hidden higher risk of cardiac failure or death, researchers report in the Dec. 8 *Journal of the American Medical Association.*

Although factors such as obesity, diabetes, or high blood pressure hike heart disease risk, many people without these problems have heart attacks. Efforts to identify other warning signs have focused largely on two componds, C-reactive protein and B-type natriuretic peptide (BNP). But only blood levels of BNP have shown predictive ability.

Two new studies suggest that a blood compound called cardiac troponin T might outperfom both as a risk indicator.

In one analysis, Christopher deFilippi of the University of Maryland School of Medicine in Baltimore and his colleagues sampled blood from more than 5,000 people nationwide who were 65 or older and had no history of heart failure. During nearly 12 years of follow-up, on average, people with the highest levels of cardiac troponin T at the study outset were at least 51 percent more likely to develop heart failure and 70 percent more apt to die from cardiovascular causes than those with the lowest levels. The researchers accounted for factors such as blood pressure, previous heart disease, and smoking.

In another study, researchers evaluated blood from nearly 3,500 people without coronary heart disease, age 30 to 65, between 2000 and 2002. By 2007, people with the highest levels of troponin T at the start of the study were at least 40 percent more likely to have died of any cause compared with those with the lowest levels. That group also acccounted for differences among the participants.

Combining cardiac troponin T measurements with BNP as a cardiac risk test "definitely would make sense," says cardiologist James de Lemos of the University of Texas Southwestern Medical Center at Dallas, who coauthored both papers.

83. Name three factors that can increase a person's chances of developing heart disease.

84. According to the article, what relationship exists between levels of cardiac troponin T and the risk of heart disease?

85. Christopher deFilippi sampled blood from 5,000 people age 65 or older and followed them for 12 years in his study. Describe one possible change in his research method that would make the results even more reliable.

3 Maintenance in Living Things

Most living organisms perform all the same life functions. They obtain and process food, and distribute nutrients and other essential materials to their cells. They get rid of wastes produced as a result of cell metabolism. All of these life functions must be regulated.

Different kinds of organisms have specific structures and behavioral patterns that enable them to perform the life functions efficiently within their physical surroundings, or *environment*. These structures and behavioral patterns are called **adaptations**.

NUTRITION

Nutrition includes those activities by which organisms obtain and process food for use by the cells. The cells use **nutrients** from foods for energy, growth, repair, and regulation. Nutrition may be autotrophic or heterotrophic. In **autotrophic** nutrition, the organism can synthesize organic substances (nutrients) from inorganic substances obtained from the environment. In **heterotrophic** nutrition, the organism must ingest needed organic substances from other organisms in the environment.

Photosynthesis

The most common type of autotrophic nutrition is **photosynthesis**. Organisms that carry out photosynthesis are called *autotrophs*—a group that includes all

plants, some **bacteria** (eubacteria) and **algae** (types of protists). In photosynthesis, the organism uses carbon dioxide and water taken from the environment along with energy from sunlight to synthesize the organic compound glucose. Most of the chemical energy available to living organisms comes either directly or indirectly from photosynthesis. Also, most of the oxygen in the air comes from photosynthesis.

Photosynthetic Pigments. Photosynthesis requires the presence of certain colored substances called *pigments,* which "trap" light energy and convert it to a form of chemical energy that can be used by living things. *Chlorophylls* are the green pigments found in photosynthetic organisms. In most of these organisms, the chlorophyll is found in organelles called *chloroplasts* (Figure 3-1). In addition to the chlorophylls, chloroplasts may contain a variety of

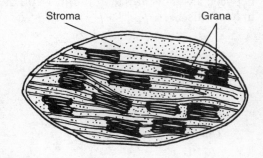

FIGURE 3-1 Structure of a chloroplast.

accessory pigments, which trap those wavelengths of light that chlorophyll cannot trap. For example, chlorophyll cannot trap green light. That is why plants appear green; their chlorophyll reflects the green light. The orange pigment carotene, however, can trap green light and thus makes its energy available for photosynthesis.

Chemistry of Photosynthesis. The process of photosynthesis is complex, involving several series of reactions. However, it can be summarized by the following equation:

$$\text{carbon dioxide} + \text{water} \xrightarrow[\substack{\text{chlorophyll} \\ \text{enzymes}}]{\text{light energy}} \text{glucose} + \text{water} + \text{oxygen}$$

Carbon dioxide and water are the raw materials of photosynthesis. Light energy absorbed by the chlorophyll is converted to chemical energy, which is used to synthesize glucose from the raw materials. Water and oxygen are released as waste products of photosynthesis.

The glucose produced by photosynthesis is used, when needed, as an energy source in cellular respiration. It can also be converted to starch, an insoluble food-storage compound. Before starch can be used in any cellular process, it must be broken down to glucose by enzymes within the cell. The glucose can be used in the synthesis of other organic compounds, such as lipids and proteins.

QUESTIONS
Part A

1. By which process are carbon dioxide and water converted to carbohydrates? (1) transpiration (2) respiration (3) fermentation (4) photosynthesis

2. Why is a plant considered an autotroph? (1) It ingests its food. (2) It divides by mitosis. (3) It converts light energy to chemical energy. (4) It obtains nutrients from its environment.

3. Glucose molecules may be stored in plants in the form of (1) oxygen (2) starch (3) nucleic acids (4) amino acids

4. Organisms capable of manufacturing organic molecules from inorganic raw materials are classified as (1) autotrophs (2) heterotrophs (3) aerobes (4) anaerobes

5. The basic raw materials for photosynthesis are (1) water and carbon dioxide (2) oxygen and water (3) sugar and carbon dioxide (4) carbon dioxide and oxygen

6. Which word equation represents the process of photosynthesis?

(1) carbon dioxide + water → glucose + oxygen + water
(2) glucose → alcohol + carbon dioxide
(3) maltose + water → glucose + glucose
(4) glucose + oxygen → carbon dioxide + water

7. Autotrophic activity in plant cells is most closely associated with the organelles called (1) mitochondria (2) ribosomes (3) vacuoles (4) chloroplasts

8. In terms of nutrition, the functional difference between animals and plants is that green plants are able to (1) synthesize glucose (2) break down carbohydrates (3) carry on aerobic respiration (4) form ATP molecules

Part B-2

Base your answers to questions 9 and 10 on the following statement and on your knowledge of biology.

Carbon exists in a simple organic molecule in a leaf and in an inorganic molecule in the air that humans exhale.

9. Identify the simple organic molecule formed in the leaf and the process that produces it.

10. Identify one molecule that humans exhale and the process that produces it.

Part C

11. State one function of each of the following in the process of photosynthesis:
    - light
    - chlorophyll
    - carbon dioxide
    - water

12. Why is photosynthesis called one of the most important processes on Earth? Give at least one example to support your answer.

13. Bromthymol blue turns to bromthymol yellow in the presence of carbon dioxide. When the carbon dioxide is removed, the solution returns to a blue color. Two green water plants were placed in separate test tubes, each containing water and bromthymol yellow. Both test tubes were corked. One tube was placed in the light, the other in the dark. After several days, the liquid in the tube exposed to the light turned blue. Based on these results, answer the following:
    - Why did the bromthymol solution turn blue in one of the tubes?
    - What does it illustrate about the activity of plants during photosynthesis?
    - What do you think occurred in the tube that was placed in the dark?

Use the information below and your knowledge of biology to answer the following question.

14. A suspension (of chloroplasts in water) from spinach leaves was kept under a bright light at a temperature of 25°C. Another suspension was kept in a dark corner of the same room. Each container had attached to it a small pipette by which the amount of oxygen released by the chloroplasts could be measured. The data table below shows the volume of oxygen produced by each suspension over a 24-hour period.

Total Volume of Oxygen Produced by Chloroplast Suspension (mL)		
Time (hours)	Incubated in Light	Incubated in Dark
0	0.00	0.00
6	0.42	0.01
12	0.96	0.01
18	1.78	0.01
24	2.36	0.01

- Describe the difference recorded in the amount of oxygen produced by the two chloroplast suspensions.
- Explain why there was a difference in the volume of oxygen produced by the two chloroplast suspensions.
- Give a scientific reason why the suspension incubated in the dark produced only 0.01 mL of oxygen.
- Make a line graph showing the results of the experiment. Use different colors to plot the data for each suspension.
- State one way the researcher could modify the experiment to show that the results are reliable.

Adaptations for Photosynthesis

Algae and green plants are autotrophic organisms that carry on photosynthesis. A large percentage of Earth's photosynthesis occurs in unicellular algae present in the oceans. The raw materials necessary for photosynthesis are absorbed directly from the water into the cells of the algae. Most photosynthesis in terrestrial (land-dwelling) plants occurs in leaves.

Structure of Leaves. Most leaves are thin and flat, providing the maximum surface area for the absorption of light. The outermost cell layer of the leaf is the *epidermis,* which protects the internal tissues from water loss, mechanical injury, and attack by fungi (Figure 3-2). In some plants, the epidermis is covered by a waxy coating, called the *cuticle,* which provides additional protection against water loss and infection.

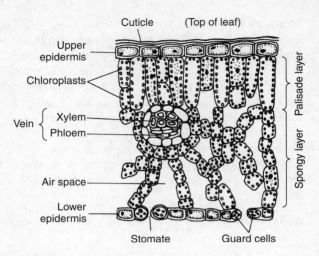

FIGURE 3-2 Cross section of a typical leaf.

There are many tiny openings in the epidermis and cuticle, mainly on the undersurface of the leaf. These openings, called *stomates,* allow the exchange of carbon dioxide, oxygen, and water vapor between the environment and the moist, inner tissues of the leaf. Each stomate is surrounded by a pair of chloroplast-containing guard cells. By changing shape (due to water pressure), the guard cells open or close the stomate opening.

Beneath the upper epidermis is the *palisade layer,* which is made up of tall, tightly packed cells filled with chloroplasts. Most of the photosynthetic activity of the leaf occurs in this layer. The cells of the epidermis are clear, so that light striking the leaf passes through to the chloroplasts in the palisade layer.

Between the palisade layer and the lower epidermis of the leaf is the *spongy layer,* which is made up of loosely arranged cells separated by interconnecting air spaces. The air spaces are continuous with the stomates. Gases from the environment enter the leaf through the stomates and diffuse from the air spaces into the cells. Other gases diffuse out of the cells into the air spaces and then out of the leaf through the stomates. The cells of the spongy layer contain chloroplasts and carry on some photosynthesis.

The conducting tissues of the leaf are found in bundles called *veins.* The tissue called *xylem* carries water and dissolved minerals from the roots through the stems to the leaves, and the tissue called *phloem* carries food from the leaves to the rest of the plant.

QUESTIONS
Part A

15. Water is lost from the leaves of a plant through its (1) spongy cells (2) root hairs (3) veins (4) stomates

16. Most of the photosynthetic activity in a leaf occurs in its (1) palisade layer (2) cuticle (3) stomates (4) spongy layer

Base your answers to questions 17 through 20 on the following diagram, which shows a leaf cross section, and on your knowledge of biology.

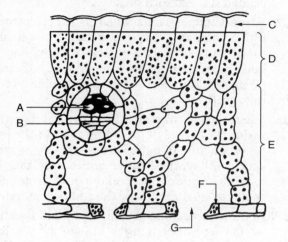

17. Which letter indicates the principal region of food manufacture? (1) *E* (2) *B* (3) *C* (4) *D*

18. Which letter indicates the area where carbon dioxide passes out of the leaf? (1) *A* (2) *G* (3) *C* (4) *D*

19. Which letter indicates a structure that regulates the size of a stomate? (1) *A* (2) *B* (3) *F* (4) *G*

20. Water and dissolved nutrients are carried by the tissues labeled (1) *D* and *E* (2) *C* and *D* (3) *A* and *B* (4) *E* and *F*

Refer to the following diagrams of three different leaf types to answer question 21.

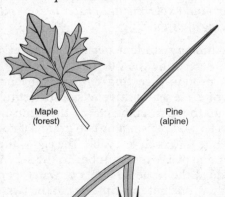

Maple (forest)

Pine (alpine)

Grass (prairie)

21. How is each leaf adapted to carry out photosynthesis in the particular habitat in which the plant lives? (See diagrams for typical habitat of each leaf type.) State one adaptation for each leaf.

22. A student placed one of her tropical houseplants outside on her porch during the summer to receive some natural sunshine. A few days later, a rubbish fire broke out in a nearby vacant lot, spreading soot all over the neighborhood. Within two weeks, the plant's leaves started to turn yellow and drop off the stem. Give two scientific explanations of how the soot may have negatively affected the plant.

23. Explain why a cactus's leaves are not broad and flat but are reduced in size to the form of spines. How is this an adaptation that helps the cactus survive?

24. How is the typical leaf adapted for carrying out photosynthesis? Include the functions of the following leaf parts:
- cuticle
- chloroplasts
- stomates
- guard cells

Heterotrophic Nutrition

Organisms that cannot synthesize organic molecules from inorganic raw materials are *heterotrophs* and must obtain preformed organic molecules from the environment. Heterotrophic organisms include most bacteria, some protists, and all **fungi** and animals. Heterotrophic nutrition involves the processes of ingestion (taking in food), digestion, and egestion (discharging waste). In animals, it generally begins with the mechanical breakdown of food, during which large pieces of food are broken down into smaller pieces by cutting, grinding, and tearing. The smaller pieces provide greater surface area for the action of enzymes during chemical digestion.

Digestion. In some heterotrophs, chemical digestion is *intracellular*—it occurs within the cell (or cells) of the organism. In most heterotrophs, however, digestion is *extracellular*—it occurs in a sac or a tube outside the cells. The end products of digestion are then absorbed into the cells.

Adaptations for Heterotrophic Nutrition

Heterotrophs obtain nutrients in a variety of ways.

Protists. In protists, such as the ameba and paramecium, digestion is intracellular. In the ameba, food particles are surrounded and engulfed by extensions of the cell called *pseudopods*. This process is known as *phagocytosis*. Within the cell, the food particle is enclosed in a food vacuole. In the paramecium, food particles are ingested through a fixed opening called the *oral groove*. They are moved into this opening by the beating of tiny "hairs" called *cilia*. The food particles are then enclosed in a food vacuole, which circulates in the cytoplasm (Figure 3-3).

In both the ameba and paramecium, the food vacuole merges with a *lysosome,* which is an organelle that contains digestive enzymes. The food within the vacuole is digested by these enzymes, and the end products of digestion are then absorbed into the cytoplasm. In the ameba, wastes are expelled from the cell through the cell membrane. In the paramecium, wastes are expelled through a fixed opening called the *anal pore*.

Humans. The human digestive system is essentially like that of most other **multicellular** (many-celled) animals. Food moves in one direction through a tube, and specialized organs carry out its mechanical breakdown and chemical digestion.

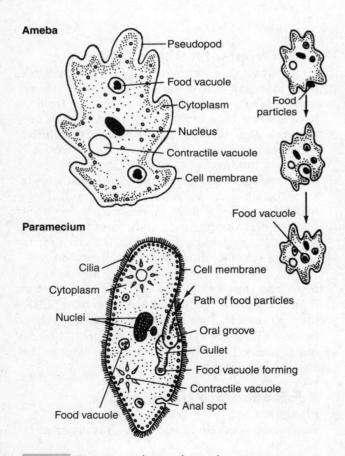

FIGURE 3-3 Nutrition in the ameba and paramecium.

25. Based on their pattern of nutrition, all animals are classified as (1) autotrophic (2) heterotrophic (3) photosynthetic (4) phagocytic

26. Digestion that occurs in a sac or a tube is referred to as (1) phagocytic (2) intracellular (3) extracellular (4) heterotrophic

27. A grasshopper is classified as a heterotroph, rather than an autotroph, because it is unable to (1) transport needed materials throughout its body (2) release energy from organic molecules (3) manufacture its own food (4) divide its cells mitotically

28. The principal function of mechanical digestion is the (1) storage of food molecules in the liver (2) production of more surface area for enzyme action (3) synthesis of enzymes necessary for food absorption (4) breakdown of large molecules to smaller ones by the addition of water

29. In the paramecium, most intracellular digestion occurs within structures known as (1) ribosomes (2) endoplasmic reticula (3) mitochondria (4) food vacuoles

30. Which organism ingests food by engulfing it with pseudopods? (1) grasshopper (2) paramecium (3) ameba (4) earthworm

Part B-2

31. How does mechanical digestion aid the process of chemical digestion?

32. Briefly compare intracellular digestion and extracellular digestion.

Part C

Use the information below and your knowledge of biology and experimental procedures to answer the following questions.

33. A biology student performed an experiment to determine the rate of digestion by protease (a protein-digesting enzyme) on cooked egg white. He set up three sets of six test tubes each. Into the first set, he placed the same amount of water and pepsin plus two grams of cooked egg white into each test tube. The egg white was left in one piece in each tube. To the second set, he added the same amounts of water, pepsin, and egg white, but this time he cut the two grams of egg white into eight small pieces before placing it into each test tube. The third set of test tubes also received the same amounts of water, pepsin, and

egg white, but the egg white was finely chopped up before being placed into each test tube.

- What hypothesis was the student most likely testing?
- Predict what should occur in each setup and give a scientific explanation for your prediction.
- The student omitted a control in his experiment. Describe the appropriate control that could be used in this investigation.

TRANSPORT

Transport involves the absorption of materials through an organism's cell membranes and into its body fluids, and the circulation of materials throughout its body.

The Cell Membrane
The cell membrane surrounds the cell and regulates the passage of materials into and out of the cell.

Structure of the Cell Membrane. The currently accepted model of the structure of the cell membrane is called the *fluid mosaic model*. According to this model, the cell membrane consists of a double layer of lipids in which large protein molecules float (Figure 3-4).

Function of the Cell Membrane. The cell membrane selectively regulates the passage of substances into and out of the cell. Small molecules, including water, carbon dioxide, oxygen, and the soluble end products of digestion, pass easily through the cell membrane. Most larger molecules, such as proteins and starch, cannot pass through the cell membrane. However, molecular size is not the only factor that affects the movement of substances into or out of a cell. Other factors include polarity (the positive or negative charge on a molecule), solubility in water or lipids, and pH.

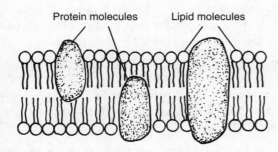

Protein molecules   Lipid molecules

FIGURE 3-4 The fluid mosaic model of cell membrane structure.

The cell membrane may contain a number of special *receptor sites* to which molecules bind as they enter or leave the cell. Binding to the receptor site is often the only way these molecules can enter or leave a cell. The shape of these receptor site molecules is highly specific to the shape of the molecule being transported. For example, a common receptor site on many cell membranes regulates the passage of sodium ions and potassium ions. The maintenance of homeostasis is largely dependent on the proper functioning of receptor sites on cells. The failure of a receptor site can lead to a serious illness. The disease cystic fibrosis is linked to the failure of chloride ion receptor sites on the cell membranes of afflicted people. This results in the accumulation of mucus in a person's lungs and, eventually, death.

Diffusion and Passive Transport
All ions and molecules are in constant, random motion. When such particles collide, they bounce off each other and travel in new directions. As a result of their motion and collisions, the particles tend to spread out from an area of high concentration to an area of low concentration, a process known as **diffusion**. The difference in concentration between two such areas is known as the *concentration gradient*.

Molecules and ions that can pass through a cell membrane tend to move into or out of the cell by diffusion. The direction of diffusion depends on the relative concentration of the substance inside and outside the cell and usually results in a balance, or **equilibrium**, in the substance's concentration. Diffusion is a type of **passive transport**; it occurs because of the kinetic energy of the molecules and ions and does not require the use of additional energy by the cell.

The diffusion of water through a membrane is called *osmosis*. In osmosis, water molecules move from a region of higher concentration of water to a region of lower concentration of water until they reach an equilibrium.

Active Transport
Processes that require **active transport** involve the movement of particles through a membrane with the use of energy by the cell. In some cases, substances are moved by active transport from a region of lower concentration to a region of higher concentration (against the concentration gradient). In active transport, protein molecules embedded in the cell membrane act as carriers that aid in the transport of materials across the membrane.

Pinocytosis and Phagocytosis
Large dissolved molecules can pass through a cell membrane by the process of *pinocytosis*. In

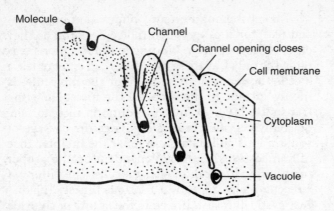

Molecule

Channel

Channel opening closes

Cell membrane

Cytoplasm

Vacuole

FIGURE 3-5 Pinocytosis (in a section of cell membrane).

pinocytosis (Figure 3-5), the cell membrane folds inward. The outer surface of the cell membrane then closes over, and the large molecule is enclosed in a vacuole inside the cell. In contrast, *phagocytosis* is the process by which a cell engulfs large undissolved particles by flowing around them and enclosing them in a vacuole. For example, amebas use their pseudopods to engulf food particles during phagocytosis (refer to Figure 3-3 on page 36).

Circulation

Circulation involves the movement of materials both within cells and throughout multicellular organisms. The movement of materials within a cell, *intracellular circulation*, takes place by diffusion and by *cyclosis*. Cyclosis is the natural streaming of cytoplasm that occurs within all cells. Intracellular circulation may also involve the movement of materials through the channels of the endoplasmic reticulum. The transport of materials throughout multicellular organisms is called *intercellular circulation*. Depending on the complexity of the organism, intercellular circulation may occur by diffusion or it may involve a specialized circulatory system with conducting, or vascular, tissues.

QUESTIONS
Part A

34. Which process describes the movement of sugar molecules through a membrane from a region of higher concentration to a region of lower concentration? (1) osmosis (2) cyclosis (3) passive transport (4) active transport

35. In the human body, the potassium ion can pass easily through cell membranes, yet the potassium ion concentration is higher inside many cells than it is outside these cells. This condition is mainly the result of (1) passive transport (2) active transport (3) osmosis (4) pinocytosis

36. Chemical analysis indicates that the cell membrane is composed mainly of (1) proteins and starch (2) proteins and cellulose (3) lipids and starch (4) lipids and proteins

37. The flow of materials through the membrane of a cell against the concentration gradient is known as (1) passive transport (2) active transport (3) osmosis (4) pinocytosis

38. A biologist observed a plant cell in a drop of water and illustrated it as in diagram A. He added a 10 percent salt solution to the slide, observed the cell, and illustrated it as in diagram B. The change in appearance of the cell resulted from more (1) salt flowing out of the cell than into the cell (2) salt flowing into the cell than out of the cell (3) water flowing into the cell than out of the cell (4) water flowing out of the cell than into the cell

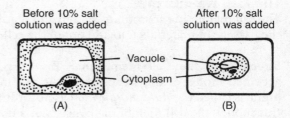

Before 10% salt solution was added

After 10% salt solution was added

Vacuole

Cytoplasm

(A)   (B)

39. The natural streaming of the cytoplasm that occurs within all cells is called (1) pinocytosis (2) phagocytosis (3) osmosis (4) cyclosis

40. Protein molecules in the cell membrane act as carriers to aid in the transport of materials during (1) osmosis (2) active transport (3) diffusion (4) passive transport

41. The diffusion of water molecules into and out of cells is called (1) cyclosis (2) pinocytosis (3) osmosis (4) active transport

42. The net movement of molecules into cells is most dependent on the (1) selectivity of the cell membrane (2) selectivity of the cell wall (3) number of vacuoles (4) number of chromosomes

43. The process by which amebas ingest food particles is called (1) pinocytosis (2) osmosis (3) phagocytosis (4) cyclosis

Part B-1

Base your answers to questions 44 and 45 on the information and diagram on page 39 and on your knowledge of biology.

An investigation was set up to study the movement of water through a membrane. The results are shown in the diagram on page 39.

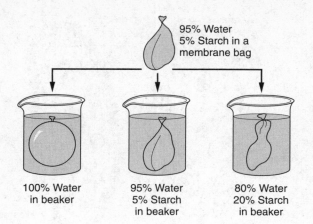

95% Water
5% Starch in a
membrane bag

100% Water
in beaker

95% Water
5% Starch
in beaker

80% Water
20% Starch
in beaker

44. Based on these results, which statement correctly predicts what will happen to red blood cells when they are placed in a beaker containing a water solution in which the salt concentration is much higher than the salt concentration in the red blood cells? (1) The red blood cells will absorb water and increase in size. (2) The red blood cells will lose water and decrease in size. (3) The red blood cells will first absorb water, then lose water and maintain their normal size. (4) The red blood cells will first lose water, then absorb water, and finally double in size.

45. A red blood cell placed in distilled water will swell and burst due to the diffusion of (1) salt from the red blood cell into the water (2) water into the red blood cell (3) water from the red blood cell into its environment (4) salt from the water into the red blood cell

Base your answers to questions 46 and 47 on the diagram below, which illustrates a process by which protein molecules may enter a cell, and on your knowledge of biology.

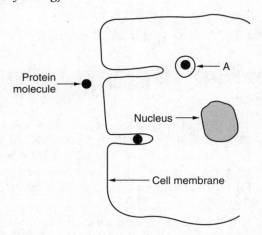

Protein
molecule

A

Nucleus

Cell membrane

46. Which process is illustrated in this diagram? (1) pinocytosis (2) osmosis (3) diffusion (4) passive transport

47. Structure *A* is most likely a (1) ribosome (2) mitochondrion (3) nucleolus (4) vacuole

48. Describe the differences between active transport and passive transport. Give one example of each type of transport.

49. Freshwater protozoa (single-celled organisms) live in an environment that is very close to 100 percent water. The inside of the cell (cytoplasm) is about 90 percent water. Explain the problem these protozoa face in their environment with respect to maintaining homeostasis. Briefly describe how they have adapted to deal with the problem.

Use the information in the paragraph and table below to answer the following questions.

50. A biology student was attempting to determine the percent of water present in the cells of elodea (an aquatic plant). She placed leaves of elodea in varying concentrations of saltwater solutions and observed when plasmolysis (cell shrinking) occurred. The table summarizes the results of her experiment.

Solution Concentration	Observed Plasmolysis
0.5% NaCl	None
1.0% NaCl	None
1.5% NaCl	None
2.0% NaCl	Very slight
2.5% NaCl	Pronounced
3.0% NaCl	Pronounced

- According to the data in the table, what percent of elodea cells is water? Explain how you arrived at this conclusion.

- Give a scientific explanation for what caused the cells to shrink at a certain concentration of salt water. What process causes plasmolysis of the cells?

Transport in Plants

The transport of materials in plants involves cyclosis, osmosis, diffusion, and active transport. Some plants contain specialized transport, or *vascular*, tissues while others do not.

Roots. Roots are structures that are specialized for the absorption of water and minerals from the soil and the conduction of these materials to the stem. Roots also anchor the plant in the soil and may contain stored nutrients in the form of starch.

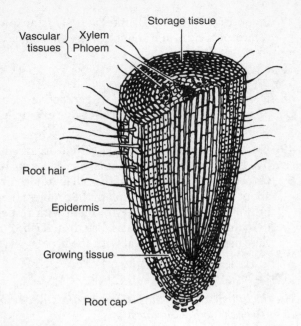

FIGURE 3-6 Structure of a root tip.

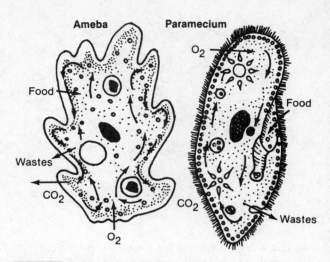

FIGURE 3-7 Transport in ameba and paramecium.

The surface area of the root is increased (for greater absorption) by the presence of *root hairs* just behind the growing tip (Figure 3-6). Water and minerals from the soil are absorbed through the membranes of the root hairs by osmosis, diffusion, and active transport. Materials are transported throughout the plant by two kinds of vascular tissues, *xylem* and *phloem.*

Stems. Although the structure of stems is more complex than that of roots, the xylem and phloem of the stem are continuous with the xylem and phloem of the roots.

Leaves. The xylem and phloem of the leaves, which are in bundles called *veins,* are also continuous with the xylem and phloem of the roots and stem.

Transport in Protists

Protists and other unicellular organisms have no specialized transport system. Materials enter and leave the cell by diffusion and active transport, and are circulated within the cell by diffusion and cyclosis (Figure 3-7).

Transport in Animals

Simple multicellular animals, whose cells are in direct contact with the surrounding water, have no specialized transport system. All other (that is, more complex) multicellular animals do have a specialized system for the transport of materials.

Humans. The human circulatory system is a closed system. Blood is moved through vessels by the pump-ing action of the heart (Figure 3-8). Human blood contains the pigment *hemoglobin,* which carries oxygen to the body tissues.

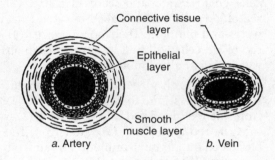

c. Capillary

FIGURE 3-8 The three types of blood vessels.

QUESTIONS
Part A

51. The primary function of the root hairs in a plant is to (1) prevent excessive loss of water (2) provide increased surface area for absorption (3) conduct water and minerals upward (4) conduct organic food materials upward and downward

52. A circulatory system in which the blood remains within vessels is called (1) a closed circulatory system (2) an open circulatory system (3) an internal circulatory system (4) an external circulatory system

53. The epidermal (outermost) cells of a plant's roots can continue to absorb water even when the concentration of water in the soil is very low, even lower than that in its cells. Explain the biological process that enables the root's epidermal cells to do this.

54. Use your knowledge of biology to answer the following questions comparing a single-celled organism (such as an ameba) and a multicelled organism (such as a human):

   • What are two similarities in their transport systems?

   • What are two differences in their transport systems?

RESPIRATION

The life processes of all organisms require energy. There is potential energy in the chemical bonds of organic molecules such as glucose. However, this energy cannot be used directly in cell metabolism. During *cellular respiration,* these bonds are broken; the energy that is released is temporarily stored in the bonds of the energy-transfer compound called ATP (adenosine triphosphate). This process occurs continuously in the cells of all organisms.

Cellular Respiration

Cellular respiration involves a series of enzyme-controlled reactions in which the energy released by the breakdown of the chemical bonds in glucose is transferred to the high-energy bonds of ATP. When ATP is broken down by hydrolysis (the addition of water), ADP (adenosine diphosphate) and phosphate (P) are produced, and energy is released for use by the cell.

The conversion of ATP to ADP is a reversible reaction catalyzed by the enzyme ATP-ase. In living organisms, ATP is constantly being converted to ADP, and the energy released is used for the reactions of cell metabolism. The ADP is then converted back to ATP by the reactions of cellular respiration. Depending on the type of organism, oxygen may or may not be required in the process of respiration.

Anaerobic Respiration. In a few kinds of organisms, free oxygen is not used, and the process is known as *anaerobic respiration,* or *fermentation.* Some cells, such as muscle cells, which normally carry on aerobic respiration, can carry on anaerobic respiration in the absence of oxygen. Other cells, such as yeast and some bacteria, which carry on anaerobic respiration, lack the enzymes necessary for aerobic respiration.

There is a net gain of only two ATP molecules for each molecule of glucose used in anaerobic respiration.

$$H_2O + ATP \xrightleftharpoons{ATP\text{-}ase} ADP + P + energy$$

Aerobic Respiration. In most organisms, cellular respiration requires the presence of free oxygen, and the process is known as *aerobic respiration.* In aerobic respiration, glucose is broken down completely to carbon dioxide and water by a series of enzyme-controlled reactions. Under ideal circumstances, these reactions, which take place mainly in the mitochondria, produce a net gain of 36 ATP molecules. However, the actual number of ATP molecules produced can vary from as few as 20 to as many as 38 per glucose molecule broken down, depending on various factors in the cell's environment.

$$glucose + oxygen \xrightarrow{enzymes} water + carbon\ dioxide + ATP$$

$$C_6H_{12}O_6 + 6O_2 \xrightarrow{enzymes} 6H_2O + 6CO_2 + 36\ ATP$$

Adaptations for Respiration

The oxygen used in aerobic cellular respiration comes from the environment, and the carbon dioxide produced must be excreted into the environment. Although the chemical processes of respiration are similar in most organisms, living things show a variety of adaptations for the exchange of these respiratory gases.

Protists. In simple organisms, such as protists, all or most of the cells are in direct contact with the environment. So the exchange of respiratory gases takes place by diffusion through the thin, moist cell membranes (Figure 3-9).

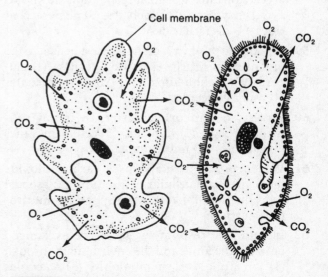

FIGURE 3-9 Respiration in ameba and paramecium.

Plants. In plants, respiratory gases are exchanged through the leaves, stems, and roots. The exchange of respiratory gases occurs by diffusion through the cell membranes of internal cells, which are surrounded by intercellular spaces. The intercellular spaces open to the environment through the stomates, openings on the undersurface of the leaf. In some plants, especially aquatic plants, the stomates are found on the upper surface of the leaf.

Humans. In humans, the exchange of respiratory gases takes place at thin, moist membranes within the lungs. Hemoglobin aids in the transport of oxygen in the blood. Carbon dioxide and oxygen are carried between the respiratory surface in the lungs and the environment by a system of air tubes.

QUESTIONS
Part A

55. Most animals make energy available for cell activity by transferring the potential energy of glucose to ATP. This process occurs during (1) aerobic respiration only (2) anaerobic respiration only (3) both aerobic and anaerobic respiration (4) neither aerobic nor anaerobic respiration

56. In animal cells, the energy to convert ADP to ATP comes directly from (1) hormones (2) sunlight (3) organic molecules (4) inorganic molecules

57. The organelles in which most of the reactions of aerobic cellular respiration take place are the (1) ribosomes (2) chloroplasts (3) lysosomes (4) mitochondria

58. The substances that most directly control the rate of reaction during cellular respiration are known as (1) enzymes (2) phosphates (3) monosaccharides (4) disaccharides

59. Which end product is of the greatest benefit to the organism in which respiration occurs? (1) glucose (2) carbon dioxide (3) ATP molecules (4) water molecules

60. Protists obtain oxygen from their environment through (1) stomates (2) cell membranes (3) vacuoles (4) mitochondria

61. Which process usually uses carbon dioxide molecules? (1) cellular respiration (2) asexual reproduction (3) active transport (4) autotrophic nutrition

62. In humans, respiratory gases are exchanged between the lungs and the environment through (1) air tubes (2) hemoglobin (3) vacuoles (4) stomates

63. Arrows *A*, *B*, and *C* in the diagram below represent the processes necessary to make the energy stored in food available for muscle activity. The correct sequence of processes represented by *A*, *B*, and *C* is (1) diffusion → synthesis → active transport (2) digestion → diffusion → cellular respiration (3) digestion → excretion → cellular respiration (4) synthesis → active transport → excretion

Food $\xrightarrow{A}$ Simpler molecules $\xrightarrow{B}$ Mitochondria $\xrightarrow{C}$ ATP in muscle cells

Part B-1

Base your answers to questions 64 through 68 on the diagram below, which represents a cellular process in animals, and on your knowledge of biology.

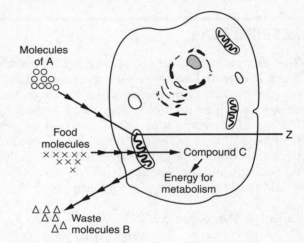

64. The items labeled as food molecules most likely represent (1) starch (2) glucose (3) phosphate (4) chlorophyll

65. Compound *C* most likely represents some molecules of (1) oxygen (2) glucose (3) ATP (4) DNA

66. If this cell is carrying on aerobic respiration, *B* represents molecules of a waste product known as (1) carbon dioxide (2) ATP (3) ethyl alcohol (4) phosphate

67. If this represents a kidney cell from the human body, the molecules of *A* are most probably (1) carbon dioxide (2) enzymes (3) lipids (4) oxygen

68. The cell organelle labeled *Z* is called a (1) chloroplast (2) mitochondrion (3) nucleolus (4) vacuole

Part B-2

69. Why must all organisms carry out cellular respiration?

70. Briefly compare the processes of cellular respiration in aerobic and anaerobic organisms. Include the following:
- the function of oxygen
- the net gain of ATP molecules

Part C

Base your answers to question 71 on the following information and on your knowledge of biology.

71. A biologist was culturing some muscle cells from a mouse (an aerobic organism) in a petri dish. He was interested in measuring the amount of ATP produced by the muscle cells when the cells were supplied with glucose. At the beginning of the experiment, the cells were producing large quantities of ATP. He then added a substance called malonic acid to the cell culture, and the amount of ATP produced fell to near zero.

- Which organelles in the muscle cells were most likely affected by the malonic acid?
- Propose a testable hypothesis concerning respiration in cells treated with malonic acid.
- Predict the effect of malonic acid on an anaerobic organism and explain your prediction.

EXCRETION

The metabolic activities of living cells produce waste materials. The life process by which the wastes of metabolism are removed from the body is called *excretion*.

Wastes of Metabolism

The wastes of various metabolic processes are shown in Table 3-1. Some wastes are **toxins** (compounds that are poisonous to body tissues), while other wastes are nontoxic. In animals, toxic wastes are excreted from the body. In plants, toxic wastes are sealed off and stored, sometimes in vacuoles. Some nontoxic wastes are excreted, while others are recycled and used in metabolic activities.

TABLE 3-1
Waste Products of Metabolism

Metabolic Activity	Wastes
Respiration	Carbon dioxide and water
Dehydration synthesis	Water
Protein metabolism	Nitrogenous wastes
Certain metabolic processes	Mineral salts

Nitrogenous, or nitrogen-containing, wastes are produced by the breakdown of amino acids. Different kinds of organisms produce different kinds of nitrogenous wastes, including *uric acid,* which is minimally toxic; *urea,* which is moderately toxic; and *ammonia,* which is highly toxic.

Adaptations for Excretion

In the simplest organisms, wastes pass from the cells directly into the environment. More complex organisms have a specialized excretory system.

Protists. In general, the excretion of wastes in protists is accomplished by diffusion through the cell membrane (Figure 3-10). In freshwater protozoans, such as the ameba and paramecium, water continuously enters the cell by osmosis. In these organisms, the excess water collects in organelles called *contractile vacuoles.* The contractile vacuoles burst at the surface of the cell, expelling the water back into the environment. This process involves active transport.

In freshwater protozoans, the nitrogenous waste product is ammonia. Although it is very toxic, ammonia is also very soluble in water, and thus it can be easily excreted from the cells of these organisms.

In photosynthetic protists, such as algae, some of the carbon dioxide produced by cellular respiration can be recycled and used in photosynthesis. Some of the oxygen produced by photosynthesis can be used in cellular respiration.

Plants. In plants, as in algae, some of the waste gases produced by photosynthesis and cellular respiration are recycled. Excess gases diffuse out of the plant through stomates on the leaves, tiny openings on the stems, and epidermal cells on the roots.

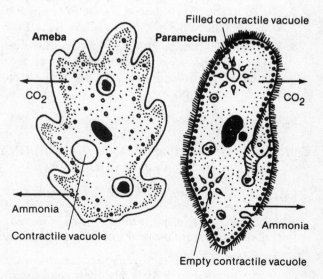

FIGURE 3-10 Excretion in ameba and paramecium.

Humans. In humans, carbon dioxide is excreted by the lungs. Water, salts, and urea are excreted by the kidneys. These waste products are passed out of the body through various specialized tubes, or passageways.

QUESTIONS
Part A

72. Metabolic wastes of animals most likely include (1) water, carbon dioxide, oxygen, and salts (2) carbon dioxide, nitrogenous compounds, water, and salts (3) hormones, water, salts, and oxygen (4) glucose, carbon dioxide, nitrogenous compounds, and water

73. Which activity would most likely produce nitrogenous waste products? (1) protein metabolism (2) glucose metabolism (3) lipid metabolism (4) starch metabolism

74. The leaf structures that are closely associated with both respiration and excretion are the (1) root hairs (2) stomates (3) waxy surfaces (4) epidermal cells

75. Protists can function without an organized excretory system because their cells (1) do not produce wastes (2) change all wastes into useful substances (3) remove only solid wastes (4) are in direct contact with a water environment

76. Which statement best describes the excretion of nitrogenous wastes from paramecia? (1) Urea is excreted by nephrons. (2) Uric acid is excreted by nephrons. (3) Urea is excreted through tiny tubules. (4) Ammonia is excreted through cell membranes.

77. Most toxic products of plant metabolism are stored in the (1) stomates (2) vacuoles (3) root cells (4) chloroplasts

78. In freshwater protozoans, the organelles involved in the maintenance of water balance are (1) food vacuoles (2) mitochondria (3) contractile vacuoles (4) pseudopods

Part B-2

79. Identify two functions the kidneys perform that help maintain homeostasis in a human.

Part C

Base your answers to question 80 on the following table, above right, and on your knowledge of biology.

80. The table compares three nitrogenous waste products, their toxicity levels, their solubility in

Type of Waste	Toxicity	Solubility	Habitat of Organism
Ammonia	Very high	Very good	Aquatic (in water)
Urea	Moderate	Good	Land, most generally
Uric acid	Low	None	Land, often desert

water, and the habitats in which the organisms that produce them typically live.

- What connection exists between the habitat of an organism and the toxicity of its nitrogenous waste?
- What connection exists between the solubility of each nitrogenous waste and its toxicity?
- State a possible biological benefit of the connections among waste toxicity, waste solubility, and an organism's habitat.

81. Organisms produce waste products as a result of their metabolic activities. These wastes include carbon dioxide; water; mineral salts, and nitrogenous wastes such as ammonia, urea, and uric acid. Select any three of these metabolic wastes and answer the following:

- How are these wastes produced in an organism?
- Why must these wastes be removed from an organism?

REGULATION

Regulation involves the control and *coordination* of life activities. In all organisms, there are chemicals that regulate life activities. In multicellular animals, there is nerve control in addition to chemical control. Both nerve control and chemical control aid organisms in their maintenance of homeostasis.

Nerve Control
Nerve control depends mainly on the functioning of **nerve cells**, or *neurons,* which are specialized for the transmission of impulses from one part of the body to another.

Structure of a Nerve Cell. The three parts of a nerve cell are the *dendrites*; the cell body, or *cyton*; and the *axon* (Figure 3-11). Dendrites are composed of many branches, but the axon has branches mainly at the end that is farthest from the cell body. Impulses are received by the dendrites and passed to the cell body, which contains the nucleus and other organelles.

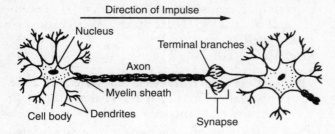

FIGURE 3-11 Structure of a typical nerve cell.

From the cell body, impulses pass along the axon to its terminal (end) branches.

Impulses. An *impulse* is a region of electrical and chemical, or *electrochemical,* change that travels over the membrane of a nerve cell. When electrochemical impulses reach the terminal branches of an axon, they stimulate the release of chemicals called *neurotransmitters.*

Neurotransmitters and Synapses. The junction between adjacent nerve cells is called a *synapse.* At the synapse, the nerve cells do not touch; there is a small gap between them. When impulses reach the terminal branches (end brush) of the axon of one nerve cell, they stimulate the release of neurotransmitters, such as acetylcholine, which diffuse across the gap of the synapse. The neurotransmitter stimulates impulses (electrochemical waves) in the dendrites of the second nerve cell. In this way, impulses pass from one nerve cell to another (Figure 3-12).

The axons of some nerve cells have junctions with a muscle or a gland. In such cases, the chemicals released by the terminal branches of the axon stimulate contraction of the muscle or secretion by the gland.

Stimulus and Receptors. Any change in the external or internal environment that initiates impulses is called a **stimulus** (plural, *stimuli*). Stimuli are detected by specialized structures called **receptors**. Each kind of receptor is sensitive to a particular kind of stimulus; for example, eyes are sensitive to light, ears to sound, and so on.

Responses and Effectors. The reaction of an organism to a stimulus is called a **response**. The response to a stimulus is carried out by *effectors,* generally the muscles or glands.

Adaptations for Nerve Control
Even the simplest animals have some type of nerve cells that transmit impulses.

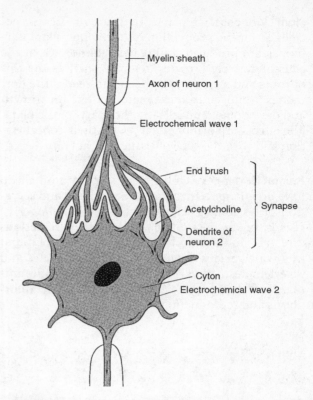

FIGURE 3-12 Nerve impulses are transmitted from one nerve cell to the next by chemicals that diffuse across the gap (at the synapse).

Simple Animals. In some animals, there is no brain, but there is a structure called a *nerve net* that transmits messages throughout the body. An example of such an animal is the *hydra,* a relative of jellyfish. In other animals, such as the earthworm, there is a primitive brain, a *nerve cord* that runs the length of the body, *peripheral nerves* that serve all parts of the body, and, in some, sense receptors.

Humans. Humans have a central nervous system that consists of a highly developed brain and a dorsal (spinal) nerve cord that runs down the back. The central nervous system permits impulses to travel in one direction along definite pathways. There is also a peripheral nervous system that consists of an elaborate network of nerves. The peripheral nervous system carries signals between the central nervous system and all parts of the body. In addition, there are many highly developed sense organs with receptors for senses such as smell, sight, hearing, taste, and touch.

Chemical Control
In both plants and animals, various aspects of their life activities are controlled by chemicals called **hormones**.

Plant Hormones. In plants, there are no organs specialized for the production of hormones. Plant hormones are produced in greatest abundance in the cells of actively growing regions, such as the tips of roots and stems and in buds and seeds. The hormones produced in these regions affect the growth and development of cells in other parts of the plant. The effects of hormones vary with their concentration and with the type of tissue they act on.

Animal Hormones. Unlike plants, many animals do have organs specialized for the synthesis and secretion of hormones. These organs, called *endocrine glands,* or ductless glands, release their secretions directly into the bloodstream. Hormones are found in a wide variety of animals, both vertebrates and invertebrates. The various hormones control the animals' metabolic activities, as well as their metamorphosis and reproduction.

QUESTIONS
Part A

82. Animal cells that are specialized for conducting electrochemical impulses are known as (1) nerve cells (2) synapses (3) nephrons (4) neurotransmitters

83. A hawk gliding over a field suddenly dives toward a moving rabbit. The hawk's reaction to the rabbit is known as a (1) stimulus (2) synapse (3) response (4) impulse

84. The transmission of nerve impulses at synapses involves chemicals called (1) hormones (2) neurotransmitters (3) enzymes (4) nucleic acids

85. Neurotransmitters, such as acetylcholine, are initially detected by which part of a nerve cell? (1) dendrites (2) nucleus (3) terminal branches (4) mitochondrion

86. The nucleus of a nerve cell is found in the (1) dendrite (2) axon (3) synapse (4) cell body

87. Structures that detect stimuli are called (1) effectors (2) receptors (3) synapses (4) cell bodies

88. The secretions of endocrine glands are known as (1) enzymes (2) hormones (3) pigments (4) neurotransmitters

89. A chemical injected into a tadpole caused the tadpole to undergo rapid metamorphosis into a frog. This chemical was most probably (1) an enzyme (2) a neurotransmitter (3) a hormone (4) a blood protein

90. The two systems that directly control homeostasis in most animals are the (1) nervous and endocrine (2) endocrine and excretory (3) nervous and circulatory (4) excretory and circulatory

Part B-2

91. Compare the central nervous system and the peripheral nervous system. What are the main structures and functions of each system?

92. Explain why the endocrine glands are also referred to as ductless glands. How is this related to their function?

LOCOMOTION

Locomotion is the ability to move from place to place. Among many protists and animals, locomotion improves the organism's ability to survive. It increases chances of finding food and shelter, avoiding predators and other dangers, and finding a mate.

Adaptations for Locomotion
Many protists and almost all animals are capable of some form of locomotion, or **movement**. Such organisms are said to be *motile*. The hydra is generally a *sessile* organism; it tends to remain in one place, fastened to another structure. However, it does have fibers that permit some limited movements.

Protists. There are three basic forms of locomotion among protists. In the ameba, locomotion is by ameboid motion, in which the cell cytoplasm flows into the pseudopods. This causes the organism to move in the direction of the newly formed extension of its cytoplasm. In the paramecium, locomotion involves cilia, which are short hairlike organelles that cover the outer surface of the cell. The cilia wave back and forth in a coordinated way, moving the cell through the water. Some algae and other protozoans move by means of *flagella*, long hairlike organelles that can pull the cell through the water (Figure 3-13).

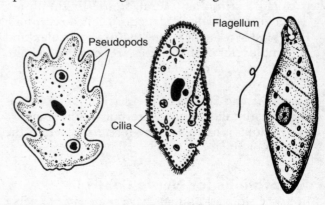

FIGURE 3-13 Locomotion in ameba, paramecium, and euglena (an alga). (Not drawn to scale.)

Humans. Humans have an internal skeleton, or *endo-skeleton*. Locomotion is accomplished by the interaction of muscles and jointed appendages (bones and cartilage).

QUESTIONS
Part A

93. Locomotion increases an animal's opportunity to do all of the following *except* (1) obtain food (2) find a mate and reproduce (3) escape from predators (4) transmit impulses

94. Which structures are *not* associated with locomotion among protists? (1) flagella (2) cilia (3) pseudopods (4) tentacles

95. Which organism is able to move due to the interaction of its muscles and skeleton? (1) ameba (2) paramecium (3) human (4) hydra

Part B-2

96. Describe four survival advantages of locomotion.

97. Some organisms are sessile, or incapable of movement. Explain how their survival might be aided in other ways.

LITERACY SKILL: READING FOR COMPREHENSION

Base your answers to questions 98 through 101 on the information below and on your knowledge of biology. Source: Science News *(March 12, 2011): vol. 179, no. 6, p. 16. Reprinted with permission of* Science News.

Bears Slow Way Down in Winter: Ursine Hibernation Turns Out to Be Deeper than Expected

There's something as yet unknown going on with black bear hibernation that slows metabolic rates more than lower body temperature alone can explain.

In the depths of Alaskan winters, closely monitored black bears dropped their temperatures only a modest 5.5 degrees Celsius on average. A standard physiological calculation predicts that such a chill would slow metabolism to 65 percent of nonhibernating resting rates. But the bears' metabolisms plunged down to even more energy-saving zones, averaging only 25 percent of the basic summer rate, ecological physiologist Oivind Toien of the University of Alaska Fairbanks and colleagues reported February 17 and in the Feb. 18 *Science.*

Such a major disconnect hasn't shown up in research on any other hibernating mammal, said study coauthor Brian M. Barnes, also of UA Fairbanks.

The study is the first to manage continuous monitoring of metabolic rate and body temperature throughout bear hibernation with little disturbance of the animals, Toien said. Other studies based on intermittent sampling with older instruments, indirect evidence or studying bears with lots of people nearby have left the matter "uncertain," as he put it.

The researchers monitored five bears, setting the animals up in wooden den boxes in an enclosure deep in the woods. The boxes were rigged to allow a bear to break out anytime it wanted. While the bears were inside, researchers measured metabolic rate, muscle movement and heart function.

Reports of large drops in bear metabolic rates during hibernation cheer Eric Hellgren of Southern Illinois University Carbondale, who admits to "a biased view as a bear biologist." He said the Alaska study may lay to rest some of the long-running discussions from physiologists who treat bear hibernation as "a different and 'lesser' form" compared with the big metabolic shifts seen in small animals such as ground squirrels.

Heart rate tracking for three of the Alaska bears showed a drop from 55 steady beats per minute on average before hibernation to 14 erratic beats per minute in winter. Physiological ecologist Hank Harlow of the University of Wyoming in Laramie said that he too has listened to hibernating bear hearts going still for a stretch then kerthumping arrhythmically. Maybe it saves energy, he said.

The Alaska team also found that when bears got moving again in spring, their metabolisms took several weeks to creep back to normal. Monitoring data showed that bears with half-speed metabolic rates still display normal bearish behavior, however.

98. Describe what is surprising about black bears' hibernation patterns.

99. What is the advantage to black bears that they hibernate during the winter?

100. Briefly describe how the research on the black bears was carried out.

101. Speculate why it is possible for a hibernating bear's heart rate to drop from 55 to 14 beats per minute.

4 Human Biology

NUTRITION

Humans are heterotrophs—they must ingest the nutrients they need, including carbohydrates, proteins, lipids, vitamins, minerals, and water. Carbohydrates, lipids, and proteins are made up of large molecules that must be digested before they can be absorbed and used by the cells. Vitamins, minerals, and water are made up of small molecules that can be absorbed without being digested. Specific nutritional requirements of humans depend on the age, gender, and activity of the individual.

Human Digestive System

The human digestive system is an **organ system** that consists of a one-way digestive tube called the *gastrointestinal,* or GI, tract and accessory **organs** (Figure 4-1). Food is moved through the GI tract by rhythmic, muscular contractions called *peristalsis.* As food moves through the tract, it is broken down mechanically and chemically. The accessory organs (liver, gallbladder, and pancreas) secrete enzymes and other substances into the digestive tract that aid in digestion.

Oral Cavity. The mouth, or oral cavity, contains the teeth, tongue, and openings from the salivary glands. Food is ingested through the mouth, and digestion begins there. The teeth function in the mechanical breakdown of food into smaller pieces, which provides a larger surface area for the chemical action of digestive enzymes.

The *salivary glands* secrete saliva, a fluid that passes into the mouth through ducts. Saliva contains

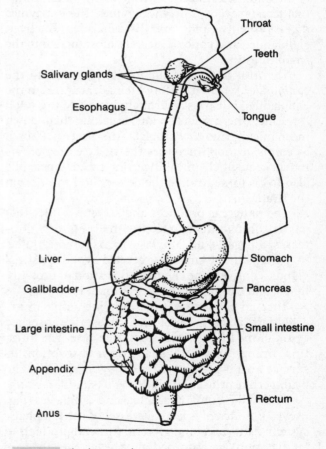

FIGURE 4-1 The human digestive system.

an enzyme, amylase, which begins the chemical digestion of starch. The tongue aids in chewing and in mixing saliva with the food by moving the food around in the mouth. The tongue also moves the food mass (or *bolus*) to the back of the mouth for swallowing.

Esophagus. When the food is swallowed, it passes into the esophagus, and peristalsis of the esophagus wall moves it downward to the stomach. Digestion of starch continues while the food is in the esophagus.

Stomach. Food reaching the lower end of the esophagus enters the stomach, a muscular sac in which it is mixed and liquefied (mechanical digestion). Gastric glands in the stomach lining secrete hydrochloric acid and the enzyme gastric protease. Hydrochloric acid provides the proper pH (acidic) required for effective functioning of gastric protease, which begins the chemical digestion of proteins.

Small Intestine. Partially digested food moves from the stomach into the small intestine, a long, convoluted tube in which most digestion occurs. The walls of the small intestine are lined with intestinal glands that secrete several different enzymes. These enzymes digest proteins, lipids, and disaccharides. The liver, gallbladder, and pancreas secrete substances into the small intestine.

The *liver* produces *bile,* which passes into the *gallbladder,* where it is stored temporarily. From the gallbladder, bile passes through ducts into the small intestine, where it acts on fats, breaking them down mechanically into tiny droplets. This process, known as *emulsification,* increases the surface area of fats for subsequent chemical digestion by enzymes. Bile also helps to neutralize the acidic food mass from the stomach.

The **pancreas** produces and secretes a juice that passes through ducts into the small intestine. Proteases, lipases, and amylase in pancreatic juice, together with the enzymes secreted by the intestinal glands, complete the chemical digestion of proteins, lipids, and carbohydrates in the small intestine.

The end products of digestion, including amino acids, fatty acids, glycerol, and glucose, are absorbed through the lining of the small intestine. The intestinal lining is specially adapted for absorption. Its surface area is greatly increased by many folds and by fingerlike projections called *villi* (singular, *villus*).

Each villus contains a lacteal and capillaries (Figure 4-2). A *lacteal* is a small vessel of the lymphatic system. Fatty acids and glycerol (the end products of fat digestion) are absorbed into the lacteals; they are transported in the lymph, which is eventually added to the blood. Glucose and amino acids are absorbed into the blood of the capillaries and transported to the liver for temporary storage. From the liver, glucose and amino acids are distributed by the blood to all the cells, as they are needed.

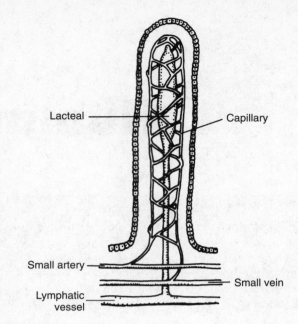

FIGURE 4-2 Structure of a villus.

When excess glucose is removed from the blood in the liver, it is converted to, and stored as, glycogen, an insoluble polysaccharide. When the concentration of glucose in the blood drops below a certain level, the glycogen is broken down to glucose, which is then returned to the blood. The storage of excess glucose as glycogen is an adaptation for the maintenance of a constant blood glucose level and is an example of homeostasis.

Large Intestine. Undigested and indigestible foods (roughage) and water move from the small intestine into the *large intestine,* which is shorter and wider than the small intestine. Water is reabsorbed from the undigested food into the capillaries in the wall of the large intestine. This reabsorption helps the body to conserve water. The remaining wastes, called *feces,* are moved through the large intestine by strong peristaltic action to the rectum, where they are stored temporarily. The feces are periodically egested (discharged) from the body through the anus.

Mechanism of Chemical Digestion

In digestion, large, insoluble molecules are broken down into small soluble molecules by the process of *hydrolysis.* Each of the many hydrolytic reactions of digestion is regulated by a specific hydrolytic enzyme.

Chemically, hydrolysis is the opposite of dehydration synthesis; large molecules are split with the addition of water. In a series of reactions, polysaccharides, such as starch, are also broken down by hydrolysis into monosaccharides (simple sugars).

In the presence of water and protein-digesting

enzymes (proteases), proteins are broken down into their constituent amino acids. In the hydrolysis of proteins, peptide bonds are broken.

In the presence of water and lipid-digesting enzymes (lipases), lipid molecules are broken down by hydrolysis into fatty acids and glycerol.

Nutritional Requirements

A balanced diet must contain carbohydrates, proteins, and fats, as well as vitamins, minerals, and water. Ingredients labels that are printed on all packaged food items indicate how much of a particular nutrient is supplied per serving, as well as the serving's calorie content. In addition to a balanced diet, exercise is recommended to maintain proper health. (*Note:* You can see the current recommended daily allowances for all the major food groups by checking the Website www.myplate.gov.)

Carbohydrates. Carbohydrates serve as the major source of energy in the body. Excess carbohydrates are converted to glycogen or fat and stored in the body as an energy reserve. *Cellulose,* a complex carbohydrate found in the cell walls of fruits, vegetables, and whole grains, provides indigestible material that serves as *roughage.* Roughage, also called *fiber,* helps to move the food mass through the intestines.

Proteins. Proteins in food are broken down into their constituent amino acids, which are then used to synthesize human proteins. Twenty different amino acids are needed for the synthesis of human proteins. Twelve of these can be synthesized in the body from other amino acids; but the other eight, called the *essential amino acids,* must be obtained from the food.

All necessary amino acids must be present at the same time for protein synthesis to occur. An inadequate supply of any essential amino acid limits protein synthesis. Meat proteins generally contain all of the essential amino acids. Such foods are called complete protein foods. Vegetable proteins are generally incomplete protein foods—they lack one or more essential amino acids. However, a variety of vegetable proteins, if eaten together, can complement each other and provide all the essential amino acids. For example, a meal of rice and beans supplies complete protein.

Fats. Fats contain relatively large amounts of potential energy and serve as an energy-storage compound in organisms. Fats are also a structural component of cell membranes.

Fats are classified as saturated and unsaturated. *Saturated fats,* which are found in meats, butter, and other animal products, are solid at room temperature. Chemically, saturated fats contain the maximum number of hydrogen atoms and have no double bonds. *Unsaturated fats* contain one or more double bonds and, thus, could hold additional hydrogen atoms. An excess of saturated fats, as well as another type of fat called a *trans fat,* in the diet is thought to contribute to cardiovascular disease. Fortunately, some forms of unsaturated fats are thought to protect against cardiovascular disease. However, it is generally considered wise to limit one's intake of all kinds of fats in order to maintain good health.

Disorders of the Digestive System

An *ulcer* is an open sore in the lining of the stomach or intestines. Ulcers may be caused by the presence of excess amounts of hydrochloric acid, which breaks down the lining of the digestive tract, or by bacterial infection. Ulcers are painful and sometimes cause bleeding.

Constipation is a condition marked by difficulty in eliminating feces from the large intestine. Constipation occurs when too much water is removed from the feces in the large intestine or when there is a reduction in peristaltic activity, slowing down the movement of waste through the large intestine. Insufficient roughage in the diet may also be a cause of constipation.

Diarrhea is a gastrointestinal disturbance characterized by frequent elimination of watery feces. This condition may result from decreased water absorption in the large intestine and increased peristaltic activity. Prolonged diarrhea may result in severe dehydration.

Appendicitis is an inflammation of the appendix, a small pouch located at the beginning of the large intestine. *Gallstones* are small, hardened cholesterol deposits that sometimes form in the gallbladder. When gallstones enter the bile duct and block the flow of bile, they cause severe pain.

QUESTIONS
Part A

1. Into which parts of the human digestive system are digestive enzymes secreted? (1) mouth, esophagus, stomach (2) stomach, small intestine, large intestine (3) mouth, stomach, small intestine (4) esophagus, stomach, large intestine

2. In humans, excess glucose is stored as the polysaccharide known as (1) glycogen (2) glycerol (3) maltose (4) cellulose

3. After a person's stomach was surgically removed, the chemical digestion of ingested protein would

probably begin in the (1) mouth (2) small intestine (3) large intestine (4) liver

4. Which organ forms part of the human gastrointestinal tract? (1) trachea (2) esophagus (3) diaphragm (4) aorta

5. The intestinal folds and villi of the human small
intestine function primarily to (1) increase the
surface area for absorption of digested nutrients
(2) excrete metabolic wastes (3) circulate blood
(4) force the movement of food in one direction
through the digestive tract

6. Lipase aids in the chemical digestion of (1) fats
(2) proteins (3) enzymes (4) salts

7. In humans, which is true of carbohydrate digestion? (1) It begins in the oral cavity and ends in
the esophagus. (2) It begins in the oral cavity
and ends in the small intestine. (3) It begins in
the small intestine and ends in the large intestine. (4) It begins and ends in the small intestine.

8. Organisms are classified as heterotrophs if they
derive their metabolic energy from (1) photosynthesis (2) inorganic raw materials (3) lightning (4) preformed organic compounds

9. Glands located within the digestive tube include
(1) gastric glands and thyroid glands (2) gastric
glands and intestinal glands (3) thyroid glands
and intestinal glands (4) adrenal glands and
intestinal glands

10. The small lymphatic vessels that extend into
the villi are (1) veins (2) lacteals (3) glands
(4) capillaries

11. The principal function of mechanical digestion
is the (1) hydrolysis of food molecules for storage in the liver (2) production of more surface
area for enzyme action (3) synthesis of enzymes
necessary for food absorption (4) breakdown of
large molecules to smaller ones by the addition
of water

12. In which organ's walls does peristalsis occur? (1)
liver (2) pancreas (3) oral cavity (4) esophagus

13. A person who consumes large amounts of saturated fats may increase his or her chances
of developing (1) meningitis (2) hemophilia
(3) pneumonia (4) cardiovascular disease

Part B-1

*Base your answers to questions 14 through 18 on your
knowledge of biology and on the following graph, above
right, which shows how much carbohydrates, proteins,
and fats are chemically digested as food passes through
the digestive tract. The letters represent body structures, in sequence, that make up the digestive tract.*

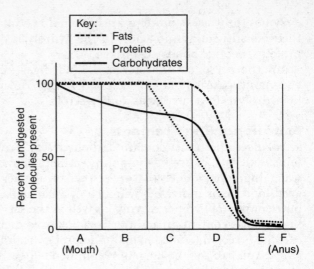

14. Proteins are digested in both (1) A and B (2) B
and C (3) C and D (4) A and C

15. The organ represented by letter C is most probably the (1) esophagus (2) stomach (3) small
intestine (4) large intestine

16. Enzymes secreted by the pancreas enter the system at (1) A (2) B (3) C (4) D

17. The final products of digestion are absorbed
almost entirely in (1) F (2) B (3) C (4) D

18. Water is removed from the undigested material
in (1) A (2) B (3) E (4) D

Part B-2

19. Use your knowledge of biology to complete the
following table.

Nutrient	Digestive End Products	Where Chemical Digestion Begins	End Products Absorbed by
Starches	Simple sugars		Villi capillaries
Lipids		Small intestine	
Proteins	Amino acids		

Part C

*Base your answers to questions 20 and 21 on the food
pyramid on page 53, which shows suggested daily servings for several types of food.*

20. Select and record a balanced, daily meal plan for
breakfast, lunch, and dinner for one person.

21. Explain why people are advised to ingest fats
"sparingly," that is, in low amounts.

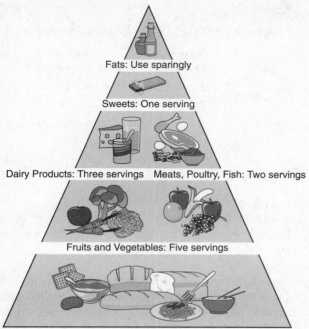

Fats: Use sparingly

Sweets: One serving

Dairy Products: Three servings   Meats, Poultry, Fish: Two servings

Fruits and Vegetables: Five servings

Bread, Grains, Cereals: Five or six servings

22. Based on your knowledge of human biology:
    - Identify three organs of the human digestive system.
    - Describe the type of digestion that occurs in each organ.
23. Explain why most foods (nutrients) eaten by humans must be digested before they can be used by the body.

TRANSPORT

Transport includes the absorption and distribution of materials throughout the body. In humans, dissolved and suspended materials are transported in the blood, which is moved throughout the body by the circulatory system.

Blood

Blood consists of a fluid called *plasma* in which red blood cells, white blood cells, and platelets are suspended (Figure 4-3).

Plasma. Blood plasma consists mostly of water. It contains many dissolved materials, including inorganic ions, wastes, nutrients, and a variety of proteins. The proteins include antibodies, enzymes, hormones, and clotting factors.

Red Blood Cells. The most numerous cells in the plasma are the *red blood cells*, which are produced in

the marrow of certain bones. Mature red blood cells do not have a nucleus. Within red blood cells is the red iron-containing pigment hemoglobin, which carries oxygen between the lungs and the body tissues.

White Blood Cells. The **white blood cells** are larger than the red blood cells and contain one or more nuclei. White blood cells are produced in the bone marrow and in lymph nodes. There are several types of white blood cells, including phagocytes and lymphocytes.

Phagocytes are white blood cells that engulf and destroy bacteria at the site of an infection. The phagocytes leave the capillaries, by means of ameboid motion, and enter the body tissues. There, they engulf bacteria and other foreign matter in the same way that amebas engulf food.

Lymphocytes are white blood cells that produce special protein molecules called **antibodies**. Antibodies react chemically with foreign substances or microorganisms in the blood and inactivate them. The substances that cause antibody production are called **antigens**. Most antigens are protein in nature. An antigen-antibody reaction is referred to as an *immune response*. (The immune response is discussed in greater detail in Chapter 5.)

Platelets. The small cell fragments that are involved in the clotting of blood are called *platelets*. A platelet consists of cytoplasm surrounded by a cell membrane; it has no nucleus.

Blood Clotting. When an injury occurs, blood vessels break and blood is released. To stop the loss of blood, a blood clot forms, blocking the wound. Clotting involves a series of enzyme-controlled reactions. All the substances required for clotting are normally present in the blood, but clot formation does not take place unless there is a break in a blood vessel. When this occurs, blood platelets are ruptured and they release an enzyme that starts the clotting reactions. The plasma protein *fibrinogen* is converted to *fibrin*, which forms a meshwork of solid fibers across the wound. Blood cells become trapped in the fibers, forming the clot.

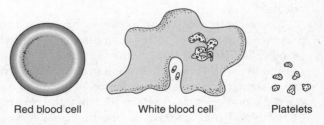

Red blood cell   White blood cell   Platelets

FIGURE 4-3 Three important components of blood.

Immunity

The ability of the body to resist a specific disease is called **immunity**. Immunity, which is provided by the **immune system** and depends on the action of antibodies in the bloodstream, can develop in two ways.

Active immunity results when antibodies are produced in response to a foreign substance (antigen) in the body. When a person catches a disease, for example chicken pox, antibodies develop against the disease-causing agent. After the illness is over, antibodies against this agent remain in the blood and protect against reinfection by the same substance or microorganism.

Active immunity is also produced by **vaccination** against a particular disease. A *vaccine* contains dead or weakened microorganisms that can stimulate antibody production but cannot cause disease.

Passive immunity develops when an individual receives antibodies from the blood of another person or from an animal. These antibodies provide temporary immunity to a particular disease. However, the "borrowed" antibodies are gradually destroyed, and the immunity they provided ends.

Allergies. In some people, exposure to certain common foreign substances, such as dust, pollen, insect bites, foods, and medications, causes an immune response known as an *allergy*. These responses, or **allergic reactions**, are actually overreactions of the body's immune system to a foreign substance. The antibodies produced may stimulate the release of a substance called *histamine,* which causes typical allergic responses, such as sneezing, coughing, or a rash.

Blood-typing. Knowledge of immunity has made possible the transplanting of organs and the transfusion of blood from one person to another. In both organ transplants and blood transfusions, an immune response is stimulated if the body of the recipient recognizes foreign antigens in the tissue or blood from the donor. In organ transplants, an antigen-antibody reaction against the transplanted organ is called *rejection*. Donor tissue proteins must be carefully matched to those of the recipient to avoid rejection.

Blood-typing for transfusions is based on the presence or absence of antigens on the surface of red blood cells. The most important blood group system in blood-typing is the ABO blood group system. In this system, two kinds of antigens may be found on the red blood cells: A and B. In addition, the plasma of the blood may contain antibodies: anti-A and anti-B. Table 4-1 shows the antigens and antibodies for each type of blood.

TABLE 4-1
Antigens and Antibodies of the ABO Blood Group System

Blood Type	Antigens on Red Cells	Antibodies in Plasma
A	A	Anti-B
B	B	Anti-A
AB	A and B	Neither Anti-A nor Anti-B
O	Neither A nor B	Anti-A and Anti-B

Transport Vessels

Blood circulates through the human body within the blood vessels, which include *arteries, capillaries,* and *veins.* (Refer to Figure 3-8, page 40.)

Arteries. Blood is carried from the heart to all parts of the body in arteries, which are thick-walled muscular vessels that expand and contract to accommodate the forceful flow of blood from the heart. The rhythmic expansion and contraction of the arteries produced by the heartbeat aids the flow of blood to all parts of the body; it is called the *pulse.*

Capillaries. With increasing distance from the heart, arteries branch into smaller and smaller vessels, finally forming capillaries, tiny blood vessels with walls only one cell layer thick. Capillaries are the site of exchange of materials between the blood and the body tissues.

Veins. Blood flows from the capillaries into the veins, thin-walled vessels that carry the blood back to the heart. Veins contain flaps of tissue that act as valves (Figure 4-4). The valves allow the blood in the veins to flow in only one direction—back toward the heart.

Intercellular Fluid and Lymph

As blood passes through the capillaries of the body, some of the plasma is forced out of the vessels and into the surrounding tissues. This fluid, which bathes all the cells of the body, is called *intercellular fluid,* or *ICF.* Materials diffusing between the

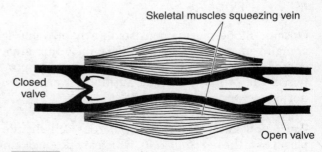

FIGURE 4-4 Blood flow in a vein.

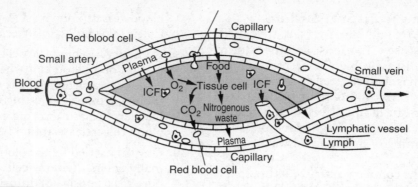

FIGURE 4-5 Molecules diffuse between the capillaries, intercellular fluid, and body cells.

cells and the blood of the capillaries are dissolved in the ICF.

Excess intercellular fluid is drained from the tissues by tiny *lymph vessels,* which are part of the *lymphatic system.* Once inside these vessels, the fluid is called *lymph.* The lymph vessels merge, forming larger vessels. Eventually, all lymph flows into two large lymph ducts, which empty into veins near the heart. In this way, the fluid lost from the blood is returned to the blood (Figure 4-5).

Major lymph vessels have enlarged regions called *lymph nodes* in which phagocytic cells filter bacteria and dead cells from the lymph. Some lymph vessels contain valves that, like those in the veins, keep the lymph flowing back toward the heart.

The Heart

Blood is pumped through the blood vessels of the body by the contractions of the heart.

Structure of the Heart. The heart has four chambers (Figure 4-6). The two upper chambers, the *atria*

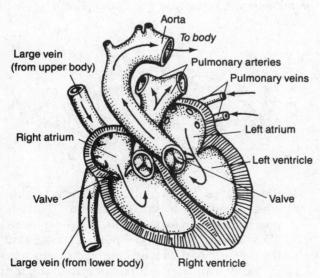

FIGURE 4-6 Structure of the human heart.

(singular, *atrium*), receive blood returning to the heart from the rest of the body. The two lower chambers, the *ventricles,* pump blood out of the heart into the arteries. The walls of the ventricles are thicker and more muscular than those of the atria.

Circulation Through the Heart. The deoxygenated (oxygen-poor) blood from the body is returned to the right atrium of the heart through two large veins—one from the upper part of the body and one from the lower part of the body. This deoxygenated blood flows down from the right atrium into the right ventricle; from there it is pumped out of the heart through the pulmonary arteries to the lungs. When in the lungs, the blood gives up carbon dioxide and picks up oxygen. The oxygenated (oxygen-rich) blood is then returned through the pulmonary veins to the left atrium of the heart. The blood then passes from the left atrium into the left ventricle, which pumps it through the *aorta,* the largest artery in the body.

This one-way flow of blood through the heart is controlled by valves that prevent backflow of the blood. There are valves between the atria and the ventricles, between the right ventricle and the pulmonary arteries, and between the left ventricle and the aorta.

Blood Pressure. The pressure exerted by the blood on the walls of the arteries during the pumping action of the heart is referred to as *blood pressure.* During the contraction phase of the heartbeat cycle, arterial blood pressure is highest. During the relaxation phase of the heartbeat cycle, blood pressure is lowest.

Pathways of Circulation

The pathway of blood between the heart and the lungs is called the *pulmonary circulation.* The circulatory pathway between the heart and all other parts of the body except the lungs is called the *systemic circulation.* The system of blood vessels that supplies the heart itself is called the *coronary circulation.*

Disorders of the Transport System

Diseases of the heart and blood vessels are called *cardiovascular* diseases. The most common form of cardiovascular disease is high blood pressure, or *hypertension,* which is characterized by elevated arterial blood pressure. This condition can be caused by a number of factors, including stress, diet, heredity, cigarette smoking, and aging. High blood pressure can damage the lining of arteries and weaken the muscle of the heart.

A blockage of the coronary artery or its branches is a *coronary thrombosis,* or heart attack. As a result of the blockage, some of the muscle tissue of the heart is deprived of oxygen and is damaged.

A narrowing of the coronary arteries may cause temporary shortages of oxygen to the heart muscle, resulting in intense pain in the chest and sometimes in the left arm and shoulder. This condition is called *angina pectoris.*

Anemia is a condition in which the blood cannot carry sufficient amounts of oxygen to the body cells. Anemia may be due to inadequate amounts of hemoglobin in the red blood cells or to too few red blood cells. One form of anemia is caused by a shortage of iron in the diet.

Leukemia is a form of cancer in which the bone marrow produces abnormally large numbers of white blood cells.

QUESTIONS
Part A

24. Which is a characteristic of lymph nodes? (1) They carry blood under great pressure. (2) They move fluids by means of a muscular pump. (3) They produce new red blood cells. (4) They contain phagocytic cells.

25. The accumulation of specific antibodies in the plasma, due to the presence of an antigen, is characteristic of (1) an immune response (2) angina pectoris (3) a coronary thrombosis (4) cerebral palsy

26. An organism develops active immunity as a result of (1) manufacturing its own antigens (2) producing antibodies in response to a vaccination (3) receiving an injection of antibodies produced by another organism (4) receiving an injection of a dilute glucose solution

27. In the human body, which blood components engulf foreign bacteria? (1) red blood cells (2) white blood cells (3) antibodies (4) platelets

28. In humans, the exchange of materials between blood and intercellular fluid directly involves blood vessels known as (1) capillaries (2) arterioles (3) venules (4) arteries

29. An injury to a blood vessel may result in the formation of a blood clot when (1) bone marrow cells decrease platelet production (2) kidney tubules synthesize clotting factors (3) ruptured platelets release enzyme molecules (4) white blood cells release antibodies

30. Oxygen carried by the blood in capillaries normally enters the body cells by (1) active transport (2) osmosis (3) diffusion (4) pinocytosis

31. Which type of vessel normally contains valves that prevent the backward flow of blood? (1) artery (2) arteriole (3) capillary (4) vein

32. The blood vessels that transport deoxygenated blood to the heart are known as (1) capillaries (2) lymph vessels (3) veins (4) arteries

33. The right ventricle is the chamber of the heart that contains (1) deoxygenated blood and pumps this blood to the lungs (2) deoxygenated blood and pumps this blood to the brain (3) oxygenated blood and pumps this blood to the lungs (4) oxygenated blood and pumps this blood to the brain

34. Which two systems are most directly involved in providing human cells with the molecules needed for the synthesis of fats? (1) digestive and circulatory (2) excretory and digestive (3) immune and muscular (4) reproductive and circulatory

Part B-1

Base your answers to questions 35 through 39 on your knowledge of biology and on the diagram below, which represents the exchange of materials between capillaries and cells.

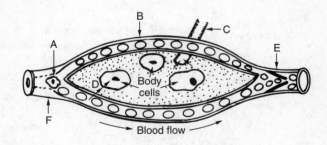

35. Blood vessel *B* has walls that are very thin, which enables this type of vessel to (1) transport hemoglobin to body cells (2) transport red blood cells into the tissue spaces (3) withstand the pressure of the blood coming in from veins (4) easily transport substances into and out of the blood

36. A function of cell *A* is to (1) carry oxygen (2) engulf disease-producing bacteria (3) transport digested food (4) produce hemoglobin

37. A substance that diffuses in the direction indicated by *D* is most likely (1) fibrin (2) oxygen (3) urea (4) bile

38. Which vessel most likely contains the greatest amount of carbon dioxide? (1) *F* (2) *B* (3) *C* (4) *E*

39. Excess intercellular fluid (ICF) is constantly drained off by the lymphatic vessels. Which letter represents such a vessel? (1) *E* (2) *B* (3) *C* (4) *F*

Base your answers to questions 40 through 43 on the following diagram and on your knowledge of biology. The diagram represents the human heart; the arrows indicate the direction of blood flow.

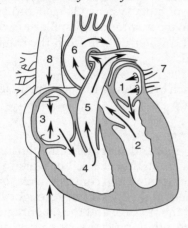

40. The aorta is represented by number (1) 1 (2) 6 (3) 8 (4) 4

41. Deoxygenated blood returns to the heart through the structure represented by number (1) 8 (2) 7 (3) 3 (4) 5

42. The chamber that pumps blood to all parts of the body except the lungs is represented by number (1) 1 (2) 2 (3) 3 (4) 4

43. Blood passes from the heart to the lungs through the structure represented by number (1) 5 (2) 6 (3) 7 (4) 8

Part B-2

44. Explain what effects faulty valves would have on a human's blood flow.

45. Describe the relationship that exists between the circulatory system and the lymphatic system.

46. The four major blood components are red blood cells, white blood cells, plasma, and platelets. Describe one major function for each blood component listed.

47. Arteries generally contain blood that has higher oxygen content than that of blood in the veins. Give a scientifically valid explanation for this observation.

48. Why are people who are anemic (have too little hemoglobin and/or too few red blood cells) often advised to take in extra iron in their diets?

49. Using appropriate information, fill in spaces *A* and *B* in a copy of the chart below. In space *A* identify an organ in the human body where molecules diffuse into the blood. In space *B* identify a specific molecule that diffuses into the blood at this organ.

An organ in the human body where molecules diffuse into the blood	A specific molecule that diffuses into the blood at this organ
A	B

Part C

50. Describe the pathway of blood flow through the heart, beginning and ending with the point at which the blood returns to the heart from the body organs.

51. Compare the structure and function of these three major types of blood vessels: arteries, veins, and capillaries.

RESPIRATION

Respiration includes cellular respiration and gas exchange. The process of cellular respiration in humans is basically the same as that in other aerobic organisms (see Chapter 3). Glucose is broken down completely to yield carbon dioxide and water, and ATP is formed from ADP and phosphate.

Anaerobic respiration occurs in human skeletal muscle during prolonged exercise when the amount of oxygen supplied by the circulatory system becomes inadequate for aerobic respiration. Under these circumstances, glucose is broken down in the muscle to lactic acid. The accumulation of lactic acid in skeletal muscle is thought to be responsible for muscle fatigue. When adequate oxygen is again available, the lactic acid is broken down to carbon dioxide and water.

Human Respiratory System

The human respiratory system moves respiratory gases between the external environment and the

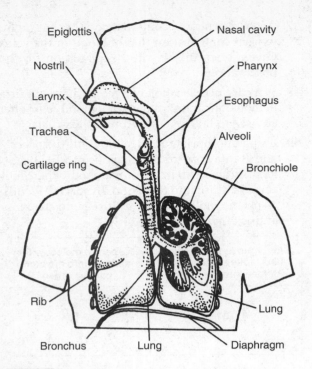

Epiglottis

Nostril

Larynx

Trachea

Cartilage ring

Rib

Bronchus

Lung

Nasal cavity

Pharynx

Esophagus

Alveoli

Bronchiole

Lung

Diaphragm

FIGURE 4-7 The human respiratory system.

internal surfaces for gas exchange within the lungs. The respiratory system consists of a network of passageways that permit air to flow into and out of the lungs (Figure 4-7).

Nasal Cavity. Air generally enters the respiratory system through the nostrils and passes into the *nasal cavity.* This cavity is lined with a ciliated mucous membrane that cleans, warms, and moistens the air.

Pharynx. From the nasal cavity, air passes into the *pharynx,* the area where the oral cavity and nasal cavity meet. Air passes through the pharynx on its way to the trachea.

Trachea. The *trachea,* or windpipe, is a tube through which air passes from the pharynx to the lungs. The opening (from the pharynx) to the trachea is protected by a flap of tissue called the *epiglottis.* During swallowing, the epiglottis covers the opening of the trachea so that food and liquids cannot enter the air passages. During breathing, the opening of the trachea is uncovered. (At the top of the trachea is the *larynx,* or voice box, which functions in speech.) The walls of the trachea contain rings of cartilage that keep the trachea open so that the passage of air remains unobstructed. The trachea is lined with a ciliated mucous membrane. Microscopic particles in the inhaled air are trapped by mucus, and the beating of the cilia sweeps the mucus upward toward the

pharynx (to be expelled from the body by coughing or sneezing).

Bronchi and Bronchioles. The lower end of the trachea splits, forming two tubes called the *bronchi* (singular, *bronchus*). The bronchi, like the trachea, are lined with a mucous membrane and ringed with cartilage. Each bronchus extends into a lung, where it branches into smaller and smaller tubes called *bronchioles.*

The bronchioles are lined with a mucous membrane, but they lack cartilage rings. At the end of each bronchiole is a cluster of tiny hollow air sacs called *alveoli.*

Alveoli. The lungs contain millions of alveoli (singular, *alveolus*). The walls of the alveoli are thin and moist and are surrounded by capillaries. The alveoli are the functional units for gas exchange in the human respiratory system. Oxygen diffuses from the alveoli into the surrounding capillaries, while carbon dioxide and water diffuse from the capillaries into the alveoli.

Lungs. Each bronchus with its bronchioles and alveoli make up a *lung.*

Breathing

Air moves into and out of the lungs during *breathing.* The lungs are highly elastic but contain no muscle tissue. They expand and contract in response to pressure changes in the chest cavity brought about by the actions of the rib cage and the diaphragm.

During *inhalation,* the ribs push upward and outward and the diaphragm moves down, enlarging the chest cavity. The enlargement of the chest cavity reduces the pressure around the lungs, which expand, and air flows into the lungs. In *exhalation,* the ribs move inward and downward and the diaphragm moves up. The chest cavity becomes smaller and air is forced out of the lungs (Figure 4-8).

Gas Exchange. The air that enters the alveoli is rich in oxygen. The blood in the capillaries surrounding the alveoli is oxygen-poor and contains the wastes of cellular respiration—carbon dioxide and water. The oxygen diffuses from the alveoli into the blood, where it enters the red blood cells and becomes loosely bound to the hemoglobin.

The oxygen and hemoglobin separate in the capillaries of the body tissues. The oxygen diffuses out of the capillaries, through the intercellular fluid, and into the body cells. Carbon dioxide and water diffuse out from the cells and into the blood. When the blood returns to the lungs, these wastes diffuse into the alveoli and are expelled from the body in the exhaled air.

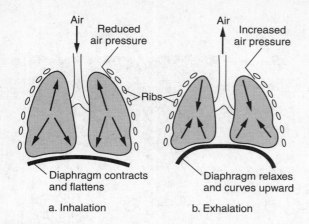

a. Inhalation   b. Exhalation

FIGURE 4-8 Movement of diaphragm as air goes into and out of the lungs.

Breathing Rate. The rate of breathing is controlled by the *breathing center* in the medulla of the brain. The breathing center is sensitive to the concentration of carbon dioxide in the blood. When the carbon dioxide level is high, nerve impulses from the breathing center are sent to the rib muscles and to the diaphragm to increase the breathing rate, which speeds up the rate of excretion of carbon dioxide from the body. As the carbon dioxide level in the blood drops, the breathing rate decreases. This regulation of carbon dioxide levels is one example of the **feedback mechanisms** by which the body maintains homeostasis.

Disorders of the Respiratory System

Bronchitis is an inflammation of the linings of the bronchial tubes. As a result of such swelling, the air passages become narrowed and filled with mucus, causing breathing difficulties and coughing. *Asthma* is an allergic reaction characterized by a narrowing of the bronchial tubes, which results in difficulty breathing. *Emphysema* is a disease in which the walls of the alveoli break down, decreasing the surface area for gas exchange. Emphysema is marked by shortness of breath, difficulty breathing, and decreased lung capacity.

QUESTIONS
Part A

52. The alveoli in humans are structures most closely associated with (1) gas exchange (2) anaerobic respiration (3) glandular secretion (4) neural transmission

53. In humans, the center that detects and regulates the amount of carbon dioxide in the blood is situated in the (1) cerebrum (2) diaphragm (3) medulla (4) rib muscles

54. The exchange of air between the human body and the environment is a result of the rhythmic contractions of the rib cage muscles and the (1) diaphragm (2) lungs (3) trachea (4) heart

55. The breathing rate of humans is regulated mainly by the concentration of (1) carbon dioxide in the blood (2) oxygen in the blood (3) platelets in the blood (4) white blood cells in the blood

Part B-1

Base your answers to questions 56 through 60 on the diagram below, which represents part of the human respiratory system.

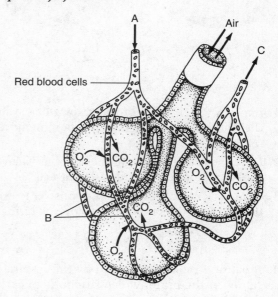

56. The blood vessels labeled *B* that are surrounding these air sacs are called (1) arteries (2) capillaries (3) veins (4) lymphatic ducts

57. These air sacs are known as (1) alveoli (2) bronchi (3) bronchioles (4) tracheae

58. The heart chamber that most directly pumps blood to the vessel network at *A* is the (1) right atrium (2) left atrium (3) right ventricle (4) left ventricle

59. The process most directly involved in the exchange of gases between these air sacs and blood vessels is called (1) active transport (2) pinocytosis (3) hydrolysis (4) diffusion

60. Compared to blood entering at *A*, blood leaving the vessel network at *C* has a lower concentration of (1) oxygen (2) hemoglobin and carbon dioxide (3) carbon dioxide (4) oxygen and hemoglobin

Base your answers to questions 61 through 63 on your knowledge of biology and on the diagram below, which represents a model of the human respiratory system.

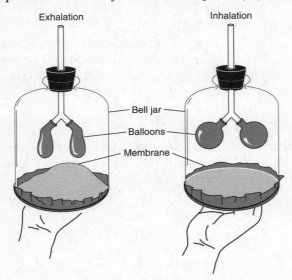

61. Explain which parts of the respiratory system the Y-tube, balloons, and rubber membrane represent.

62. Describe what happens to the balloons when the rubber membrane is pulled downward.

63. Give a scientific reason for your answer to question 62. How does this process apply to humans?

Part C

64. Breathing rate is controlled by the respiratory center in the brain, which responds to carbon dioxide levels in the blood. High levels of carbon dioxide increase the breathing rate; low levels decrease the breathing rate. Give a scientific reason why a person's breathing rate increases during and after vigorous exercise.

65. State how the alveoli in our lungs satisfy the conditions needed to be a good respiratory surface. Include at least two conditions that allow gas exchange to take place.

66. Place the following terms in a sequence that shows the correct pathway air takes during breathing in a human (starting with taking it in from the environment): *bronchi, alveoli, nose/ mouth, trachea,* and *bronchioles.*

EXCRETION

The metabolic wastes of humans include carbon dioxide, water, salts, and urea. Excretory wastes

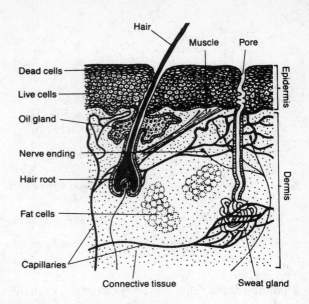

FIGURE 4-9 Structure of the skin.

pass from the cells into the blood and are carried to the excretory organs that expel them from the body. The excretory organs include the lungs, liver, sweat glands, and kidneys.

Lungs. The *lungs* function in the excretion of carbon dioxide and water vapor, which are the wastes of cellular respiration.

Liver. The *liver* is a large organ that performs many functions essential to human survival. One of the excretory functions of the liver is to get rid of excess amino acids. The amino groups are removed and converted into *urea,* which is excreted by the kidneys. The remaining amino acid molecules are broken down by cellular respiration. The liver is also responsible for the breakdown of red blood cells.

Sweat Glands. The *sweat glands* of the skin excrete wastes, including water, salts, and a small amount of urea. These wastes pass by diffusion from capillaries into the sweat glands and then through ducts to pores on the surface of the skin (Figure 4-9). The mixture of wastes and water excreted by the sweat glands is called sweat, or *perspiration.*

Perspiration functions primarily in the regulation of body temperature. The evaporation of sweat from the surface of the skin occurs when heat is absorbed from skin cells, and it serves to lower the body temperature. This method of temperature regulation is another example of homeostasis.

Urinary System

The human urinary system consists of the kidneys, ureters, urinary bladder, and urethra (Figure 4-10).

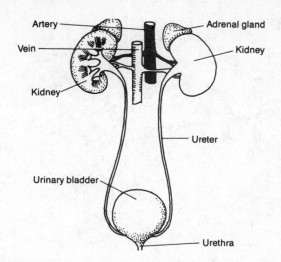

FIGURE 4-10 Structure of the human urinary system.

Kidneys. Human *kidneys* perform two major functions: they remove urea from the blood, and they regulate the concentrations of most of the substances in the body fluids. Blood is carried to each kidney by a large artery. Within the kidney, the artery divides and subdivides into smaller and smaller arteries and then into balls of capillaries called *glomeruli* (singular, *glomerulus*). Each glomerulus is part of a *nephron*, the functional unit of the kidney (Figure 4-11). There are about one million nephrons in each kidney.

A nephron consists of a glomerulus surrounded by a cup-shaped structure called *Bowman's capsule*. Extending from the capsule is a long coiled tubule that is surrounded by capillaries. As blood flows through the glomerulus, water, salts, urea, glucose, and some amino acids diffuse out of the blood into Bowman's capsule. This process is called *filtration*.

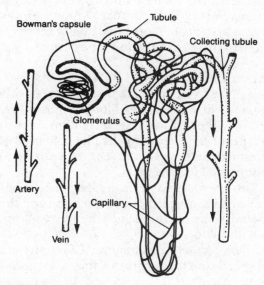

FIGURE 4-11 Structure of a nephron.

As these substances—referred to as the *filtrate*—pass through the long coiled tubule of the nephron, glucose, water, amino acids, and some of the salts are reabsorbed by active transport into the blood in the capillaries surrounding the tubule. The fluid that remains in the tubules consists of water, urea, and salts, and is called *urine*. Urine passes from the small tubule of the nephron into larger tubules and then to the ureter.

Ureters and Urinary Bladder. Urine flows from each kidney into a large tubule called the *ureter*. The ureters carry the urine to the urinary bladder, a muscular organ in which urine is stored temporarily.

Urethra. Urine is periodically expelled from the bladder into a tube called the *urethra*. This tube leads to the outside of the body.

Diseases of the Urinary System

Diseases of the kidneys affect the body's ability to eliminate normal amounts of metabolic wastes. *Gout* is a condition that produces symptoms similar to arthritis and is caused by deposits of uric acid in the joints. Victims of gout suffer from severe pain and stiffness in the joints. Diets that are extremely high in protein result in the production of large amounts of urea, which the kidneys must remove from the blood. The extra strain on the kidneys in eliminating these wastes may result in a kidney disorder, or **malfunction**.

QUESTIONS
Part A

67. Which human body system includes the lungs, liver, skin, and kidneys? (1) respiratory (2) digestive (3) transport (4) excretory

68. In humans, the filtrate produced by the nephrons is temporarily stored in the (1) glomerulus (2) alveolus (3) gallbladder (4) urinary bladder

69. What is the principal waste from excess amino acids in humans? (1) salt (2) urea (3) uric acid (4) carbon dioxide

70. In humans, the organ that breaks down red blood cells and amino acids is the (1) kidney (2) liver (3) gallbladder (4) small intestine

71. The main components of urine, besides water, are (1) amino acids and fatty acids (2) urea and salts (3) ammonia and bile (4) hydrochloric acid and bases

72. In humans, urine is eliminated from the bladder through the (1) urethra (2) ureter (3) nephron (4) collecting tubule

73. The basic structural and functional excretory units of the human kidney are known as (1) nephridia (2) nephrons (3) alveoli (4) ureters

74. The excretory organ that is also associated with the storage of glycogen is the (1) stomach (2) lung (3) kidney (4) liver

Part B-1

Base your answers to questions 75 through 77 on your knowledge of biology and on the diagram below, which illustrates a nephron and its capillaries.

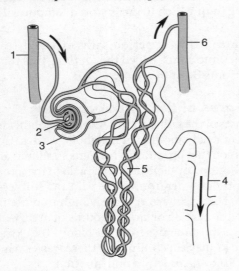

75. Into which structure does the filtrate first pass? (1) 5 (2) 6 (3) 3 (4) 4

76. In which area is water being reabsorbed? (1) 5 (2) 2 (3) 3 (4) 4

77. In which area does urine collect? (1) 1 (2) 2 (3) 6 (4) 4

Part B-2

78. Briefly describe how each of the following functions as an excretory organ:
    • the liver
    • the skin
    • the lungs

Part C

Base your answers to questions 79 and 80 on the following diagram and information above. The diagram represents a nephron from which samples of fluid were extracted. The samples were recovered from the areas labeled A and B in the diagram. The concentrations of five substances in the fluid extracted from both sites were compared and the results are listed in the table.

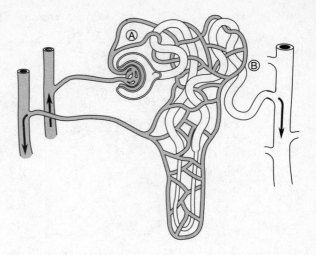

Substance	Concentration at A	Concentration at B
Water	High	Low
Urea	Moderate	High
Glucose	Moderate	Zero
Amino acids	High	Zero
Salts	Low	High

79. Explain the change in the concentrations of water and urea from area *A* to area *B*.

80. Why are there no amino acids present in the fluid extracted from area *B*, yet the concentration at area *A* was high?

NERVOUS SYSTEM

Regulation in humans involves the interaction of the nervous and endocrine systems. The two systems are similar in that they both secrete chemicals and both play a major role in the maintenance of homeostasis. In general, they differ in that the responses of the nervous system are more rapid and of shorter duration than those of the endocrine system.

Nerve Cells

The nervous system is made up of **nerve cells**, or *neurons,* which are adapted for the transmission of impulses. The nervous system contains three different types of nerve cells, which differ both in structure and function; these are the sensory neurons, motor neurons, and interneurons.

Sensory neurons transmit impulses from the sense organs, or receptors, to the brain and the spinal cord. Sense organs include the eyes, ears, tongue, nose, and skin.

Motor neurons transmit impulses from the brain and spinal cord to the *effectors,* that is, to the muscles and the glands.

Interneurons are found in the spinal cord and brain; they transmit nerve impulses from sensory neurons to motor neurons.

Nerves

The nerve cells, or parts of nerve cells, are bound together in bundles called *nerves.* There are three kinds of nerves: *sensory nerves,* which contain only sensory neurons; *motor nerves,* which contain only motor neurons; and *mixed nerves,* which contain both sensory and motor neurons.

Central Nervous System

The two main divisions of the human nervous system are the *central nervous system,* which includes the brain and spinal cord, and the *peripheral nervous system,* which includes all the nerves outside the central nervous system.

The Brain. The *brain* is a large mass of nerve cells located in the cranial cavity. It is surrounded and protected by the bones of the skull. The three major parts of the brain are the cerebrum, the cerebellum, and the medulla (Figure 4-12). Each controls different functions of the body.

In humans, the *cerebrum* is the largest part of the brain. It is the center for thought, memory, and learning; it receives and interprets messages from the sense organs; and it initiates all voluntary, or conscious, movements.

The *cerebellum* is located below and behind the cerebrum. It coordinates all motor activities and is involved in maintaining the body's balance.

The *medulla* is located at the base of the brain and connects the brain and the spinal cord. The medulla controls many important involuntary activities in the body, including breathing, heartbeat, blood pressure, and peristalsis.

The Spinal Cord. The medulla of the brain is continuous with the *spinal cord,* which is surrounded

and protected by the vertebrae of the backbone, or spinal column. The spinal cord coordinates activities between the brain and other body structures. Impulses from sense receptors throughout the body are transmitted by sensory neurons to the spinal cord. In the spinal cord, impulses are transmitted by interneurons to the brain. Impulses from the brain are carried by motor neurons through the spinal cord and then to the appropriate effectors.

Peripheral Nervous System

The peripheral nervous system includes all neurons, both sensory and motor, outside the central nervous system. These nerve cells carry impulses between the central nervous system and the rest of the body. The two main divisions of the peripheral nervous system are the somatic nervous system and the autonomic nervous system.

The *somatic nervous system* includes all the nerves that control the movements of the voluntary muscles of the body, as well as the sensory neurons that transmit impulses from sense receptors to the central nervous system.

The *autonomic nervous system* consists of the nerves that control the activities of smooth muscle, cardiac muscle, and glands. The activities of this system, which are involuntary (not under voluntary control), include regulation of the heartbeat and circulation, respiration, and peristalsis.

Behavior and the Nervous System

All animals, including humans, have behaviors that help them maintain homeostasis and aid their survival. These behaviors are controlled by the nervous system. Some behaviors are inborn, while others are learned.

Habits. A *habit* is a kind of learned behavior that becomes automatic through repetition. The repetition establishes pathways for nerve impulse transmission that permit a rapid, automatic response to a particular stimulus.

Reflexes. An automatic, inborn response to a particular stimulus is called a *reflex.* In a reflex response, impulses follow a set pathway called a *reflex arc* (Figure 4-13, page 64). In this pathway, impulses pass from a receptor to a sensory neuron to an interneuron (in the spinal cord) to a motor neuron to an effector. Although impulses may also pass from an interneuron to the brain, the reflex response is controlled by the spinal cord and occurs without the involvement of the brain. Reflexes are generally protective in nature, allowing a rapid response to a potentially dangerous stimulus.

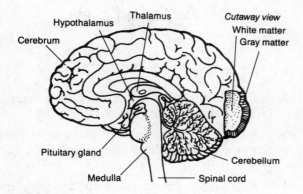

FIGURE 4-12 Structure of the human brain.

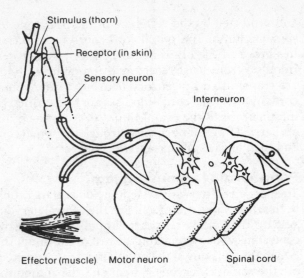

Stimulus (thorn)

Receptor (in skin)

Sensory neuron

Interneuron

Effector (muscle)   Motor neuron

Spinal cord

FIGURE 4-13 A typical reflex arc.

Disorders of the Nervous System

Cerebral palsy is a group of diseases caused by damage to the parts of the brain that control voluntary movement. This damage occurs during embryonic development. *Meningitis* is an inflammation of the membranes that surround the brain and spinal cord. Meningitis may be caused by viral or bacterial infections, and symptoms include headache, muscle stiffness, fever, and chills. A *stroke* is a disorder in which the brain is damaged as a result of a *cerebral hemorrhage* (a broken blood vessel) or a blood clot (in a blood vessel) in the brain. *Polio* is a disease that affects the central nervous system; it may result in paralysis. Polio is caused by a virus and can be prevented by immunization. *Alzheimer's* is a degenerative disease in which neurons in the brain are gradually destroyed. This fatal illness generally strikes older people and begins with such symptoms as forgetfulness, mood swings, and unusual behavior. As the disease progresses, the person becomes less and less capable of handling simple daily tasks such as dressing, bathing, and eating on his or her own.

QUESTIONS
Part A

81. The major function of a motor neuron is to (1) transmit impulses from the spinal cord to the brain (2) act as a receptor for environment stimuli (3) transmit impulses from sense organs to the central nervous system (4) transmit impulses from the central nervous system to muscles or glands

82. Nerves are composed of bundles of (1) muscle cells (2) neurons (3) phagocytes (4) bone cells

83. Which part of the human central nervous system is involved primarily with sensory interpretation and thinking? (1) spinal cord (2) medulla (3) cerebrum (4) cerebellum

84. The somatic nervous system contains nerves that run from the central nervous system to the (1) muscles of the skeleton (2) heart (3) smooth muscles of the gastrointestinal tract (4) endocrine glands

85. If the cerebellum of a human were damaged, which condition would probably result? (1) inability to reason (2) difficulty breathing (3) loss of sight (4) loss of balance

86. Which is the correct route of an impulse in a reflex arc?

    (1) receptor → sensory neuron → interneuron → motor neuron → effector
    (2) effector → receptor → motor neuron → sensory neuron → interneuron
    (3) sensory neuron → effector → motor neuron → receptor → interneuron
    (4) motor neuron → sensory neuron → interneuron → effector

87. The brain and the spinal cord make up the (1) autonomic nervous system (2) peripheral nervous system (3) central nervous system (4) somatic nervous system

88. Impulses are transmitted from receptors to the central nervous system by (1) receptor neurons (2) sensory neurons (3) interneurons (4) motor neurons

Part B-1

Base your answers to questions 89 through 92 on the following diagram of the human brain.

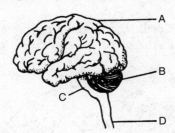

89. Injury to which part would most likely result in loss of memory? (1) *A* (2) *B* (3) *C* (4) *D*

90. Which part of the brain controls the involuntary movements of the digestive system? (1) *A* (2) *B* (3) *C* (4) *D*

91. Which part of the brain is involved with balance and the coordination of body movements? (1) *A* (2) *B* (3) *C* (4) *D*

92. Sight and hearing are functions of the structure labeled (1) *A* (2) *B* (3) *C* (4) *D*

Base your answers to questions 93 and 94 on the diagram below and on your knowledge of biology.

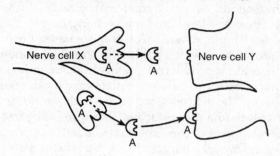

93. The process represented in the diagram best illustrates (1) cellular communication (2) muscle contraction (3) extraction of energy from nutrients (4) waste disposal

94. Which statement best describes the diagram? (1) Nerve cell *X* is releasing receptor molecules. (2) Nerve cell *Y* is signaling nerve cell *X*. (3) Nerve cell *X* is attaching to nerve cell *Y*. (4) Nerve cell *Y* contains receptor molecules for substance *A*.

Part B-2

95. Use the following terms to complete the chart below, which outlines the human nervous system: *somatic nervous system, brain, cerebrum, cerebellum, autonomic nervous system, medulla, spinal cord.*

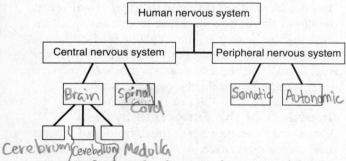

96. Briefly describe the main functions of the three major regions of the human brain:
- the cerebrum
- the cerebellum
- the medulla

Part C

97. Explain how a reflex arc works to protect the human body from a potentially dangerous stimulus. Provide an example.

98. The human nervous system is complex. Give one example of how our brains have led to the progress that we consider to be "advanced" compared to that of other animals.

ENDOCRINE SYSTEM

The human endocrine system is made up of the endocrine glands, which secrete **hormones** directly into the blood. The hormones (which are chemical messengers that bind with receptor proteins to affect gene activity, resulting in long-lasting changes in the body) are transported by the circulatory system to the organs and tissues on which they act.

Endocrine Glands

The glands of the human endocrine system are the hypothalamus, pituitary, thyroid, parathyroids, adrenals, islets of Langerhans, and gonads (ovaries and testes) (Figure 4-14).

Hypothalamus. Hormone-secreting cells are present in a small part of the brain called the *hypothalamus.* The hormones of the hypothalamus influence the activities of the pituitary gland.

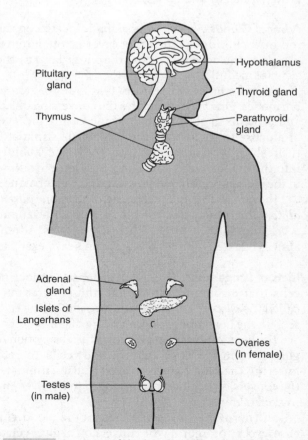

FIGURE 4-14 Structure of the human endocrine system.

Pituitary Gland. Many hormones are secreted by the *pituitary gland,* which is located at the base of the brain. Some pituitary hormones regulate the activities of other endocrine glands.

Growth-stimulating hormone is a pituitary hormone that has widespread effects in the body in addition to stimulating the growth of long bones.

Thyroid-stimulating hormone (TSH) is a pituitary hormone that stimulates the secretion of the thyroid hormone thyroxin.

Follicle-stimulating hormone (FSH) is a pituitary hormone that stimulates the development of follicles in the ovaries of females. In males, it influences sperm production.

Thyroid Gland. The iodine-containing hormone *thyroxin* is produced by the *thyroid gland,* which is located in the neck. Thyroxin regulates the rate of metabolism in the body cells and is essential for normal physical and mental development.

Parathyroid Glands. Embedded in the back of the thyroid gland are the *parathyroid glands,* which secrete the hormone *parathormone.* Parathormone controls calcium metabolism. Calcium is required for normal nerve function, blood clotting, and the growth of teeth and bones.

Adrenal Glands. An *adrenal gland* is located on the top of each kidney. The outer layer of the adrenal glands is the adrenal cortex; the inner layer is the adrenal medulla.

The *adrenal cortex* secretes two types of steroid hormones. One type stimulates the conversion of fats and proteins to glucose, thereby increasing the level of glucose in the blood. The other type stimulates the reabsorption of sodium from the kidney tubules into the bloodstream. The concentration of sodium in the blood affects blood pressure and water balance.

The *adrenal medulla* secretes the hormone *adrenaline,* which increases the blood glucose level and accelerates the heartbeat and breathing rates. Adrenaline is released in times of stress and heavy exercise.

Islets of Langerhans. The small groups of endocrine cells that are found throughout the pancreas are called the *islets of Langerhans.* These endocrine cells secrete the hormones insulin and glucagon.

The hormone **insulin** promotes the absorption of glucose from the blood into the body cells, thereby lowering the blood glucose level. It also stimulates the conversion of glucose to glycogen in the liver and in skeletal muscle.

The hormone *glucagon* increases the blood glucose level by promoting the conversion of glycogen to glucose in the liver and skeletal muscle. The glucose then passes from the organs back into the blood. Through their opposite effects, insulin and glucagon function to help the body maintain homeostasis by keeping the blood glucose level within certain limits.

The Gonads. The male and female *gonads*—the testes and ovaries—both function as endocrine glands. The **testes** (singular, *testis*) secrete the male sex hormone **testosterone**, which stimulates the development of the male reproductive organs and secondary sex characteristics; it also stimulates the production of **sperm**. The **ovaries** secrete the female sex hormones **estrogen** and **progesterone**. Estrogen influences the development of the female reproductive organs and secondary sex characteristics; it also stimulates the production of **egg** cells. Progesterone stimulates the thickening of the uterine lining in preparation for the implantation of an **embryo** (the fertilized egg cell).

Negative Feedback

The secretion of hormones by the endocrine glands is regulated by a mechanism known as *negative feedback.* In many cases, the level of one hormone in the blood stimulates or inhibits the production of a second hormone. The blood level of the second hormone in turn stimulates or inhibits the production of the first hormone. For example, the relationship between the pituitary's secretion of thyroid-stimulating hormone (TSH) and the thyroid's secretion of the hormone thyroxin is a classic type of a *negative feedback mechanism.*

When the concentration of thyroxin in the blood drops below a certain level, the pituitary is stimulated to secrete TSH. This hormone, in turn, then stimulates the secretion of thyroxin by the thyroid. When the blood thyroxin concentration reaches a certain level, the further secretion of TSH by the pituitary is inhibited. In this way, the body can regulate thyroxin levels—just as it regulates carbon dioxide levels—in order to maintain **stability**, or homeostasis.

Disorders of the Endocrine System

A *goiter* is an enlargement of the thyroid gland that is most commonly caused by a lack of iodine in the diet. *Diabetes* is a disorder in which the islets of Langerhans do not secrete adequate amounts of insulin into the bloodstream and, as a result, the blood glucose level is elevated. Disorders in the pituitary gland may affect the release of growth hormone, resulting in a negative effect on a person's growth.

Recent advances in recombinant DNA technology have allowed the synthesis of human growth hormone, as well as insulin. These hormones (made by genetically engineered bacteria) can be used to replace or supplement the inadequate amount of hormone being made by the person with the disorder.

99. Which is *not* an endocrine gland? (1) thyroid (2) salivary gland (3) pancreas (4) testis

100. The part of the brain that is most directly related to the endocrine system is the (1) cerebrum (2) medulla (3) hypothalamus (4) cerebellum

101. Which structure secretes the substance it produces directly into the bloodstream? (1) gallbladder (2) salivary gland (3) adrenal gland (4) skin

102. The hormones insulin and glucagon are produced by the (1) thyroid (2) pituitary (3) pancreas (4) liver

103. Which hormone lowers blood sugar levels by increasing the rate of absorption of glucose by the body cells? (1) follicle-stimulating hormone (2) insulin (3) parathormone (4) adrenaline

104. A person was admitted to the hospital with an abnormally high blood sugar level and a very high sugar content in his urine. Which gland most likely caused this condition by secreting lower than normal amounts of its hormone? (1) pancreas (2) parathyroid (3) salivary (4) thyroid

105. Which hormone stimulates activity in the ovaries? (1) testosterone (2) thyroid-stimulating hormone (3) insulin (4) follicle-stimulating hormone

106. A person's rate of metabolism is regulated by a hormone secreted by the (1) parathyroids (2) thyroid (3) pancreas (4) adrenals

107. Estrogen, which influences the development of secondary sex characteristics, is secreted by the (1) pituitary (2) adrenals (3) parathyroids (4) ovaries

108. In humans, the level of calcium in the blood is regulated by the (1) pancreas (2) thyroid (3) adrenals (4) parathyroids

109. The mechanism that regulates the secretion of hormones by endocrine glands is called (1) peristalsis (2) active transport (3) negative feedback (4) filtration

110. Insufficient iodine in the diet may cause goiter, a disorder of the (1) adrenal glands (2) pancreas (3) pituitary gland (4) thyroid gland

Base your answers to questions 111 through 114 on the graph above, which shows the levels of glucose and insulin present in a person's blood after eating a meal.

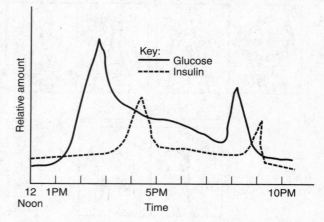

111. At approximately what times did the glucose level spike in this person?

112. What effect does insulin seem to have on the blood glucose level?

113. Describe the relationship between the levels of glucose and the levels of insulin.

114. What is the most probable reason for the time lag between the spikes in glucose level and the spikes in insulin level?

115. Use your knowledge of biology to answer the following questions about how a negative feedback mechanism works:

   • How do the pituitary gland and thyroid gland affect each other?

   • How does this feedback mechanism help in the maintenance of homeostasis?

   • What hormones produced by each gland are part of this feedback mechanism?

116. The diagrams below represent some of the systems that make up the human body. Select one of the pairs of systems and:

Pair 1   Pair 2

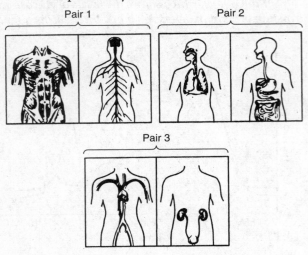

Pair 3

- identify each system in the pair you selected
- state one function of each system in the pair
- explain how the two systems work together to help maintain homeostasis

Smooth muscle

Cardiac muscle

Skeletal muscle

FIGURE 4-15 Smooth, cardiac, and skeletal muscle.

LOCOMOTION

Movement, or *locomotion,* in humans involves the interaction of bones, cartilage, muscles, tendons, and ligaments.

Bones

The human skeleton is made up mainly of bones of various shapes and sizes. All bones are made of *bone tissue,* which is quite hard and rigid. Bones provide support and protection for the soft parts of the body; they are the sites of attachment for muscles; and at joints, bones act as levers, enabling the body to move when the attached muscles contract. The production of new red blood cells and white blood cells occurs in the marrow of certain long bones.

Cartilage

In addition to bone, the human skeleton contains *cartilage,* a type of flexible, fibrous, elastic connective tissue. In embryos, most of the skeleton is made of cartilage. After birth, a child's cartilage is gradually replaced by bone, so that in adults, almost all of the cartilage has been replaced. In adults, cartilage is found at the ends of ribs, between vertebrae, at the ends of bones, and in the nose, ears, and trachea. Cartilage provides cushioning and flexibility at joints, and support and pliability in structures such as the nose and ears.

Joints

The places in the skeleton where the bones are connected to each other are called *joints.* Joints make movement of the skeleton possible. There are several kinds of movable joints in the human body. *Hinge joints,* which can move back and forth, are in the elbow and knee. *Ball-and-socket joints,* which are capable of circular movements, are found in the shoulder and hip. The neck has a *pivot joint,* which can move in a half circle. The bones of the skull are joined in *immovable joints.*

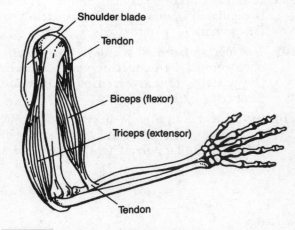

FIGURE 4-16 Muscles and bones of the upper arm.

Muscles

Unlike other body tissues, muscle tissue has the capacity to contract, or shorten. All movement in the body involves muscle tissue. There are three types of muscle tissue in the human body: skeletal muscle, smooth muscle, and cardiac muscle (Figure 4-15).

Skeletal Muscle. The voluntary muscles attached to the bones of the skeleton are made of *skeletal muscle* tissue. Muscle tissue of this type appears striated, or striped, when viewed with a microscope, and is also known as *striated muscle*. The contraction of skeletal muscle is controlled by the nervous system, which makes coordinated movements possible.

Skeletal muscles generally operate in antagonistic pairs; the contraction of one muscle of the pair extends the limb, while contraction of the other muscle flexes the limb. Figure 4-16 shows the muscles of the upper arm. The triceps is the extensor, while the biceps is the flexor. When the biceps contracts, the triceps relaxes, and the arm flexes, bending at the elbow. When the triceps contracts, the biceps relaxes, and the arm is extended.

Smooth Muscle. When viewed with a microscope, *smooth muscle* tissue does not appear striated. This type of muscle, which is also called *visceral muscle,* is found in the walls of the digestive organs and arteries, as well as in other internal organs. Smooth muscles are not under voluntary control.

Cardiac Muscle. The *cardiac muscle* tissue is found only in the heart. Although it appears striated when viewed with a microscope, cardiac muscle tissue is not under voluntary control, and its structure is different from that of skeletal muscle tissue.

Tendons and Ligaments. Muscles are attached to bones by tough, inelastic, fibrous cords of connective tissue called *tendons.* Bones are connected together at movable joints by *ligaments,* which are composed of tough, elastic connective tissue.

Disorders of Locomotion

Arthritis is an inflammation of the joints, which can be very painful and make movement difficult. *Tendonitis* is an inflammation of a tendon, usually where it is attached to a bone. This condition occurs most commonly in athletes.

117. Which type of muscle tissue found in the walls of the human stomach is most closely associated with the process of peristalsis? (1) striated (2) cardiac (3) voluntary (4) smooth

118. Bones are attached to each other at movable joints by (1) elastic ligaments (2) cartilaginous tissues (3) smooth muscles (4) skeletal muscles

119. Which is *not* a major function of cartilage tissues in a human adult? (1) giving pliable support to body structures (2) cushioning joint areas (3) adding flexibility to joints (4) providing skeletal levers

120. Which type of connective tissue makes up the greatest proportion of the skeleton of a human embryo? (1) ligaments (2) cartilage (3) tendons (4) bone

121. Which structure contains pairs of opposing skeletal muscles? (1) stomach (2) small intestine (3) heart (4) hand

122. Which statement most accurately describes human skeletal muscle tissue? (1) It is involuntary and striated. (2) It is involuntary and lacks striations. (3) It is voluntary and striated. (4) It is voluntary and lacks striations.

123. In the human elbow joint, the bone of the upper arm is connected to the bones of the lower arm by flexible connective tissue called (1) tendons (2) ligaments (3) muscles (4) neurons

For each phrase in questions 124 through 128, select the human body structure in the list below that is best described by that phrase.

Human Body Structure

A. bones

B. cartilage tissues

C. ligaments

D. smooth muscles

E. tendons

F. voluntary muscles

124. Cause peristalsis in the digestive tract (1) *B* (2) *C* (3) *D* (4) *F*

125. Serve as extensors and flexors (1) *A* (2) *D* (3) *E* (4) *F*

126. Serve as levers for body movements (1) *A* (2) *B* (3) *C* (4) *E*

127. Bind the ends of bones together (1) *B* (2) *C* (3) *D* (4) *E*

128. Attach the muscles to bones (1) *B* (2) *C* (3) *D* (4) *E*

Refer to Figure 4-16 on page 68, which shows the bones and (upper arm) muscles of the human arm to answer questions 129 through 131.

129. What happens to the arm when the biceps contracts?

130. What happens to the arm when the triceps contracts?

131. Why are the biceps and triceps considered an opposing pair of muscles?

132. Briefly compare the functions of the following paired structures of the muscular and skeletal systems:

- smooth muscle and skeletal muscle
- tendon and ligament
- bone and cartilage

133. How do the skeletal and muscular systems work together to produce locomotion?

134. State two advantages that locomotion gives to an organism. Explain how they aid survival.

LITERACY SKILL: READING FOR COMPREHENSION

Base your answers to questions 135 through 137 on the information below and on your knowledge of biology. Source: Science News *(February 12, 2011): vol. 179, no. 4, p. 16. Reprinted with permission of* Science News.

Quality May Trump Quantity in HDL: Good Cholesterol's Effectiveness at Clearing Fats Is Crucial

How much good cholesterol a person has is not as important as how well the beneficial substance works to stop heart disease, a new study suggests.

High-density lipoprotein—also known as HDL, or "good" cholesterol—is healthy for the heart, previous studies have indicated. Higher blood levels of the molecule tend to decrease risk of developing heart disease.

But a new study indicates that HDL levels may not be the most important factor in protecting against clogged arteries and cardiovascular disease. The study, published January 13 in the *New England Journal of Medicine,* shows that HDL's efficiency at removing fats from arteries is a better predictor of who will develop heart disease than its levels in the blood.

"Just measuring HDL levels isn't enough to figure out what's going on," says Jay Heinecke, an endocrinologist at the University of Washington in Seattle.

Some people's HDL was more efficient than other people's, found researchers led by Daniel Rader of the University of Pennsylvania School of Medicine in Philadelphia. Healthy people with this trait had less thickening of the carotid arteries than people with less efficient cholesterol-clearing HDL. In a separate group of people, HDL functioning was a better indicator than HDL levels of whether the person had heart disease, the team found.

Doctors won't be able to test their patients' HDL efficiency anytime soon. "We don't yet have an assay or a test that can be used in a clinical setting," Rader says. But the work does shed light on questions about how good cholesterol might fight heart disease.

135. Why are high levels of HDL (good cholesterol) beneficial to humans?

136. According to the researchers, what factor about HDL may be more effective in reducing heart disease risk than just the levels of HDL?

137. What indicator of better heart health was observed in people with more efficient cholesterol-clearing HDL?

5 Homeostasis and Immunity

A DYNAMIC EQUILIBRIUM

Under normal circumstances, an organism is able to maintain stability, or homeostasis, in relation to both its internal and external environments. This maintaining of a **dynamic equilibrium** means that despite the fact that environmental conditions may change, an organism responds by taking corrective actions that restore healthy conditions within its body.

For example, to maintain its normal temperature of about 37°C, the human body can make simple adjustments to keep its temperature within a safe range. If the body is too cold, small blood vessels in the skin may constrict in order to direct blood flow to the vital internal organs. In addition, the body may shiver to generate more heat. If the body is overheated, blood vessels near the skin surface can dilate (open wider) to promote blood flow to the skin in order to lose heat to the surrounding air. The skin may also produce perspiration (sweat) as a means of lowering the body temperature.

Feedback Mechanisms

Many homeostatic adjustments in organisms involve interactions called *negative feedback mechanisms,* or feedback loops. An initial change in one part of the loop (in response to some changing condition) stimulates a reaction in another part of the system. When the condition has been corrected, the second part of the loop feeds back information to the first part, shutting it off. This, in turn, shuts off the response that it initially caused in the second part. Homeostasis is maintained. If conditions in the body change, the feedback system is triggered into action again.

A common negative feedback loop involves the

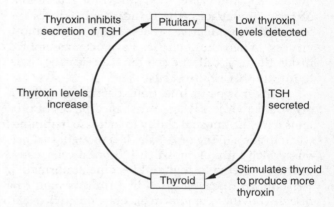

FIGURE 5-1 A negative feedback loop, involving the pituitary and thyroid glands.

pituitary gland, the thyroid gland, and their hormones. If the level of thyroxin (a thyroid hormone that regulates metabolism) is too low, the pituitary gland secretes thyroid-stimulating hormone (TSH). This causes the thyroid to increase its production of thyroxin. As the levels of thyroxin in the blood increase, the pituitary gland stops secreting TSH. Without the TSH, the thyroid slows down its secretion of thyroxin. In this way, the levels of thyroxin are maintained within normal limits (Figure 5-1).

WHEN HOMEOSTASIS FAILS: ILLNESS AND DISEASE

Causes of Disease

Any breakdown in an organism's ability to maintain or restore equilibrium can result in illness, disease, or even death. The causes of disease are many and varied. Diseases that are caused by factors inside the body are usually inherited and due to defective genetic traits. Diseases that are caused by factors outside the body, and that can be passed from one organism to another, are called **infectious diseases**. Factors that cause such diseases include microorganisms, or **microbes**, that are harmful. These disease-causing microbes, called **pathogens**, may include bacteria, fungi, protozoa, and worms, as well as nonliving particles of protein and nucleic acid, called *viruses*. Viruses normally invade healthy cells by binding to specific sites on their cell membranes. Once inside, the virus may infect the cell by inserting its nucleic acid into the DNA of the host cell. The functions of the host cell are thus disrupted and it can no longer carry on its life activities in a normal fashion. Moreover, when the cell reproduces, it also copies the inserted viral nucleic acid and passes it on to further generations of cells. Sometimes, the invading virus uses the host cell's reproductive process to synthesize more viruses. When these viruses have been assembled inside the host cell, the cell bursts, releasing them to infect other healthy cells.

Another type of infectious particle is called a *prion*. Like viruses, these misshaped pieces of proteins have the unusual ability to increase in number when inside a living organism. It is thought that prions, which form clumps that kill brain cells, cause normal proteins to fold and become abnormal. A well-known disease caused by prions is *mad cow disease* (bovine spongiform encephalopathy), a fatal illness that destroys the nervous system in cattle. Sheep also may suffer from a nervous-system disease caused by prions, called *scrapie*. The degenerative nervous disorder Creutzfeldt-Jakob disease, or *kuru,* which infects some people, is also caused by prions.

Sometimes, unhealthy habits and/or risky behaviors can jeopardize health and lead to illness. Poor nutrition, cigarette smoking, and abuse of alcohol and drugs can all result in serious illness and a breakdown of homeostasis. For example, excessive consumption of alcoholic beverages can cause cirrhosis of the liver, a fatal disease.

Cancer. Disease may also occur when certain cells in the body behave abnormally due to a genetic mutation. Such cells can divide uncontrollably and result in the growth of *tumors*. Tumors may be benign (not spreading) or malignant (spreading). Uncontrolled growth, or *metastasis,* of malignant cells is known as **cancer**. When cancer cells spread throughout the body, they interfere with the functioning of normal cells. In such cases, the cancer can become life-threatening. Although cancer may occur spontaneously, certain factors are known to increase the risk of developing it. Tobacco smoking, poor diet, some microbes, genetic factors, and exposure to **radiation** and certain chemicals called *carcinogens* are all thought to play a part in causing cancer.

Symptoms of Disease. Some diseases show their symptoms as soon as they begin to develop or soon after they are triggered by a pathogen. An example is influenza (the flu), which is caused by viruses. Other diseases may take several days, weeks, or even years before their symptoms appear. **AIDS** (*a*cquired *i*mmuno*d*eficiency *s*yndrome) and cancer are examples of diseases that may develop in the body for years before their symptoms appear.

QUESTIONS
Part A

1. The term that describes a body's overall ability to maintain homeostasis is (1) negative loop system (2) low maintenance (3) dynamic equilibrium (4) infectious

2. Many viruses infect only a certain type of cell because they bind to (1) other viruses on the surface of the cell (2) mitochondria in the cell (3) hormones in the cell (4) receptor sites on the surface of the cell

3. Viruses differ from other pathogens in that *only* viruses (1) contain a true nucleus (2) can reproduce on their own every 20 minutes (3) consist only of protein and nucleic acid (4) are able to infect healthy cells

4. Which represents a correct cause-and-effect sequence? (1) cirrhosis of the liver → excessive alcohol consumption (2) low thyroxin levels → increase in TSH secretion (3) symptoms of disease → exposure to pathogen (4) dilation of blood vessels in skin → overheating of the body

5. Infectious particles known as prions, which cause nervous system diseases such as scrapie and kuru, consist of misshaped pieces of (1) bacteria (2) fungi (3) proteins (4) viruses

6. When a certain plant is without water for an extended period of time, guard cells close openings in the leaves of the plant. This activity conserves water and illustrates (1) cellular communication involving the action of nerve cells and receptor sites (2) an increase in rate of growth due to a low concentration of water (3) maintenance of a dynamic equilibrium through detection and response to stimuli (4) a response to one biotic factor in the environment

Base your answer to the following question on the diagram below and on your knowledge of biology.

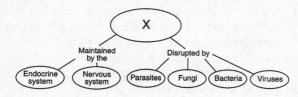

7. What term or phrase does letter *X* most likely represent?

8. Select two of the following risk factors: drug abuse, poor nutrition, genetic factors, radiation, tobacco smoking.
   - Define each of the two risk factors you have selected.
   - Explain how each risk factor can interfere with proper functioning of the immune system.

Base your answers to questions 9 through 11 on the diagram of a negative feedback loop, shown below, and on the following data: Structure A releases a substance, X, that can stimulate structure B to release its substance, Y.

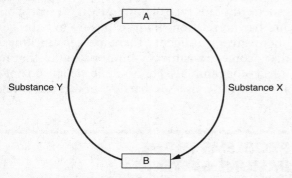

9. Under what conditions would structure *A* probably release substance *X*?

10. Explain what happens when the levels of substance *Y* get too high.

11. What type of substances are *X* and *Y* most likely to be?

THE IMMUNE SYSTEM: PROTECTION AGAINST DISEASE

The human body is well protected against invading pathogens. The first line of defense prevents harmful microorganisms from getting into the body by blocking their entry. The skin, when unbroken, provides an effective physical barrier to nearly all pathogenic organisms. Secretions such as tears, saliva, and mucus provide an effective physical and chemical barrier; they contain enzymes that destroy pathogens or help trap and flush them out of the body.

Nevertheless, some pathogens manage to elude the first line of defense and gain entry. They may do so through breaks in the skin (cuts and scrapes) or through the eyes and natural openings in the body, such as the mouth and nostrils. The mucous membrane is yet another easy route into the body. The mucous membrane is soft, moist thin tissue such as is found inside the mouth and rectum. Once inside, these invaders are confronted by the *immune system,* the body's primary defense mechanism. Invaders may be destroyed by being engulfed by special cells or by being chemically marked for destruction and elimination.

Functions of the Immune System

How does the immune system function? All cells have very specific proteins on their plasma membrane surfaces. The immune system is able to recognize proteins on cells that are foreign and to distinguish them from its own body's proteins. These invading foreign proteins are referred to as *antigens*.

Specialized Blood Cells. The human immune system consists of specialized white blood cells and lymphatic organs such as the spleen, thymus, and tonsils. The system also has a number of *lymph nodes* that participate in defense mechanisms. Some white blood cells, called *macrophages,* engulf and digest pathogens (Figure 5-2). After destroying the pathogens, these white cells often die, too.

White blood cells called *T cells* are specialized to kill pathogens or mark them for destruction. Other white blood cells, called *B cells,* produce very specific *antibodies* against the pathogens. Antibodies have a

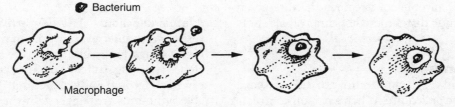

FIGURE 5-2 The macrophage is a type of white blood cell that engulfs and destroys invading pathogens.

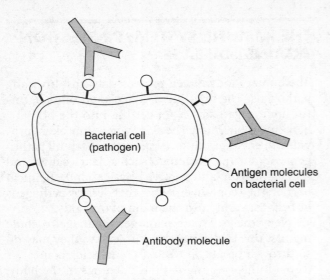

FIGURE 5-3 The immune system produces antibodies that are specific to the invading foreign antigens.

chemical structure that precisely matches the shape of the antigen with which they react. Once the match has been made, the pathogen is destroyed. Some of the antibody-producing blood cells remain in the body's immune system as "memory cells." These specialized cells can quickly mount an attack if the body is invaded again by the same pathogen (Figure 5-3).

Vaccinations

A *vaccine* is a weakened pathogen or its antigen that is injected into an organism. *Vaccinations* are given to people and animals to provide *immunity* against particular pathogens. Once recognized by the immune system, the invading antigen causes antibodies that are specific to it to be made. The cells that produce the antibodies remain as memory cells in the body. Thus, vaccinations provide *active acquired immunity* (see following section). If the actual pathogen invades the body at a later time, these memory cells can launch an immediate response and attack the invaders, often before they have a chance to cause any disease symptoms. Examples of vaccines that are given to people include those for the flu (influenza), MMR (measles, mumps, rubella), and hepatitis. Since the viruses that cause flu are different every year, it is necessary to obtain a flu vaccine yearly to maintain immunity. In the United States, state laws determine which vaccinations children must get before they attend school. Examples of vaccines that are given to animals include distemper shots and rabies shots for pet dogs.

Types of Immunity

There are several types of immunity to disease that a person may have or acquire. When a person contracts a disease (or receives a vaccination) that he or she later recovers from, his or her immune system creates antibodies that are specific to the pathogens or antigens that caused the disease. These antibodies remain in the bloodstream even after the disease symptoms have ceased. If the person becomes infected again with the same type of pathogen or antigen, the antibodies already present attack the invaders so that he or she will either recover faster or not even become ill a second time. This type of immunity is called **acquired immunity**, and it can be either *active* or *passive*.

In **active immunity**, the person is exposed to the pathogen or antigen directly. Active immunity may result from direct exposure to a pathogen or antigen from the environment or in the form of a vaccine. In either case, the person produces his or her own antibodies against the disease.

In **passive immunity**, antibodies are transferred from another source to the person. For example, during fetal development, antibodies cross the placenta from the mother to her fetus, thus providing immunity. Additionally, if a mother breast-feeds her infant, antibodies enter the baby through the mother's milk. Providing antibodies through an injection may also induce passive immunity. For example, if a person is bitten by a rabid animal, an injection containing antibodies to the rabies virus is given to the person to prevent the development of rabies, a fatal disease.

Innate immunity in a person is determined genetically. This type of immunity is present at birth and has no relationship to exposure to pathogenic organisms or antigens. There are certain illnesses that people are naturally immune to but that may infect other animals. For example, people do not get all of the same diseases that dogs or cats can develop.

PROBLEMS IN THE IMMUNE SYSTEM

Overreactions of the Immune System

In some individuals, the immune system overreacts to certain stimuli or antigens that are harmless to most other people. Unfortunately, these severe reactions cause, rather than prevent, suffering and illness for the person.

Allergic Reactions. An *allergic reaction* is a strong response to *allergens* in pollen, animal fur, mold, insect stings, foods, and so on. The sufferer may experience sneezing, watery and itchy eyes, a runny nose, hives, coughing, and/or swelling. These uncomfortable symptoms are triggered by the immune system's release of substances called *histamines*. Although these allergy symptoms are inconvenient, they are responses made by the body in an attempt to expel the invading antigen. In some cases, the swelling may be so severe in the sinuses or throat that it interferes with breathing. An extreme type of allergic reaction, known as *anaphylactic shock*, occurs in some people in response to bee or wasp stings, certain foods, and even some medications. This condition causes severe swelling and can be truly life-threatening. In general, this type of severe reaction does not occur with the first exposure to the antigen. Rather, the person becomes sensitized on the first exposure and can go into anaphylactic shock on the second or third exposures. Such persons usually carry an EpiPen with them in case of accidental exposure to these antigens. The EpiPen contains a measured dose of epinephrine, a drug that can reduce or prevent the effects of anaphylaxis.

Autoimmune Diseases. In very rare cases, the immune system accidentally targets some of the body's own cell proteins as antigens. Once the immune system has identified an antigen as foreign, the cells bearing that protein are attacked as if they were invading foreign pathogens. This reaction produces a condition known as an **autoimmune disease** (*auto* meaning "self"). Examples of such serious diseases include rheumatoid arthritis (which causes inflammation and pain in the joint membranes) and lupus erythematosus (which causes painful swelling of the skin and joints, fever, rash, hair loss, fatigue, and sensitivity to light).

Immune Response to Transplants. People who receive transplanted organs, such as a heart, liver, or kidney (due to a *malfunction* of their own organ), may also experience problems with their immune response. Because the organ is recognized as foreign, the immune system may launch an attack against it, causing the body to reject the new organ. Physicians attempt to match the chemistry of the organ donor as closely as possible with that of the recipient, in order to minimize the risk of organ rejection. In addition, *immunosuppressant* drugs may be used to lessen the immune response. However, use of these medications can leave the transplant recipient quite vulnerable to infection by various microbes.

A Damaged or Weakened Immune System

HIV (*h*uman *i*mmunodeficiency *v*irus), the agent that causes AIDS, damages the immune system by destroying specific T cells known as *helper T cells*. This leaves the affected person with a severely limited immune response. For that reason, AIDS is called an *immunodeficiency disease*. In fact, AIDS sufferers are prone to and frequently die from a variety of diseases that a healthy person's immune system could probably conquer (especially with the use of medicine), rather than from the virus itself. In recent years, many drugs have been produced that greatly reduce AIDS symptoms or slow the reproduction of the virus. People with AIDS are now able to live much longer than previously. However, AIDS still remains incurable.

Finally, as a person gets older, his or her immune system gradually weakens in its ability to respond to pathogens or cancerous cells. Consequently, older adults may be more prone than younger individuals to becoming ill or developing (malignant) tumors. Fatigue, stress, substance abuse, and poor nutrition can also contribute to a weakened immune response.

QUESTIONS
Part A

12. Which cells are important components of the human immune system? (1) red blood cells (2) liver cells (3) white blood cells (4) nerve cells

13. A blood test showed that a person had increased levels of antibodies. This may indicate that the person has (1) an infection (2) diabetes (3) low blood pressure (4) an enlarged thyroid

14. In some people, substances such as peanuts, eggs, and milk cause an immune response. This response to usually harmless substances is most similar to the (1) action of the heart as the intensity of exercise increases (2) mechanism that regulates the activity of guard cells (3) action of white blood cells when certain bacteria enter the body (4) mechanism that maintains the proper level of antibodies in the blood

15. Substances that trigger a defensive response by the immune system are called (1) antibodies (2) antigens (3) lymph nodes (4) macrophages

16. A similarity between antibodies and enzymes is that both (1) are lipids (2) are produced by liver cells (3) can make blood vessels dilate (4) have very specific shapes and functions

17. Which statement does *not* describe an example of a feedback mechanism that maintains homeostasis? (1) The guard cells close the openings in leaves, preventing excess water loss from a plant. (2) White blood cells increase the production of antigens during an allergic reaction. (3) Increased physical activity increases heart rate in humans. (4) The pancreas releases insulin, helping humans to keep blood sugar levels stable.

18. It is recommended that people at risk for serious flu complications be vaccinated so that their bodies will produce (1) antigens to fight the flu virus (2) antibodies against the flu virus (3) toxins to fight the infection caused by the flu virus (4) antibiotics to reduce symptoms caused by the flu virus

19. A person's sneezing, coughing, and watery eyes right after exposure to cat hair are all indications of (1) an autoimmune disease (2) an infection caused by the cat (3) an allergic reaction (4) early warning signs of cancer

20. The use of a vaccine to stimulate the immune system to act against a specific pathogen is valuable in maintaining homeostasis because (1) once the body produces chemicals to combat one type of virus, it can more easily make antibiotics (2) the body can digest the weakened microbes and use them as food (3) the body will be able to fight invasions by the same type of microbe in the future (4) the more the immune system is challenged, the better it performs

Answer the following question based on your knowledge of biology and on the diagram below, which represents what can happen when homeostasis in an organism is threatened.

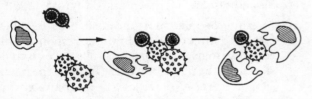

21. Which statement provides a possible explanation for these events? (1) Antibiotics break down harmful substances by the process of digestion. (2) Specialized cells tag and/or engulf invading microbes during an immune response. (3) Embryonic development of essential organs occurs during pregnancy. (4) Cloning removes abnormal cells produced during differentiation.

22. Which statement describes an example of active acquired immunity? (1) Humans generally do not get equine encephalitis, a disease of horses. (2) After having mumps as a child, an adult does not generally have a recurrence of the disease. (3) A patient receives an antibiotic to fight off a respiratory infection. (4) Breast milk provides many antibodies to a nursing infant.

23. Antibodies that cross the placenta from mother to baby during fetal development provide the child with (1) innate immunity (2) active acquired immunity (3) passive acquired immunity (4) induced passive immunity

Base your answers to questions 24 through 26 on the graph below, which shows the relationship between exposure to an antigen and the antibody response that followed.

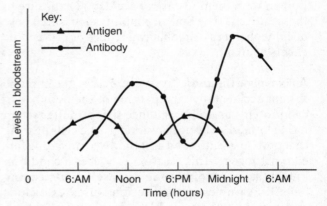

24. At what times did the antigen reach maximum levels in the bloodstream?

25. What relationship exists between the antigen levels and antibody levels in this graph?

26. The second peak of the antibody level is much greater than the first peak. Explain why.

Base your answers to question 27 through 29 on the paragraph below and on your knowledge of biology.

A boy contracted the viral disease chicken pox when he was a first grader. His doctor kept him out of school for two weeks until he recovered from the illness. Two years later, when his younger brother came down with chicken pox, the older boy did not catch it again, even though they shared a bedroom and were in close contact with one another.

27. What type of immunity to the chicken pox virus did the older boy develop? State one reason to support your answer.

28. How did the older boy's immune system protect him against chicken pox when he contracted the virus in the first grade?

29. Why didn't the older boy catch chicken pox again when his younger brother had it two years later?

30. A pharmaceutical company is proposing that its new product, Immunoblast, can help strengthen a person's immune system. Design an experiment in which you could test the effectiveness of this new product. Include the following steps:

- State the problem you are investigating.
- Propose a suitable hypothesis.
- Write the experimental procedure you would follow.
- List the data you would collect to test your hypothesis.

31. Each year, before the start of the flu season, older adults are advised to get a flu shot, or vaccination, to protect them.

- Why is the flu shot recommended more for older adults than for younger ones?
- How does the vaccine protect people from the flu?
- Why is a new flu vaccination needed every year?

32. Describe two ways that the risk of organ rejection can be minimized in a transplant patient. Discuss one problem that is associated with the use of immunosuppressant drugs.

33. AIDS is an infectious disease that has reached epidemic proportions. Briefly describe the nature of this disease and be sure to include:

- the type of pathogen that causes AIDS
- the specific body system that is attacked by that pathogen
- the effect on the body when this system is weakened by AIDS
- *two* ways to prevent or control the spread of infectious diseases such as AIDS

LITERACY SKILL: READING FOR COMPREHENSION

Base your answers to questions 34 through 37 on the information below and on your knowledge of biology. Source: Science News *(March 12, 2011): vol. 179, no. 6, p. 12. Reprinted with permission of* Science News.

Allergies Might Fight off Cancer: Elevated Immune Response Could Target Some Tumors

Hay fever, dog, peanut and other allergies may protect sufferers from certain types of brain tumors, a new study suggests.

In surveys of hospital patients, individuals with glioma—a form of brain and spinal cancer—were less likely than cancer-free individuals to report having allergies, researchers report in the February *Cancer Epidemiology, Biomarkers & Prevention*.

Epidemiologist Bridget McCarthy of the University of Illinois at Chicago and her team quizzed more than 1,000 hospital patients with or without cancer about their allergy histories. Of the 344 patients with high-grade glioma, about 35 percent reported having been diagnosed with one or more allergies in their lifetimes, compared with about 46 percent of the 612 cancer-free respondents. About 10 percent of patients with high-grade tumors had three or more allergies, as opposed to 19 percent of the controls. "The more allergies you have, the more protected you were," McCarthy says.

Glioma isn't the first cancer to be negatively correlated with common allergies, says Michael Scheurer, an epidemiologist at Baylor College of Medicine in Houston. Allergy-prone people may fight off colorectal and pancreatic cancer, and even childhood leukemia, better than sniffles-free people, according to some studies.

Just why these links exist isn't clear. Allergy sufferers mount heightened immune responses to certain foreign or dangerous cells and chemicals, says Scheurer. And cancer cells are certainly dangerous—human immune systems naturally seek the cells out. The immune systems in people with allergies may just do it better. "They have an overactive immune system, and maybe that's been protecting them from the development of tumors," he says.

In December, Scheurer and his colleagues reported finding a link between a higher risk for one type of glioma and use of antihistamine drugs such as diphenhydramine, Benadryl's active ingredient. The Illinois team did not find such a link.

Scheurer says Benadryl users shouldn't worry: "Brain tumors are very, very rare tumors, and a lot of people take antihistamines." He suspects that in a small set of individuals with a genetic predisposition to brain cancer, antihistamines may slow down the immune response, giving cancer cells an opening.

34. According to this article, what is the relationship between people who have allergies and their chances of developing the brain cancer glioma?

35. What other cancers may allergy-prone people be better able to fight off than people who do not suffer from allergies?

36. Describe the inference the researchers make concerning the immune system of allergy sufferers and its ability to protect them from cancer.

37. Why do the researchers believe that people who use antihistamines should not worry about increased chances of developing brain tumors?

6 Reproduction and Development

The survival of a species depends on reproduction, that is, the production of new individuals. There are two ways that organisms can reproduce, depending on the organism: **asexually** and **sexually**. In *asexual reproduction,* only one parent is involved, and the new organism develops from a cell or cells of the parent organism. In *sexual reproduction,* there are usually two parents, and each one contributes a specialized **sex cell** to the new organism. The two sex cells, one from each parent, fuse to form the first cell of the new generation. Some organisms can reproduce only asexually, for example, most protists. Some organisms can reproduce only sexually, for example, most animals. There are some organisms that, depending on the circumstances, can reproduce either asexually or sexually. Two examples are the hydra and many flowering plants.

MITOSIS

All cells arise from other cells by cell division, during which the nucleus duplicates, or *replicates,* and the cytoplasm divides in two, forming two cells. The process of **mitosis** (a nuclear process) is the orderly series of changes that results in the duplication of the complete set of chromosomes and the formation of two new nuclei that are identical to each other and to the nucleus of the original parent cell. (Chromosomes are structures within cells on which the genes are located.) The division of the cytoplasm occurs either during or after mitosis, and it results in the formation of two new, identical daughter cells. The effect of this is that all the cells that come from a single cell are genetically identical to it and to each other; they are all *clones.*

Events of Mitosis

During the period between cell divisions, the chromosome material is dispersed in the nucleus in the form of *chromatin.* At the beginning of mitosis, before the chromosomes become visible as distinct units, the chromatin replicates. It then contracts, forming a visible set of double-stranded chromosomes. Each double-stranded chromosome consists of two identical strands, or *chromatids,* joined by a *centromere* (Figure 6-1). It is very important to understand that the two chromatids carry the *exact* same genes and that they result from the replication process of a single chromosome prior to cell division.

During the early stages of mitosis, the nuclear membrane disintegrates and disappears, while a network of fibers called the *spindle apparatus* forms. In animal cells, two small organelles called *centrioles* move to the opposite ends, or *poles,* of the cell, where they appear to be involved in the formation of the spindle apparatus. Plant cells generally lack centrioles, but the spindle apparatus forms without them, and the movement of chromosomes is similar to that in animal cells.

The double-stranded chromosomes become attached to the spindle apparatus and line up along the cell's center, or *equator.* The two chromatids of each double-stranded chromosome separate and move to opposite poles of the cell. Current evidence

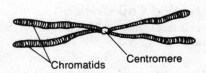

FIGURE 6-1 A double-stranded chromosome.

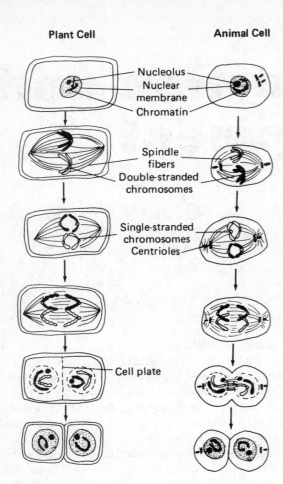

Plant Cell   Animal Cell

Nucleolus
Nuclear
membrane
Chromatin

Spindle
fibers
Double-stranded
chromosomes

Single-stranded
chromosomes
Centrioles

Cell plate

FIGURE 6-2 Stages of mitosis.

suggests that this movement results from the short-ening of the spindle fibers, which causes the chroma-tids to move to either one pole of the cell or the other. A nuclear membrane forms around each of the two sets of single-stranded chromosomes, thus forming two daughter nuclei—identical to each other and to the original nucleus (Figure 6-2).

Division of the Cytoplasm

In animal cells, the cytoplasm is divided when the cell membrane "pinches in" at the cell's center (in the process of *cytokinesis*), separating the two nuclei and dividing the cytoplasm into approximately equal halves.

In plant cells, the cytoplasm is divided when a *cell plate* forms across the center of the cell. The cell plate then forms the new cell walls.

Uncontrolled Cell Division

In multicellular organisms, cells sometimes undergo abnormal and rapid divisions, resulting in growths called *tumors,* which invade surrounding tissues and organs and interfere with their normal activi-ties. Such tumors are linked to a group of diseases

known, collectively, as *cancer.* (For more informa-tion, refer to Chapter 5, page 72.)

1. Each of the two daughter cells that result from the normal mitotic division of the original parent cell contains (1) the same number of chromo-somes but has genes different from those of the parent cell (2) the same number of chromosomes and has genes identical to those of the parent cell (3) one-half the number of chromosomes but has genes different from those of the parent cell (4) one-half the number of chromosomes and has genes identical to those of the parent cell

2. The following list describes some of the events associated with normal cell division:

   A. nuclear membrane formation around each set of newly formed chromosomes

   B. pinching in of cell membrane to separate daughter nuclei and divide cytoplasm

   C. replication of each chromosome to form sets of double-stranded chromosomes

   D. movement of single-stranded chromosomes to opposite ends of the spindle fibers

   What is the normal sequence in which these events occur? (1) $A \rightarrow B \rightarrow C \rightarrow D$ (2) $C \rightarrow B \rightarrow D \rightarrow A$ (3) $C \rightarrow D \rightarrow A \rightarrow B$ (4) $D \rightarrow C \rightarrow B \rightarrow A$

3. What is the result of normal chromosome repli-cation? (1) Lost or worn-out chromosomes are replaced. (2) Each daughter cell is provided with twice as many chromosomes as the parent cell. (3) The exact number of centrioles is produced for spindle fiber attachment. (4) Two identical sets of chromosomes are produced.

4. Normally, a complete set of chromosomes is passed on to each daughter cell as a result of (1) reduction division (2) mitotic cell division (3) meiotic cell division (4) nondisjunction

5. In nondividing cells, the chromosome material is in the form of (1) chromatids (2) centrioles (3) spindle fibers (4) chromatin

6. Organelles that play a role in mitotic divi-sion in animal cells but not in plant cells are (1) centrioles (2) chromatids (3) cell plates (4) chromosomes

7. In plant cells, after the cytoplasm divides, a cell plate forms across the center of the cell and forms the new (1) cell membranes (2) chromosomes (3) cell walls (4) centrioles

8. Colchicine is a drug that prevents chromosomes from separating during cell division. Describe how colchicine might affect daughter cells produced by a cell during mitosis.

9. Red blood cells lose their nuclei when they become fully mature. How does this explain the fact that red blood cells cannot undergo mitosis?

10. Compare the process of mitosis in a plant cell and in an animal cell.

11. Using the Internet, research how a tumor forms. How is mitosis related to the formation of a tumor? How is a benign tumor different from a malignant tumor?

TYPES OF ASEXUAL REPRODUCTION

Asexual reproduction is the production of new organisms without the joining of nuclei from two specialized sex cells. In asexual reproduction, the new organism develops by mitotic cell divisions, and the offspring are genetically identical to the parent.

Binary Fission
The form of asexual reproduction that occurs most commonly in single-celled organisms, such as the ameba and paramecium, is *binary fission* (Figure 6-3). In this type of reproduction, the nucleus divides

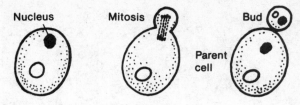

FIGURE 6-4 Budding in yeast.

by mitosis, and the cytoplasm divides, forming two daughter cells of equal size. These newly formed cells are smaller than the parent cell, but they contain the same number of chromosomes.

Budding
Yeasts and some other simple organisms carry on a form of asexual reproduction called *budding*, which is basically similar to binary fission. However, in budding, the division of the cytoplasm is unequal, so that one of the daughter cells is larger than the other. The daughter cells may separate, or they may remain attached, forming a colony (Figure 6-4).

In multicellular organisms such as the hydra, budding refers to the production of a multicellular growth, or *bud*, from the body of the parent (Figure 6-5). The bud is produced by mitotic cell division, and it develops into a new organism. The new organism may detach from the parent, or it may remain attached, forming a colony.

Sporulation
In some multicellular organisms, such as bread mold, specialized cells called *spores* are produced in large numbers by mitosis. This process is called *sporulation*. Spores are generally surrounded by a tough coat, which enables them to survive harsh environmental conditions. Each spore may then develop into a new organism when environmental conditions become favorable.

Regeneration
The process of **regeneration** refers to the replacement, or regrowth, of lost or damaged body parts. For example, a lobster may regenerate a lost claw. In

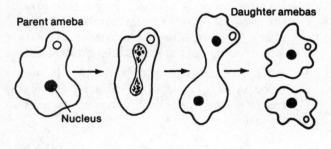

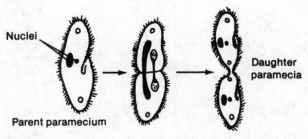

FIGURE 6-3 Binary fission in the ameba (top) and the paramecium (bottom).

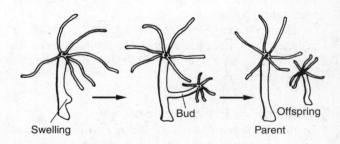

FIGURE 6-5 Budding in hydra.

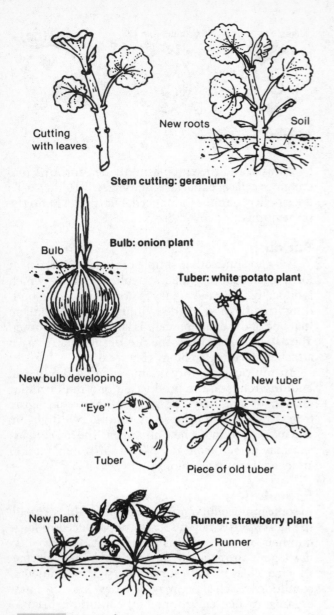

Cutting
with leaves

New roots   Soil

Stem cutting: geranium

Bulb: onion plant

Bulb

Tuber: white potato plant

New bulb developing

"Eye"   New tuber

Tuber   Piece of old tuber

New plant   **Runner: strawberry plant**

Runner

FIGURE 6-6 Forms of vegetative propagation.

some cases, an entire new animal can develop from a part of the parent organism. A new sea star can develop from one arm and part of the central disk of an existing sea star (which then regenerates the missing arm). In this case, regeneration is a type of asexual reproduction.

Invertebrates generally show a greater capacity for regeneration than vertebrates do, probably because they have many more unspecialized cells and parts than vertebrates do.

Vegetative Propagation

In plants, *vegetative propagation* involves various forms of asexual reproduction in which new plants develop from the roots, stems, or leaves of the parent

plant. Examples include new plant growth from bulbs, tubers, cuttings, and runners (Figure 6-6).

12. Compared to the parent cell, a daughter cell produced as a result of binary fission (1) has one-half as many chromosomes (2) has twice as many chromosomes (3) is the same size, but has fewer chromosomes (4) is smaller, but has the same number of chromosomes

13. A form of asexual reproduction that occurs in yeast is (1) binary fission (2) budding (3) vegetative propagation (4) spore formation

14. What is a type of asexual reproduction that commonly occurs in many species of unicellular protists? (1) external fertilization (2) tissue regeneration (3) binary fission (4) vegetative propagation

15. A type of asexual reproduction in which new plants develop from the roots, stems, or leaves of an existing plant is called (1) binary fission (2) sporulation (3) regeneration (4) vegetative propagation

16. A form of asexual reproduction found in bread mold involves the production of large numbers of specialized cells, each surrounded by a tough coat. This process is called (1) binary fission (2) budding (3) sporulation (4) regeneration

17. Compared to vertebrates, invertebrate animals exhibit a higher degree of regenerative ability because they (1) produce larger numbers of sex cells (2) produce larger numbers of spindle fibers (3) possess more chromosomes in their nuclei (4) possess more undifferentiated cells

18. What specific type of reproduction is shown below in the diagrams of an ameba? (1) vegetative propagation (2) binary fission (3) budding (4) meiosis

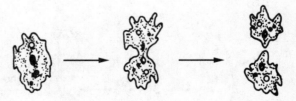

19. The chromosome content of a skin cell that is about to form two new skin cells is represented in the following diagram on page 83.

Which diagram best represents the chromosomes that would be found in the two new skin cells produced as a result of this process? (1) 1 (2) 2 (3) 3 (4) 4

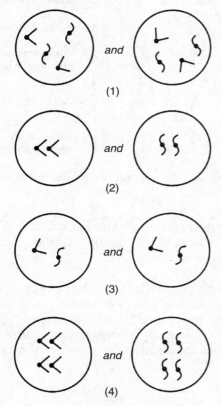

Part B-2

20. What role does mitosis play in asexual reproduction?

21. The ameba is a single-celled organism that reproduces asexually by mitosis. Explain why all of the offspring of a single ameba can be considered clones.

22. In what ways are regeneration and vegetative propagation similar? Why are the offspring identical to the parent in both processes?

23. A scientist noted that a paramecium culture in his laboratory reproduced more rapidly than average when kept in a sunny corner of the room. He also observed that other paramecium cultures kept in darker parts of the room reproduced more slowly. Use your knowledge of biology to answer the following:

- What testable question might the scientist ask based on his observations?
- State one possible hypothesis to explain the scientist's observations.
- State a procedure that the scientist could use to test the hypothesis.

Part C

24. The diagram below illustrates asexual reproduction in bread mold.

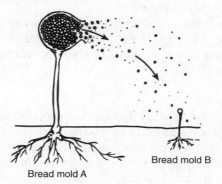

Bread mold B

Bread mold A

Reproductive structures known as spores were released from bread mold A. One of these spores developed into bread mold B. State how the genetic information in the nuclei of cells in bread mold B compares to the genetic information in the nuclei of cells in bread mold A.

MEIOSIS AND SEXUAL REPRODUCTION

In organisms that reproduce sexually, specialized sex cells, or **gametes**, are produced by *meiosis,* a special kind of cell division. One type of gamete, the *sperm cell,* is produced by the male parent, while the other type of gamete, the *egg cell,* is produced by the female parent. The fusion of the nuclei of the sperm cell and the egg cell is called **fertilization**. The resulting cell, which is called the **zygote**, undergoes repeated mitotic cell divisions to form the *embryo.*

Chromosome Number

All members of a given species have a characteristic number of chromosomes in each of their body cells. This *diploid,* or 2n, *chromosome number* normally remains constant from generation to generation. For example, all human body cells have 46 chromosomes, fruit flies have 8, and garden peas have 14.

The chromosomes of a body cell are actually in the form of *homologous pairs.* The two chromosomes of each homologous pair are similar in size and shape, and control the same traits. Thus, in human body cells there are 23 pairs of homologous chromosomes (23 from the mother and 23 from the father); in fruit flies there are 4 pairs; and in garden peas there are 7 pairs.

Mature sperm and egg cells contain half the diploid number of chromosomes—they contain one member of each homologous pair. Half the diploid chromosome number is called the *monoploid,* or *1n, chromosome number.* Mature sex cells (gametes) contain the monoploid (also called *haploid*) number of chromosomes; every other cell in the body contains the diploid number.

In sexually mature individuals, monoploid egg cells and sperm cells are formed in the gonads (ovaries and testes) by **meiosis**, the process of *reduction division.*

Meiosis

Meiosis occurs only in maturing sex cells and consists of two nuclear and cytoplasmic divisions but only one chromosome replication. The first meiotic division produces two cells, each containing the monoploid number of double-stranded chromosomes. The second meiotic division results in the formation of four cells, each containing the monoploid number of single-stranded chromosomes.

As a result of meiosis, a single primary sex cell with the diploid chromosome number gives rise to four cells, each with the monoploid (*n*) chromosome number. These cells mature into gametes—either sperm cells or egg cells.

Meiosis is a source of genetic variations because it provides new combinations of chromosomes for the resulting gametes. A gamete receives only one member of each pair of homologous chromosomes from the 2*n* primary sex cells. The sorting of these chromosomes during formation of the gametes is random.

Gametogenesis

The process by which sperm and eggs are produced is called *gametogenesis.* It involves meiotic cell division and cell maturation. Gametogenesis occurs in specialized paired sex organs, or *gonads.* The male gonads are the testes; the female gonads are the ovaries. In most animals, the sexes are separate; that is, each individual has either testes or ovaries. However, some animals, such as the hydra and the earthworm, have both male and female gonads; such animals are called *hermaphrodites.*

Spermatogenesis. The production of sperm is called *spermatogenesis* (Figure 6-7). The process begins with meiosis in primary sperm cells, which are diploid. As a result of meiosis, each primary sperm cell develops into four monoploid cells of equal size. As

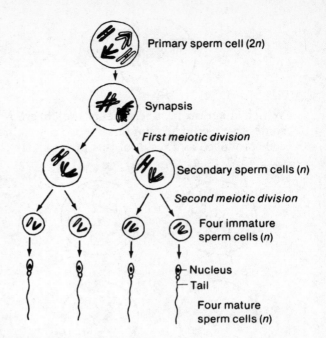

FIGURE 6-7 Spermatogenesis: the production of mature sperm cells.

they mature, these cells lose most of their cytoplasm and develop a long, whiplike flagellum that is used for locomotion.

Oogenesis. Egg cells are produced by *oogenesis* (Figure 6-8). In oogenesis, a primary egg cell undergoes meiosis. The chromosomal changes are the same as those that occur in spermatogenesis (from 2*n* to *n*). However, in oogenesis, division of the cytoplasm

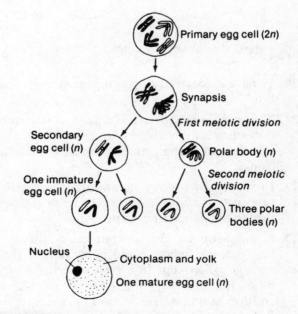

FIGURE 6-8 Oogenesis: the production of one mature egg cell.

TABLE 6-1

A Comparison of Mitosis and Meiosis

Mitosis	Meiosis
Double-stranded chromosomes line up in middle of cell in single file.	Double-stranded chromosomes line up in middle of cell in double file.
Results in diploid ($2n$) number of chromosomes in daughter cells.	Results in monoploid (n) number of chromosomes in daughter cells.
Occurs in all cells of the body.	Occurs only in maturing sex cells.
Results in very few genetic variations because chromosomes remain the same.	Results in many genetic variations because of random sorting and new combinations of chromosomes.

is unequal. The first meiotic division produces one large cell and one small one called a *polar body*. The larger cell then undergoes the second meiotic division, forming an egg cell and another polar body. The first polar body may also undergo a second meiotic division, forming two polar bodies. Oogenesis results in the production of one large monoploid egg cell and three small polar bodies. The only function of the polar bodies is to receive chromosomes as the cell undergoes meiosis; they play no role in reproduction. In fact, the polar bodies always disintegrate.

The advantage of the unequal cytoplasmic division is that the egg cell is provided with a large supply of stored nutrients in the form of yolk.

Comparison of Mitosis and Meiosis LS1.B

The daughter cells produced by mitotic cell division have the same number and kinds of chromosomes as the original parent cell. A cell with the $2n$ chromosome number produces daughter cells with the $2n$ (diploid) chromosome number. Mitosis produces extra body cells for growth and repair of tissues. It is also associated with asexual reproduction.

In contrast, as a result of meiotic cell division, the daughter cells have one-half the number of chromosomes of the original cell (see Table 6-1). A cell with the $2n$ chromosome number produces daughter cells with the n (monoploid) chromosome number. Meiosis occurs only in the gonads during the production of gametes.

QUESTIONS

Part A

25. Monoploid gametes are produced in animals as a result of (1) meiosis (2) mitosis (3) fertilization (4) fission

26. In human males, the maximum number of functional sperm cells that is normally produced from each primary sex cell is (1) one (2) two (3) three (4) four

27. Sexually reproducing species show greater variation than asexually reproducing species due to (1) lower rates of mutation (2) higher rates of reproduction (3) environmental changes (4) sorting of chromosomes during gametogenesis

28. In animals, polar bodies are formed as a result of (1) meiotic cell division in females (2) meiotic cell division in males (3) mitotic cell division in females (4) mitotic cell division in males

29. During the normal meiotic division of a diploid cell, the change in chromosome number that occurs is represented as (1) $4n \rightarrow n$ (2) $2n \rightarrow 4n$ (3) $2n \rightarrow 1n$ (4) $1n \rightarrow \frac{1}{2}n$

30. In a species of corn, the diploid number of chromosomes is 20. What would be the number of chromosomes found in each of the normal egg cells produced by this species? (1) 5 (2) 10 (3) 20 (4) 40

31. A human zygote is normally produced from two gametes that are identical in (1) size (2) method of locomotion (3) genetic composition (4) chromosome number

32. Organisms that contain both functional male and female gonads are known as (1) hybrids (2) hermaphrodites (3) protists (4) parasites

33. In sexually reproducing species, the number of chromosomes in each body cell remains the same from one generation to the next as a direct result of (1) meiosis and fertilization (2) mitosis and mutation (3) differentiation and aging (4) homeostasis and dynamic equilibrium

Part B-1

34. The diagrams below represent the sequence of events in a cell undergoing normal meiotic cell division.

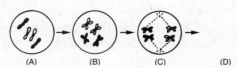

(A)   (B)   (C)   (D)

Which diagram most likely represents stage D of this sequence? (1) 1 (2) 2 (3) 3 (4) 4

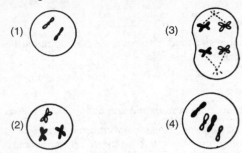

Base your answers to questions 35 through 38 on your knowledge of biology and on the diagram below, which represents a diploid cell about to undergo meiosis. The shapes inside the cell represent homologous chromosomes.

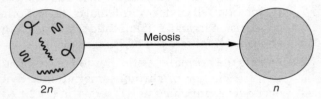

35. Copy the diagram into your notebook. In the empty circle, draw one of the resulting daughter cells produced by the diploid cell at the end of meiosis.

36. What is the diploid chromosome number of the original cell?

37. What will be the chromosome number of a daughter cell produced by this cell by meiosis?

38. Name an organ in which this cell might be found. Explain your answer.

Part C

39. Briefly compare the processes of mitosis and meiosis. What is the function of each process?

40. Compare the processes of sperm and egg production in terms of the following:
   - where each process occurs
   - the relative numbers of gametes produced by each process

41. Discuss why, in sexual reproduction, it is necessary for the gametes to have the monoploid number of chromosomes rather than the diploid number. How does the process of meiosis ensure that the gametes will be monoploid?

42. Explain how the daughter cells produced during meiosis may be genetically different from one another even though they result from the same original diploid cell. Why is this variation important? Why are cells produced by mitosis *not* genetically different from one another?

FERTILIZATION AND DEVELOPMENT

Fertilization is the union of a monoploid (*n*) sperm nucleus with a monoploid (*n*) egg nucleus to form a diploid (2*n*) cell, the *zygote,* which is the first cell of the new organism. Fertilization restores the species' diploid number of chromosomes.

External Fertilization
The union of a sperm and an egg outside the body of the female is called *external fertilization*. External fertilization generally occurs in a watery environment and is characteristic of reproduction in frogs, most fish, and many other aquatic vertebrates.

In external fertilization, large numbers of eggs and sperm are released into the water at the same time to increase the chances that fertilization will take place and to help ensure that at least some of the fertilized eggs will develop, avoid being eaten, and survive to adulthood.

Internal Fertilization
The union of a sperm and an egg inside the moist reproductive tract of the female is called **internal fertilization**. Reproduction in most terrestrial, or land-dwelling, vertebrates, including birds and mammals, is characterized by internal fertilization.

In internal fertilization, relatively few eggs are produced at one time, since the chances that fertilization will occur are much greater with internal fertilization than with external fertilization.

Stages of Development
The early stages of embryonic development are similar in all animals. The process known as **development** begins when the zygote undergoes a rapid series of mitotic cell divisions called *cleavage.*

Cleavage. During cleavage, there is no increase in the size of the embryo—just an increase in the number of cells it contains (see Figure 6-9, page 87). Cell growth and specialization begin after cleavage.

Blastula Formation. The mitotic divisions of cleavage result in the formation of the *blastula,* a hollow ball made up of a single layer of cells.

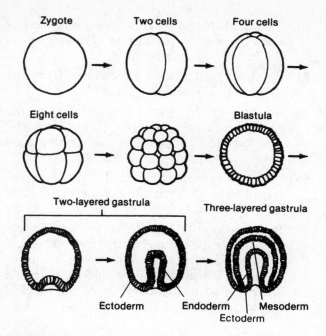

Zygote Two cells Four cells

Eight cells Blastula

Two-layered gastrula Three-layered gastrula

Ectoderm Endoderm Mesoderm
Ectoderm

FIGURE 6-9 Early stages of embryonic development.

Gastrulation. As mitotic divisions continue, one side of the blastula pushes inward, or indents, in a process called *gastrulation*. The resulting embryonic stage, called a *gastrula*, consists of an inner layer, or *endoderm*, and an outer layer, or *ectoderm*. A third layer, called the *mesoderm*, forms between the endoderm and ectoderm. The endoderm, mesoderm, and ectoderm are called the *germ layers*. Cell specialization (that is, differentiation) begins during this stage.

Differentiation and Growth. The germ layers undergo changes, or **differentiation**, to form the various tissues, organs, and organ systems of the developing animal (see Table 6-2). During differentiation, some portions of the DNA within individual cells are active, while other portions are inactive. There are numerous methods by which sections of DNA are "switched" on or off. As a result, each cell develops into a specific type of cell, based upon which portion of its DNA is active and coding within its nucleus. For example, a stomach cell differentiates in response to signals from the active DNA in that cell, which

deals with the functions of a stomach cell. Similarly, within a liver cell, different parts of the DNA—those that code for the functions of a liver cell—are active. Although each and every body cell in an animal contains the entire set of DNA for that animal, only certain parts of the DNA are active in any particular cell, depending on the type of cell it is.

Embryonic development involves growth as well as differentiation. *Growth* includes both an increase in the size of the embryonic cells and an increase in the number of cells.

External Development
Embryonic development may occur outside or inside the body of the female. Growth of the embryo outside the female's body is called *external development*.

The eggs of many fish and amphibians are fertilized externally and develop externally in an aquatic environment. The eggs of birds and many reptiles (and even a few mammals) are fertilized internally but develop externally, encased in tough, protective shells to prevent their drying out.

Internal Development
Growth of the embryo inside the female's body is called **internal development**. In most mammals, both fertilization and development are internal. The eggs of mammals have little yolk and are very small compared with the eggs of reptiles and birds. In all mammals, the young are nourished after birth by milk from the mother's mammary glands.

Placental Mammals. Most mammals are placental mammals in which the embryo develops in the **uterus**, or womb, of the female and receives food and oxygen and gets rid of wastes through the placenta.

The **placenta** is a temporary organ that forms within the uterus from embryonic and maternal tissues; it is rich in both embryonic and maternal blood vessels. Dissolved materials pass between the mother and the embryo through the blood vessels in the placenta—food and oxygen pass from the mother to the embryo, while wastes pass from the embryo to the mother. The blood of the mother and the embryo never mix.

TABLE 6-2	
Tissues and Organs Formed from the Embryonic Germ Layers	
Embryonic Layer	**Organs and Organ Systems**
Ectoderm	Nervous system; skin
Mesoderm	Muscles; circulatory, skeletal, excretory, and reproductive systems
Endoderm	Lining of digestive and respiratory tracts; liver; pancreas

43. In the early development of a zygote, the number of cells increases, without leading to an increase in size, in the process of (1) ovulation (2) cleavage (3) germination (4) metamorphosis

44. An embryo's three germ layers are formed during (1) gastrulation (2) fertilization (3) blastula formation (4) growth

45. In most species of fish, the female produces large numbers of eggs during the reproductive cycle. This would indicate that reproduction in fish is most probably characterized by (1) internal fertilization and internal development (2) internal fertilization and external development (3) external fertilization and internal development (4) external fertilization and external development.

46. Which type of fertilization and development do birds and most reptiles have? (1) internal fertilization and internal development (2) internal fertilization and external development (3) external fertilization and internal development (4) external fertilization and external development

47. The embryos of some mammals, such as the kangaroo and the opossum, complete their development externally. What is the source of nutrition for their last stage of development? (1) milk from maternal mammary glands (2) diffusion of nutrients through the uterine wall (3) food stored in the egg yolk (4) solid foods gathered and fed to them by the mother

48. In mammals, the placenta is essential to the embryo for (1) nutrition, reproduction, growth (2) nutrition, respiration, excretion (3) locomotion, respiration, excretion (4) nutrition, excretion, reproduction

49. Which characteristic of sexual reproduction specifically favors the survival of terrestrial animals? (1) fertilization within the body of the female (2) male gametes that may be carried by the wind (3) fusion of gametes in the outside environment (4) fertilization of eggs in the water

Base your answers to questions 50 through 53 on your knowledge of biology and on the diagram below, which represents the early stages of embryonic development.

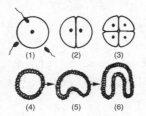

50. The structures labeled *2* and *3* are formed as a direct result of (1) meiosis (2) gastrulation (3) cleavage (4) differentiation

51. The structure in stage *4* represents a (1) zygote (2) blastula (3) gastrula (4) follicle

52. The cells of the outer layer give rise to the (1) digestive system and liver (2) excretory system and muscles (3) circulatory system and gonads (4) nervous system and skin

53. Which cells are *not* represented in any of the diagrams? (1) endoderm (2) mesoderm (3) ectoderm (4) gastrula

54. The arrows in the diagram below illustrate processes in the life of a species that reproduces sexually. Which processes result directly in the formation of cells with half the amount of genetic material that is characteristic of the species? (1) 1 and 2 (2) 2 and 3 (3) 3 and 4 (4) 4 and 5

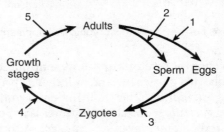

55. The development of specialized tissues and organs in a multicellular organism's embryo occurs as a result of (1) cloning (2) differentiation (3) meiosis (4) cleavage

Refer to the following four terms, which describe the early stages of embryonic development, to answer questions 56 through 58: gastrula, cleavage, zygote, blastula.

56. List these terms in the correct order, from earliest to latest stage of embryonic development.

57. For each term listed, draw a simple sketch to illustrate that stage of embryonic development.

58. Briefly describe what occurs during each of these embryonic stages.

59. Animals that are characterized by external fertilization produce many times more gametes (sperm and eggs) than do animals that have internal fertilization. Give two reasons for this observation.

60. Stem cells are cells in which the *entire* DNA is active. Explain how a stem cell is able to differentiate into any type of cell needed by the body.

HUMAN REPRODUCTION AND DEVELOPMENT

Male Reproductive System

The male reproductive system functions in the production of sperm cells, male sex hormones, and in the placement of sperm into the female reproductive system.

Sperm Production. The sperm-producing organs, the *testes,* are located in an outpocketing of the body wall called the *scrotum* (Figure 6-10). The temperature in the scrotum, which is 1 to 2°C cooler than normal body temperature, is best suited for the production and storage of sperm.

From the testes, the sperm pass through a series of ducts into which liquid is secreted by various glands. The liquid serves as a transport medium for the sperm cells and is an adaptation for life on land. The liquid and sperm together are called *semen.* Semen passes to the outside of the body through the urethra, a tube through the penis. The *penis* is used to deposit the semen in the female reproductive tract.

Hormone Production. The testes produce the male sex hormone testosterone, which regulates the maturation of sperm cells. Testosterone also regulates the development of male secondary sex characteristics, including body form, beard development, and deepening of the voice.

Female Reproductive System

The female reproductive system functions in the production of egg cells and female sex hormones.

Egg Production. The female reproductive organs, the *ovaries,* are located within the lower portion of the body cavity (Figure 6-11). In the ovaries, each egg cell

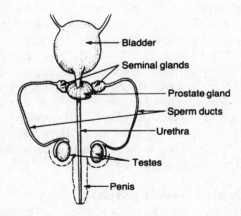

FIGURE 6-10 The human male reproductive system.

Bladder
Seminal glands
Prostate gland
Sperm ducts
Urethra
Testes
Penis

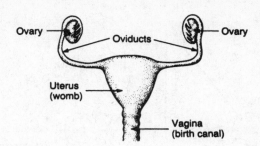

Ovary
Oviducts
Ovary
Uterus (womb)
Vagina (birth canal)

FIGURE 6-11 The human female reproductive system.

is present in a tiny sac called a *follicle.* About once a month, a follicle matures and bursts, and the egg within it is released from the surface of the ovary, a process called *ovulation.* The egg cell then passes into the oviduct, or *fallopian tube,* which leads to the *uterus.* If sperm are present, fertilization may occur. If the egg is fertilized, it passes into the uterus, where embryonic development may occur. If the egg is not fertilized, it degenerates.

The lower end of the uterus, the *cervix,* opens to a muscular tube called the *vagina,* or *birth canal.* When embryonic development is complete, the baby leaves the body of the mother through the vagina.

Hormone Production. The ovaries produce the female sex hormones estrogen and progesterone. These hormones regulate the maturation of egg cells, as well as the development of secondary sex characteristics, including the development of the mammary glands and the broadening of the pelvis. Estrogen and progesterone are also involved in the menstrual cycle and **pregnancy.**

The Menstrual Cycle

The series of events that prepares the uterus for pregnancy is called the *menstrual cycle.* The cycle begins with the thickening of the lining of the uterine wall. The lining also becomes vascularized (filled with blood vessels). If fertilization does not occur, the thickened uterine lining breaks down and the material is expelled from the body during menstruation. The cycle then begins again.

The menstrual cycle begins at *puberty,* the stage at which the individual becomes capable of reproducing. It is temporarily interrupted by pregnancy and sometimes by illness, and ceases permanently at *menopause.* The cycle is regulated by the interaction of hormones, and lasts approximately 28 days.

The menstrual cycle consists of four stages (Figure 6-12 on page 90):

(a) During the follicle stage, an egg matures and the follicle secretes estrogen, which stimulates the thickening of the uterine lining. This stage lasts about 14 days.

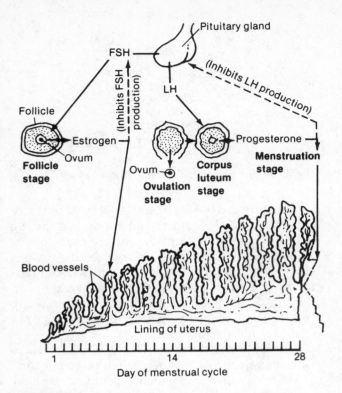

FIGURE 6-12 Stages of the human menstrual cycle.

(b) About midway in the cycle, ovulation occurs. The egg is released from the ovary and enters the oviduct.

(c) Following ovulation, the *corpus luteum* forms from the ruptured follicle. The corpus luteum secretes progesterone, which continues the vascularization of the uterine lining started by estrogen. This stage lasts about 12 days.

(d) If fertilization does not occur, the egg cell and the thickened uterine lining break down, and the extra tissue, together with some blood and mucus, pass out of the body through the vagina. The shedding of the uterine lining is called *menstruation*. This stage lasts about four to five days.

Hormones of the Menstrual Cycle

The menstrual cycle is controlled by hormones that are released by the hypothalamus, pituitary gland, and ovaries.

During the follicle stage, the pituitary gland, under the influence of hormones from the hypothalamus, secretes FSH (follicle-stimulating hormone), which in turn stimulates the follicle to secrete estrogen. Estrogen stimulates ovulation and initiates vascularization of the uterine lining.

Increased blood estrogen levels inhibit the production of FSH by the pituitary, and the secretion of LH (luteinizing hormone) by the pituitary increases.

Ovulation occurs at about this time in the cycle. After ovulation, LH stimulates the formation of the corpus luteum from the ruptured follicle. The corpus luteum secretes progesterone, which enhances the vascularization of the uterine lining.

If fertilization does not occur, the high levels of progesterone in the blood inhibit the production of LH by the pituitary. The drop in LH level causes a drop in the progesterone level. The lining of the uterus thins out, and at about the twenty-eighth day of the cycle, the shedding of the uterine lining, or menstruation, begins. The blood flow of menstruation is caused by the breakage of many small blood vessels.

The relationship between the ovarian hormones estrogen and progesterone and the pituitary hormones FSH and LH is an example of a *negative feedback mechanism*.

Fertilization and Development

If fertilization does occur in the oviduct, the zygote undergoes cleavage to form a blastula. Six to ten days later, the blastula becomes implanted in the uterine lining. Gastrulation usually occurs after implantation. The germ layers of the gastrula begin to differentiate and grow, resulting in the formation of specialized tissues and organs. The placenta and umbilical cord form, enabling the embryo to obtain nutrients and oxygen and to dispose of metabolic wastes. An amnion (membrane-enclosed sac) filled with fluid provides a watery environment that cushions the embryo, which helps to protect it from injury.

In Vitro Fertilization

Fertilization that occurs outside the body of the female (that is, by means of laboratory techniques) is known as *in vitro* (meaning "in glass") fertilization. After fertilization, the early embryo is implanted into the uterus, where development is completed.

Multiple Births

Sometimes two or more embryos develop in the uterus simultaneously. Fraternal twins develop when two eggs are released from the ovary at the same time and both are fertilized. The two eggs are fertilized by two different sperm cells. Fraternal twins may be of the same sex or opposite sexes. Identical twins develop when a zygote separates into two equal halves early in cleavage. Each half develops into an offspring. Since identical twins develop from the same zygote, they have identical genetic makeups and are always of the same sex.

Birth and Development

The time between fertilization and birth is referred to as the *gestation period*. In humans, the gestation period is about nine months. After the first three months of gestation, the embryo is referred to as a **fetus**. At the end of the gestation period, the secretion of progesterone decreases and another hormone from the pituitary causes strong muscular contractions of the uterus. The amnion bursts, and the baby is pushed out of the mother's body through the vagina.

During *postnatal development* (development after birth), humans pass through different stages, including infancy, childhood, puberty, adulthood, and old age. Puberty begins at early adolescence. In males, puberty usually occurs between the ages of 12 and 18; in females, it usually occurs between the ages of 10 and 14.

Aging is a series of complex structural and functional changes in the body that occur naturally with the passage of time. The causes of aging are not fully understood. However, it now appears that aging may result from an interaction of both genetic and environmental factors. One of the events that is known to occur as a cell ages is the shortening of the ends of its chromosomes, a region known as the *telomere*. The aging process ends in death, which may be described as an irreversible cessation of brain function.

QUESTIONS
Part A

61. Which structure *least* affects the human female menstrual cycle? (1) pituitary (2) ovary (3) pancreas (4) corpus luteum

62. A woman gave birth to twins, one girl and one boy. The number of egg cells involved was (1) 1 (2) 2 (3) 3 (4) 4

63. A diagram of the human female reproductive structures is shown below.

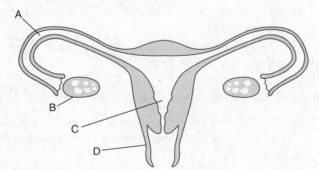

Which structure is correctly paired with its function? (1) A—releases estrogen and progesterone (2) B—produces and releases the egg (3) C—provides the usual site for fertilization (4) D—nourishes a developing embryo

64. Which structure is the membrane that serves as the protective, fluid-filled sac in which an embryo is suspended? (1) pituitary (2) placenta (3) corpus luteum (4) amnion

65. The technique of uniting a sperm cell and an egg cell outside the female's body is called (1) in vitro fertilization (2) internal fertilization (3) gametogenesis (4) artificial ovulation

66. Which hormone is *not* involved in the regulation of the human menstrual cycle? (1) progesterone (2) estrogen (3) FSH (4) testosterone

67. What normally happens immediately after fertilization in sexual reproduction? (1) specialization of cells to form a fetus from an egg (2) production of daughter cells having twice the number of chromosomes as the parent cell (3) production of daughter cells having half the number of chromosomes as the parent cell (4) division of cells resulting in the development of an embryo from a zygote

68. Some body structures of a human male are represented in the diagram below. An obstruction in the structures labeled *X* would directly interfere with the (1) transfer of sperm to a female (2) production of sperm (3) production of urine (4) transfer of urine to the external environment

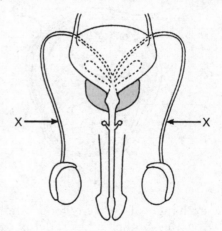

69. Fraternal twins develop from (1) one egg and two sperm (2) two eggs and one sperm (3) two eggs and two sperm (4) one egg and one sperm

70. Which statement best describes the relationship between the blood of a human fetus and the blood of the mother? (1) Their blood systems are separate only at certain times in development and connected at other times. (2) The blood flows directly from the mother into the fetus. (3) Their blood systems are separate and no materials are exchanged. (4) Their blood systems are separate, but certain materials pass from one to the other.

Base your answers to questions 71 through 73 on the diagram below, which represents a cross section of a part of the human female reproductive system, and on your knowledge of biology.

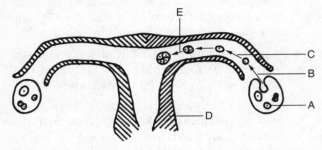

71. Which structure is prepared for the implantation of a fertilized egg as a result of the action of reproductive hormones? (1) *A* (2) *B* (3) *C* (4) *D*

72. Within which structure does fertilization normally occur? (1) *A* (2) *B* (3) *C* (4) *D*

73. Which step represents the process of ovulation? (1) *A* (2) *B* (3) *C* (4) *D*

Base your answers to questions 74 through 76 on the diagram below, which represents a stage in human embryonic development.

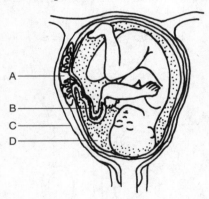

74. The exchange of oxygen, food, and wastes between the mother and the fetus occurs at structure (1) *A* (2) *B* (3) *C* (4) *D*

75. What is the function of the fluid labeled *D*? (1) nourishment (2) protection (3) excretion (4) respiration

76. The structure labeled *C*, within which embryonic development occurs, is known as the (1) oviduct (2) birth canal (3) uterus (4) placenta

For each of the processes described in questions 77 through 79, choose from the following list above the correct stage of the human menstrual cycle during which that process occurs.

Human Menstrual Cycle Stage

A. ovulation

B. follicle stage

C. menstruation

D. corpus luteum stage

77. The lining of the uterus is shed: (1) *A* (2) *B* (3) *C* (4) *D*

78. An egg is released from an ovary: (1) *A* (2) *B* (3) *C* (4) *D*

79. An egg matures in an ovary: (1) *A* (2) *B* (3) *C* (4) *D*

Base your answers to questions 80 through 83 on the following graph, which shows a woman's changing hormone levels for FSH and estrogen over a period of 21 days, and on your knowledge of human reproductive biology.

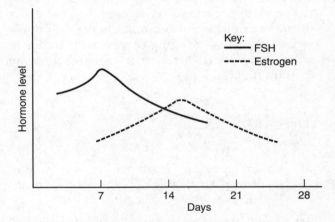

80. Describe the relationship depicted in the graph between FSH and estrogen.

81. Why does the level of estrogen begin rising *after* the FSH level rises?

82. Why does the FSH level begin to fall after the seventh day?

83. On approximately what day are the woman's estrogen levels highest?

84. List the four major hormones that play a role in the menstrual cycle and discuss how they interact during the cycle.

85. Mr. and Mrs. W have been trying to conceive their first child for over one year, with no success. They decide to visit their doctors for medical tests. Blood tests on Mrs. W reveal that her FSH levels are abnormally low. Discuss how this

finding might explain the couple's inability to conceive. What medical treatment might help Mrs. W to become pregnant?

86. Briefly discuss the function of the following structures in the development of the human embryo: *placenta, umbilical cord, amnion.*

87. A human is a complex organism that develops from a zygote. Briefly explain some of the steps in this developmental process. In your answer be sure to:

   • explain how a zygote is formed

   • compare the chromosomes in a zygote with those of a parent's body cell

   • identify one developmental process involved in the change from a zygote to an embryo

   • identify the body structure in which fetal development usually occurs

---

SEXUAL REPRODUCTION IN FLOWERING PLANTS

Flowers are the reproductive organs of the *angiosperms,* or flowering plants.

Structure of Flowers

Flowers may contain the following structures: sepals, petals, stamens, and pistils (Figure 6-13).

Sepals are leaflike structures at the base of a flower that enclose and protect the flower bud. In some species the sepals are green, while in others the sepals are white or brightly colored.

Petals are leaflike structures inside the sepals that surround the reproductive organs of the flower. Petals may be brightly colored or white and often have a sweet fragrance.

Stamens are the male reproductive organs of a flower. Each stamen consists of an oval-shaped *anther*

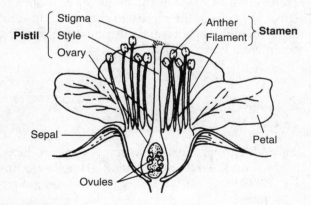

FIGURE 6-13 Structure of a flower.

supported by a stalk, or *filament. Pollen grains,* which contain monoploid sperm nuclei, are produced by meiosis by the diploid cells of the anther. The thick wall that encloses the pollen grain prevents the contents from drying out. This is an adaptation for life on land.

Pistils are the female reproductive organs of a flower. A pistil consists of a stigma, style, and ovary. The *stigma,* which is a knoblike, sticky structure, is adapted for receiving pollen grains. The stigma is supported by the *style,* a slender stalk that connects the stigma to the *ovary,* which is at the base of the pistil. In the ovary, monoploid egg cells are produced by meiosis in structures called *ovules.*

The flowers of some species contain both stamens and pistils. In other species, some flowers contain only stamens, while others contain only pistils. The flowers of some species have both sepals and petals, while the flowers of other species lack one or the other.

Pollination and Fertilization

The transfer of pollen grains from an anther to a stigma is called **pollination**. The transfer of pollen from an anther to a stigma of the same flower or to a stigma of another flower on the same plant is called *self-pollination.* The transfer of pollen from an anther of one flower to the stigma of a flower on another plant is *cross-pollination.* Cross-pollination increases the chances of genetic variation in the offspring because the pollen and the egg cells are from two different plants.

Pollination may be carried out by wind, insects, birds, or bats. Brightly colored petals and the scent of nectar attract these animals. Pollen grains from a flower adhere to their bodies and are carried to another flower, where they rub off on the sticky surface of a stigma.

When a pollen grain reaches a stigma, it *germinates,* or sprouts (Figure 6-14, page 94). A pollen tube grows from the pollen grain down through the stigma and style to an ovule within the ovary. The growth of the pollen tube is controlled by the tube nucleus. Two sperm nuclei and the tube nucleus pass down through the pollen tube. The sperm nuclei enter an ovule, where one sperm nucleus fertilizes the egg nucleus to form a diploid (2*n*) zygote. The other sperm nucleus fuses with two *polar nuclei* in the ovule to form a triploid (3*n*) *endosperm nucleus,* which divides to form a food storage tissue. The zygote undergoes repeated mitotic divisions to form a multicellular plant embryo. After fertilization, the ovule ripens to form a *seed,* while the ovary develops into a *fruit.* The seeds of flowering plants are found inside the fruits.

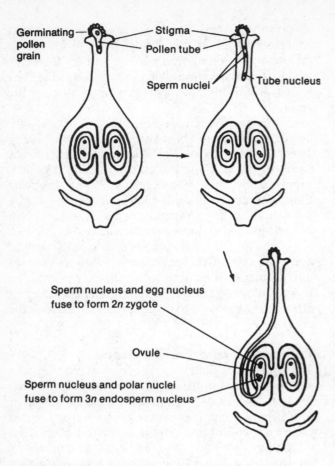

FIGURE 6-14 Fertilization in flowering plants.

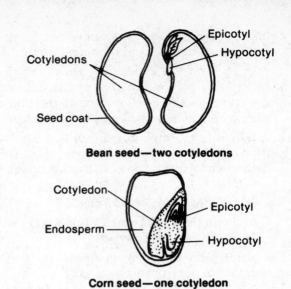

Bean seed—two cotyledons

Corn seed—one cotyledon

FIGURE 6-15 Structure of a seed.

away as they move. Fleshy fruits are eaten by animals, and their seeds are later deposited with the animal's wastes.

Seed Germination

When conditions of moisture, oxygen, and temperature are favorable, seeds germinate. The embryo plant develops leaves and roots, and begins to produce its own food by photosynthesis. The development of a mature plant from an embryo involves cell division, cell differentiation, and growth.

Plant Growth

In flowering plants, only certain regions, called *meristems,* are able to undergo cell division. There are two types of meristems: cell division in the tips of roots and stems (in apical meristems) results in an increase in length; cell division between the xylem and phloem (in lateral meristems, or *cambiums*) results in an increase in the diameter of roots and stems. The cells of the meristem regions divide and then undergo elongation and differentiation, forming the different kinds of plant tissues.

Structure of a Seed

A seed consists of a seed coat and a plant embryo with one or two cotyledons (Figure 6-15). The *seed coat,* which develops from the outer coverings of the ovule, surrounds and protects the embryo. The plant embryo consists of the epicotyl, hypocotyl, and cotyledon. The *epicotyl* is the upper portion of the embryo; it develops into the leaves and upper portion of the stem. The *hypocotyl* is the lower portion of the embryo; it develops into the roots and, in some species, the lower portion of the stem. The *cotyledons* contain endosperm, the stored food that provides nutrients for the developing plant.

Fruits

The fruits of flowering plants are structures that are specialized for seed dispersal. Fruits carry the seeds away from the parent plant, which helps to prevent overcrowding. The fruits of dandelions and maples, for example, are dispersed by wind; coconuts are dispersed by water; and cockleburs are fruits that become attached to the fur of animals and are carried

---

QUESTIONS
Part A

88. Which reproductive structures are produced within the ovaries of plants? (1) pollen grains (2) sperm nuclei (3) egg nuclei (4) pollen tubes

89. In a flowering plant, the ovule develops within a part of the (1) style (2) anther (3) pistil (4) stigma

90. Which embryonic structure supplies nutrients to a germinating bean plant? (1) pollen tube (2) hypocotyl (3) epicotyl (4) cotyledon

91. Heavy use of insecticides in springtime may lead to a decrease in apple production in the fall, which is most probably due to interference with the process of (1) pollination (2) cleavage (3) absorption (4) transpiration

92. In a bean seed, the part of the embryo that develops into the leaves and upper portion of the stem is known as the (1) seed coat (2) epicotyl (3) hypocotyl (4) cotyledon

93. A condition necessary for the germination of most seeds is favorable (1) light (2) chlorophyll concentration (3) temperature (4) nitrate concentration

94. In flowering plants, the entire female reproductive organ is called the (1) filament (2) anther (3) style (4) pistil

95. In flowering plants, pollen grains are formed in the (1) style (2) anther (3) sepal (4) stigma

96. The seeds of a flowering plant develop from the ripened (1) fruits (2) cotyledons (3) ovules (4) endosperm

97. The endosperm of a bean seed is contained within its (1) cotyledons (2) ovules (3) stamen (4) petals

98. The fruits of a flowering plant develop from the ripened (1) seeds (2) ovules (3) ovaries (4) pollen tubes

99. Which structure is *not* part of a plant embryo? (1) epicotyl (2) seed coat (3) hypocotyl (4) cotyledon

100. Which portion of a bean seed would contain the greatest percentage of starch? (1) seed coat (2) epicotyl (3) cotyledon (4) hypocotyl

Base your answers to questions 101 through 103 on the diagram below, which shows a cross section of a flower, and on your knowledge of biology.

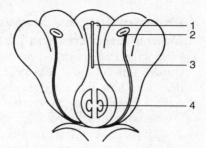

101. In this diagram, the stigma and the anther are (1) 1 and 2 (2) 1 and 4 (3) 2 and 4 (4) 2 and 3

102. Which process has occurred in this flower? (1) pollen germination (2) seed formation (3) zygote formation (4) fruit production

103. In which part would fertilization occur? (1) 1 (2) 2 (3) 3 (4) 4

Base your answers to questions 104 and 105 on the diagram below, which shows the internal structure of half of a bean seed, and on your knowledge of biology.

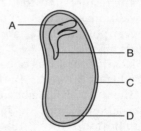

104. In which structure would most of the stored food for the embryo be found? (1) A (2) B (3) C (4) D

105. The epicotyl and the hypocotyl are represented by (1) A and C (2) B and D (3) A and B (4) C and D

106. Explain why cross-pollination increases the chances of genetic variation in the offspring of flowering plants.

107. Compare sexual reproduction in mammals and flowering plants. In what way is the process similar in these two types of organisms?

Base your answers to questions 108 through 112 on the information below and on your knowledge of biology. Source: Science News *(March 12, 2011): vol. 179, no. 6, p. 12. Reprinted with permission of* Science News.

Prenatal Surgery Shows Promise: Fetal Spina Bifida Operation Increases Likelihood of Walking

Fetal surgery performed months before birth can improve the health of children with spina bifida, a neural tube defect caused by an opening in the spine. By comparing children who had gotten surgery before or after birth, researchers found that operating preterm improves the chance that a child with spina bifida will be able to walk and lessens the risk of other neurological complications.

But these potential gains must be weighed against an increased risk of premature birth associated with surgery in the womb. The findings appear online February 9 in the *New England Journal of Medicine.*

The study focused on fetuses and newborns with myelomeningocele, the most common and severe form of spina bifida, in which the spinal cord bulges outside the spinal column. The condition can result in cognitive disabilities, fluid on the brain, bowel problems and paralysis. Usually surgeons operate on such babies a few days after birth by inserting the spinal cord back into its canal and sealing the opening with sutures. If successful, this limits fluid buildup in the brain and spinal cord and lessens the cord's pull on the brain.

In the study, researchers described 158 pregnant women who had a fetus diagnosed with myelomeningocele. Half had been randomly assigned to fetal surgery while the others delayed the procedure until after birth.

The results show that 42 percent of children who had surgery in the womb were able to walk unassisted at 30 months compared with 21 percent of those who received the surgery postnatally. There were no marked differences in mental development between the groups.

Nearly four-fifths of babies who had surgery in utero were premature, with 10 of 78 born before 30 weeks. In the other group, 15 percent were born prematurely.

The study "is a major step in the right direction," say physicians Joe Simpson of Florida International University in Miami and Michael Greene of Massachusetts General Hospital in Boston, writing online the same day in *NEJM,* but "the degree to which intrauterine repair will transform outcomes for fetuses with myelomeningocele remains unclear."

---

108. According to the article, what is one great advantage in operating on spina bifida *before* birth?

109. State three problems associated with myelomeningocele (spina bifida) in newborns.

110. Briefly describe the operation that is performed on newborns. How does this procedure prevent future problems?

111. Based on the article, how successful was the prenatal surgery on children's ability to walk unassisted at 30 months? Use data *from the article* to support your answer.

112. As with any surgery, there are risks involved. State the major risk of this operation. If you were counseling a couple to proceed with the surgery, what advice would you give? Support your answer with evidence from the article.

7 Genetics and Heredity

FOUNDATIONS OF GENETICS

Genetics is the branch of biology that deals with patterns of **inheritance**, or heredity. *Heredity* is the biological process by which parents pass on genetic information to their offspring through their gametes. The science of genetics originated with the work of an Austrian monk, *Gregor Mendel,* who performed a series of experiments on pea plants between 1856 and 1868.

Principles of Mendelian Genetics

In his breeding experiments, Mendel (who, like everyone else at that time, had no knowledge of genes or chromosomes) made careful observations of the inheritance patterns of specific contrasting traits found in pea plants. Through a mathematical analysis of the traits found in the large numbers of offspring from his experimental crosses, Mendel developed his principles of *dominance, segregation,* and *independent assortment.* Mendel also concluded that the traits he observed were controlled by pairs of inherited "factors," with one member of each pair coming from each parent organism. Thus, in organisms that reproduce sexually, half of the offspring's genetic material is contributed by the female parent and half by the male parent. As a result, the offspring has traits from both parents and is never identical to either one of them.

Gene-Chromosome Theory

The importance of Mendel's work was not recognized until the early 1900s, when the development of better microscopes enabled biologists to observe chromosome behavior during meiotic cell division. Biologists then linked the separation of homologous chromosome pairs during meiosis and their **recombination** (mixing of traits) at fertilization with the inheritance of Mendel's factors. Breeding experiments carried out by T. H. Morgan with the fruit fly, *Drosophila,* provided supporting evidence for Mendel's principles of inheritance.

Mendel's inherited, or **hereditary**, factors—now known as **genes**—are arranged in a linear fashion on the chromosomes. Each gene has a definite position, or *locus* (plural, *loci*), on the chromosome. However, it is now known that the genes are not fixed in only one position on a chromosome; they can actually change loci. The two alternate genes in any one organism that control each trait are called **alleles**, and they are located in the same position on homologous chromosomes. The *gene-chromosome theory* explains the hereditary patterns observed by Mendel. For many traits, there may exist several different alleles. The expression of the trait controlled by these alleles is dependent upon which specific ones are inherited by the organism.

Gene Expression

Every organism has at least two alleles that govern every trait. As mentioned, these two genes are passed on—one from the mother and one from the father—to the offspring. The genes encode information that is expressed as the traits of the organism, a phenomenon called **gene expression**. A single gene (that is, one set of alleles) may control one or several traits.

Alternatively, some traits are determined by more than one gene (that is, by more than one set of alleles).

Although all the body cells in an organism contain the same genetic instructions, the cells may differ considerably from one another in structure and function. The reason is that, in any given cell, only some of the genes are expressed, while all other genes are inactivated. For example, in liver cells, it is mainly the genes that pertain to liver functions that are active, while the other genes are inactive. The same is true of all other cells in a body. You can think of the genes on a cell's chromosomes as recipes in a cookbook: the book may contain hundreds of recipes, but if you are making a chocolate cake, you will read only the instructions for making that item. Likewise, the cell reads only the instructions for making its specific products.

Genes that are "on" are expressed; those that are "off" are not expressed. There are many mechanisms that can switch genes on and off, including intracellular chemicals, enzymes, regulatory proteins, and the cell's environment. In addition, a particular gene may alternately be expressed or inactivated, depending on the cell's needs at the time.

SOME MAJOR CONCEPTS IN GENETICS

Dominance

In his experiments, Mendel crossed plants that were pure for contrasting traits. For example, he crossed pure tall plants with pure short plants. All the offspring of such crosses showed only one of the two contrasting traits. In the cross of tall plants and short plants, all the offspring were tall. In this type of inheritance, the allele that is expressed in the offspring is said to be *dominant*; the allele that is present but not expressed is said to be *recessive*. This pattern illustrates Mendel's principle of dominance.

By convention, the dominant allele is represented by a capital letter, and the recessive allele is represented by the lowercase form of the same letter. For example, the allele for tallness, which is dominant, is shown as *T*; the allele for shortness, which is recessive, is shown as *t*.

If, in an organism, the two genes of a pair of alleles are the same, for example, *TT* or *tt*, the organism is said to be **homozygous**, or pure, for that trait. The genetic makeup of the organism, which is its **genotype**, is either homozygous dominant (*TT*) or homozygous recessive (*tt*). If the two genes of a pair of alleles are different, for example, *Tt*, the organism is said to be **heterozygous**, or *hybrid*, for that trait.

The physical appearance of an organism that results from its genetic makeup is called its **phenotype**. For example, a pea plant that is heterozygous for height has the genotype *Tt* and the phenotype of being tall. When an organism that is homozygous for the dominant trait is crossed with an organism that is homozygous for the recessive trait (*TT* × *tt*), the phenotype of the offspring is like that of the dominant parent. Thus, the heterozygous offspring (*Tt*) is tall. The term phenotype can be expanded to mean the expression of any genes, not only those controlling outward physical appearance. For example, the ability to synthesize a particular enzyme such as lactase as a result of gene expression is a phenotype. The opposite is also true: the inability to produce an enzyme is a phenotype. The phenotype of people who cannot produce this enzyme is called *lactose intolerant*.

In studies involving genetic crosses, the organisms that are used to begin the studies are called the *parent generation*. The offspring produced by crossing members of the parent generation are called the *first filial*, or *F₁*, *generation*. The offspring of a cross between members of the F_1 generation make up the *second filial*, or F_2, *generation*.

1. When a strain of fruit flies homozygous for light body color is crossed with a strain of fruit flies homozygous for dark body color, all the offspring have light body color. This illustrates Mendel's principle of (1) segregation (2) dominance (3) incomplete dominance (4) independent assortment

2. Two genes located in corresponding positions on a pair of homologous chromosomes and associated with the same characteristic are known as (1) gametes (2) zygotes (3) chromatids (4) alleles

3. For a given trait, the two genes of an allelic pair are not alike. An individual possessing this gene combination is said to be (1) homozygous for that trait (2) heterozygous for that trait (3) recessive for that trait (4) pure for that trait

4. In pea plants, flowers located along the stem (*axial*) are dominant to flowers located at the end of the stem (*terminal*). Let *A* represent the allele for axial flowers and *a* represent the allele for terminal flowers. When plants with axial flowers are crossed with plants having terminal flowers, all of the offspring have axial flowers. The genotypes of the parent plants are most likely (1) *aa* × *aa* (2) *Aa* × *Aa* (3) *aa* × *Aa* (4) *AA* × *aa*

5. Curly hair in humans, white fur in guinea pigs, and needlelike spines in cacti all partly describe each organism's (1) alleles (2) autosomes (3) chromosomes (4) phenotype

6. The appearance of a recessive trait in offspring of animals most probably indicates that (1) both parents carried at least one recessive gene for that trait (2) one parent was homozygous dominant and the other parent was homozygous recessive for that trait (3) neither parent carried a recessive gene for that trait (4) one parent was homozygous dominant and the other parent was hybrid for that trait

7. Which statement describes how two organisms may show the same trait yet have different genotypes for that phenotype? (1) One is homozygous dominant and the other is heterozygous. (2) Both are heterozygous for the dominant trait. (3) One is homozygous dominant and the other is homozygous recessive. (4) Both are homozygous for the dominant trait.

8. In cabbage butterflies, white color (*W*) is dominant and yellow color (*w*) is recessive. If a pure white cabbage butterfly mates with a yellow cabbage butterfly, all the resulting (*F*₁) butterflies are heterozygous white. Which cross represents the genotypes of the parent generation? (1) *Ww* × *ww* (2) *WW* × *Ww* (3) *WW* × *ww* (4) *Ww* × *Ww*

9. Most of the hereditary information that determines the traits of an organism is located in (1) only those cells of an individual produced by meiosis (2) the nuclei of body cells of an individual (3) certain genes in the vacuoles of body cells (4) the numerous ribosomes in certain cells

10. The characteristics of a developing fetus are most influenced by (1) gene combinations and their expression in the embryo (2) hormone production by the father (3) circulating levels of white blood cells in the placenta (4) milk production in the mother

Part B-2

11. Explain how two organisms can have the same phenotype but different genotypes.

12. To illustrate your answer to question 11, pick a trait and use a letter to represent it. Write the genotypes of the parents and *F*₁ generations for each organism.

Part C

13. Why do the offspring of sexually reproducing organisms resemble both parents? Why are they not identical to either one of the parents?

14. Explain why the body cells of an organism can differ in structure and function, even though they all contain the same genetic information.

Segregation and Recombination

When gametes are formed during meiosis, the two chromosomes of each homologous pair separate, or *segregate*, randomly. Each gamete contains only one allele for each trait. After the gametes fuse during fertilization, the resulting (zygote) cell contains pairs of homologous chromosomes, but new combinations of alleles may be present. This process is described by Mendel's principle of segregation.

Figure 7-1 illustrates segregation and recombination in a cross between two individuals that are heterozygous for tallness. In a large number of such crosses, with a large number of offspring, two types of numerical ratios can be observed. In terms of genotype, the ratio is 1 homozygous dominant (*TT*) : 2 heterozygous (*Tt*) : 1 homozygous recessive (*tt*). In terms of phenotype, the ratio is 3 tall : 1 short. These genotype and phenotype ratios are typical for all crosses between organisms that are hybrid for one trait.

The Testcross

To determine the genotype of an organism that shows the dominant phenotype, a testcross is performed. In a *testcross*, the organism in question is crossed with a homozygous recessive organism (Figure 7-2 on page 100). If the test organism is homozygous dominant, all the offspring will be heterozygous and show the dominant phenotype. If any offspring show the recessive phenotype, the individual being tested would have to be heterozygous. With the development of more sophisticated DNA testing that can identify particular genes, the testcross is used less frequently now. DNA testing is much quicker and more reliable, without having to wait for offspring to be produced in order to determine unknown genotypes.

Punnett Square

The possible offspring of a genetic cross are often shown with a diagram called a *Punnett square*. We can use a Punnett square to show the possible

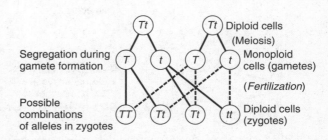

FIGURE 7-1 Segregation and recombination of alleles.

12.

	A	a
A	AA	Aa
a	Aa	aa

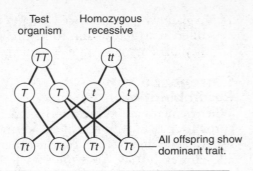

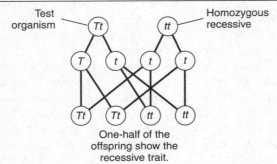

FIGURE 7-2 Use of a testcross to determine an organism's genotype.

offspring of a cross between a heterozygous tall pea plant (*Tt*) and a homozygous short pea plant (*tt*).

The first step in using a Punnett square is to determine the possible genotypes of the gametes of each parent. In this example, the heterozygous tall plant (*Tt*) produces two types of gametes: half will contain the dominant gene for height, *T*, and half will contain the recessive gene, *t*. The gametes of the homozygous short plant (*tt*) will each contain the recessive gene for height, *t*.

As shown in Figure 7-3, the letters that represent the trait carried by the gametes of one parent are written next to the boxes on the left side of the square; the letters for the gametes of the other parent are written

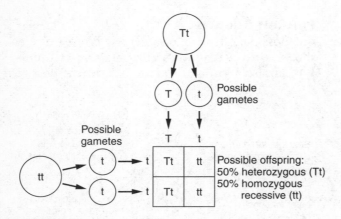

FIGURE 7-3 Use of a Punnett square to determine possible genotypes of offspring.

above the boxes on top of the square. The letters are combined to show offspring genotypes as follows: letters on top of the square are written in the boxes below them, and letters on the side are written in the boxes to the right of them. The dominant gene, when present, is written first. The pairs of letters in the four boxes represent the possible combinations of genes in the offspring of the cross. Of the possible offspring of this cross, half would be heterozygous tall (*Tt*) and half would be homozygous (recessive) short (*tt*).

Linkage
Mendel's observation of the independent inheritance of different traits was the basis for his principle of independent assortment. When the events of meiosis were discovered, it became clear that traits are inherited independently of one another only when their genes are on different chromosomes. However, when the genes for two different traits are located on the same chromosome, they tend to be inherited together. Such genes are said to be *linked*. The patterns of inheritance and phenotype ratios for linked traits are different from those of nonlinked traits (the kind observed by Mendel).

Crossing-Over
During *synapsis* in the first meiotic division, the chromatids of a pair of homologous chromosomes often twist around each other, break, exchange segments, and rejoin (Figure 7-4). This exchange

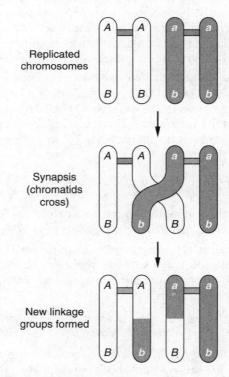

FIGURE 7-4 Crossing-over of chromatids.

of segments, called *crossing-over*, results in a rearrangement of linked genes and produces variations in offspring. Crossing-over is an important source of genetic variation in sexual reproduction. Linked genes that are located farther apart on the chromosome are much more likely to be separated during crossing-over than genes that are positioned close together. In fact, the frequency of gene separation can be used to determine the distance between specific genes and to map their loci on the chromosome.

QUESTIONS
Part A

15. Polydactyly is a characteristic in which a person has six fingers per hand. Polydactyly is dominant over the trait for five fingers. If a man who is heterozygous for this trait marries a woman with the normal number of fingers, what are the chances that their child would be polydactyl? (1) 0% (2) 50% (3) 75% (4) 100%

16. A cross between two pea plants that are hybrid for a single trait produces 60 offspring. Approximately how many of the offspring would be expected to exhibit the recessive trait? (1) 15 (2) 45 (3) 30 (4) 60

17. Which principle states that during meiosis chromosomes are distributed to gametes in a random fashion? (1) dominance (2) linkage (3) segregation (4) mutation

18. In guinea pigs, black coat color is dominant over white coat color. The offspring of a mating between two heterozygous black guinea pigs would probably show a phenotype ratio of (1) two black to two white (2) one black to three white (3) three black to one white (4) four black to zero white

19. The offspring of a mating between two heterozygous black guinea pigs would probably show a genotype ratio of (1) l *BB* : 2 *Bb* : 1 *bb* (2) 3 *Bb* : 1 *bb* (3) 2 *BB* : 2 *bb* (4) 2 *BB* : 1 *Bb* : 1 *bb*

20. If a breeder wanted to discover whether a black guinea pig was homozygous (*BB*) or heterozygous (*Bb*) for coat color, the animal in question would have to be crossed with an individual that has the genotype (1) *BB* (2) *bb* (3) *Bb* (4) *BbBb*

21. Mendel's principle of independent assortment applies to traits whose genes are found on (1) homologous chromosomes (2) sex chromosomes (3) the same chromosome (4) nonhomologous chromosomes

22. The process in which the chromatids of pairs of homologous chromosomes exchange segments is called (1) linkage (2) crossing-over (3) independent assortment (4) intermediate inheritance

23. In horses, black coat color is dominant over chestnut coat color. Two black horses produce both a black-coated and a chestnut-coated offspring. If coat color is controlled by a single pair of genes, it can be assumed that (1) in horses, genes for coat color frequently mutate (2) one of the parent horses is homozygous dominant and the other is heterozygous for coat color (3) both parent horses are homozygous for coat color (4) both parent horses are heterozygous for coat color

Part B-2

24. Based on your answer to question 23, explain how two black horses could produce a chestnut-colored offspring.

Base your answers to questions 25 through 27 on the diagram below, which represents a pair of homologous chromosomes at the beginning of meiosis. The letters A, B, C, a, b, and c represent pairs of alleles located on the chromosomes.

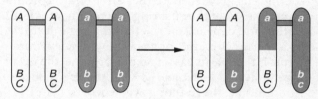

25. Compare the sets of chromosomes on the left with those on the right. Explain what has happened.

26. What process (not shown) is responsible for the observed results?

27. How does this process lead to variations among offspring?

Part C

28. When is a testcross used? Explain how it works.

29. Explain the following statement: Traits are inherited independently of one another only if their genes are on different chromosomes. You may use diagrams to support your explanation.

Sex Determination
The diploid cells of many organisms contain two types of chromosomes: *autosomes* and *sex chromosomes*. There is generally one pair of sex chromosomes, and all the other chromosomes are autosomes. In human body cells, there are 22 pairs of autosomes and one pair of sex chromosomes. The sex chromosomes are

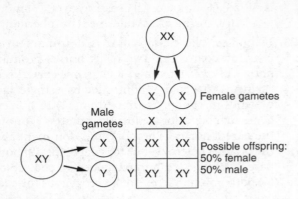

FIGURE 7-5 Sex determination of offspring.

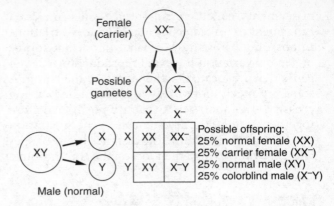

FIGURE 7-6 Inheritance of color blindness.

called the *X* and *Y* chromosomes. Females have two *X* chromosomes, and males have one *X* and one *Y* chromosome.

During meiotic cell division, the sex chromosomes, like all other chromosome pairs, are separated (Figure 7-5). The resulting gametes contain only one sex chromosome. Since females have two *X* chromosomes, each female gamete receives an *X* chromosome. Since the genotype of males is *XY*, sperm cells may receive either an *X* or a *Y* chromosome. The sex of the offspring is determined at fertilization and depends on whether the egg is fertilized by a sperm with an *X* or a sperm with a *Y* chromosome. If the sperm has an *X* chromosome, the resulting zygote will be female (*XX*). If the sperm has a *Y* chromosome, the resulting zygote will be male (*XY*).

Sex-linked Traits

T. H. Morgan, in his experiments with fruit flies, found that some rare, abnormal recessive traits appear with greater frequency in males than in females. From his observations, Morgan concluded that the genes for these traits are present on the *X* chromosome and that there are no corresponding alleles for these traits on the *Y* chromosome, because the *Y* chromosome is smaller and has far fewer genes than the *X* chromosome. Genes found on the *X* chromosome are called *sex-linked genes*. Recessive sex-linked traits appear more frequently in males than in females because in females there is usually a normal, dominant allele on the other *X* chromosome, so that the phenotype is normal. In males, there is no second allele, so the presence of one recessive gene produces a recessive phenotype.

Both *hemophilia* and *color blindness* are sex-linked disorders; they occur more frequently in males than in females. Hemophilia is a condition in which the blood does not clot properly, while color blindness is an inability to distinguish certain colors. The genes for normal blood clotting and normal color vision are dominant; the genes for hemophilia and color blindness are recessive. For a female to show either of these disorders, she must have recessive genes (alleles) on both of her *X* chromosomes. Females with one normal, dominant gene and one recessive gene for these disorders are called *carriers*. They can pass the disorder to their offspring but do not themselves show symptoms of the disorder. Figure 7-6 shows the possible genotypes of children of a normal male and a female carrier of color blindness.

QUESTIONS
Part A

30. If a color-blind man marries a woman who is a carrier for color blindness, it is most probable that (1) all of their sons will have normal color vision (2) half of their sons will be color-blind (3) all of their sons will be color-blind (4) none of their children will have normal color vision

31. A color-blind man marries a woman with normal vision. Her mother was color-blind. They have one child. What is the chance that this child will be color-blind? (1) 0% (2) 25% (3) 50% (4) 100%

32. A color-blind woman marries a man who has normal color vision. What are their chances of having a color-blind daughter? (1) 0% (2) 25% (3) 75% (4) 100%

33. Which parental pair could produce a color-blind female? (1) homozygous normal-vision mother and color-blind father (2) color-blind mother and normal-vision father (3) heterozygous normal-vision mother and normal-vision father (4) heterozygous normal-vision mother and color-blind father

34. Which statement correctly describes the normal number and type of chromosomes present in

human body cells of a particular sex? (1) Males have 22 pairs of autosomes and 1 pair of *XX* sex chromosomes. (2) Females have 23 pairs of autosomes. (3) Males have 22 pairs of autosomes and 1 pair of *XY* sex chromosomes. (4) Males have 23 pairs of autosomes.

35. Based on the pattern of inheritance known as sex linkage, if a male is a hemophiliac, how many genes for this trait are present on the sex chromosomes in each of his diploid cells? (1) 1 (2) 2 (3) 3 (4) 4

36. Traits controlled by genes on the *X* chromosome are said to be (1) sex-linked (2) mutagenic (3) incompletely dominant (4) homozygous

Part C

37. Use a Punnett square diagram to show why, for each pregnancy, the chances of giving birth to either a boy or a girl are 50-50. Explain the results shown in your diagram.

38. Explain why hemophilia occurs more often in males than in females. Use a Punnett square diagram to illustrate your answer.

GENETIC MUTATIONS

Changes in the genetic material are called **mutations**. Mutations in body cells can be passed on to new cells of the individual as a result of mitosis, but they cannot be transmitted to offspring by sexual reproduction because body cells are not passed on to offspring. However, mutations in sex cells *can* be transmitted to the next generation. Mutations may involve alterations in chromosomes or alterations in the chemical makeup of genes.

Chromosomal Alterations

Chromosomal alterations involve a change in the structure or number of chromosomes. The effects of chromosomal alterations are often seen in the phenotype of an organism because each chromosome contains many genes.

Nondisjunction. During meiosis, the two chromosomes of each homologous pair separate from each other; each gamete produced by the division receives only one member of each homologous pair. The separation of homologous chromosomes is called *disjunction*. The term *nondisjunction* refers to a type of chromosomal alteration in which one or more pairs of homologous chromosomes fail to separate normally during meiotic cell division (Figure 7-7).

As a result of nondisjunction, one of the gametes

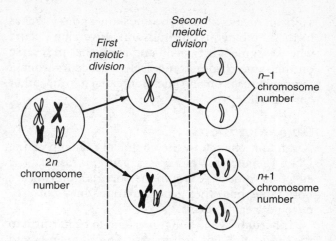

FIGURE 7-7 Nondisjunction of chromosomes.

produced contains both members of the homologous pair, while another gamete contains neither chromosome. Nondisjunction results in the production of some gametes with more chromosomes than normal and some gametes with fewer chromosomes than normal. If one of these abnormal gametes is involved in fertilization, the resulting zygote will have either more than or fewer than the normal (2*n*) number of chromosomes.

Down syndrome in humans is caused by the presence of an extra chromosome number 21. Nondisjunction during gamete production in one of the parents produces a gamete with an extra chromosome 21. As a result of fertilization, this extra chromosome is transmitted to the offspring.

Polyploidy. Occasionally during gamete formation, a complete set of chromosomes fails to undergo disjunction, and a gamete is produced that contains the diploid (2*n*) chromosome number. If a diploid gamete unites with a normal (*n*) gamete during fertilization, the resulting zygote will have a 3*n* chromosome number. If two 2*n* gametes fuse, a 4*n* zygote results. The inheritance of one or more complete extra sets of chromosomes is called *polyploidy*. This condition is common in plants but rare in animals. In plants, polyploid individuals are usually larger or more vigorous than the normal, diploid varieties. Certain strains of wheat, potatoes, alfalfa, apples, tobacco, and zinnias are polyploid. Some polyploid plants produce seedless fruit and are sterile.

Changes in the Chromosomal Structure. Changes in the makeup of chromosomes may result from random breakage and recombination of chromosome parts. Translocation occurs when a segment of one chromosome breaks off and reattaches to a nonhomologous chromosome. Addition occurs when a segment breaks off one chromosome and reattaches to the homologous chromosome. Inversion occurs when a segment breaks off and reattaches in reverse on the same chromosome. Deletion occurs when a segment breaks off and does not reattach to any other chromosome.

Gene Mutations

A random change in the chemical makeup of the DNA (genetic material) is a *gene mutation*. The effects of some gene mutations, such as albinism, are noticeable, but other gene mutations may not produce noticeable effects.

Inheritable gene mutations tend to be harmful to the individual. For example, sickle-cell anemia and Tay-Sachs disease are caused by gene mutations. Fortunately, most gene mutations are recessive and are hidden by the normal, dominant allele. However, if both parents carry the same recessive mutant gene, there is a chance that their offspring will be homozygous recessive and show the harmful trait.

Occasionally, random gene mutations produce changes that make an individual better adapted to the environment. Over time, such helpful mutant genes tend to increase in frequency within a population (because they increase the individuals' chances for survival).

Mutagenic Agents

Although mutations occur spontaneously, the rate of mutation can be increased by exposure to certain chemicals and forms of **radiation** that act as *mutagenic agents*. For example, forms of mutagenic radiation include x-rays, ultraviolet rays, radioactive substances, and cosmic rays. Mutagenic chemicals include formaldehyde, benzene, and asbestos fibers.

QUESTIONS
Part A

39. Which phrase best describes most mutations? (1) dominant and disadvantageous to the organism (2) recessive and disadvantageous to the organism (3) recessive and advantageous to the organism (4) dominant and advantageous to the organism

40. The failure of a pair of homologous chromosomes to separate during meiotic cell division is called (1) nondisjunction (2) translocation (3) addition (4) deletion

41. The condition in which a gamete contains the $2n$ or $3n$ number of chromosomes is called (1) translocation (2) a gene mutation (3) polydactyly (4) polyploidy

42. The presence of only one X chromosome in each body cell of a human female produces a condition known as Turner syndrome. This condition most probably results from the process called (1) polyploidy (2) crossing-over (3) nondisjunction (4) hybridization

43. A random change in the chemical structure of DNA produces (1) polyploidy (2) a translocation (3) nondisjunction (4) a gene mutation

44. Down syndrome in humans is characterized by the presence of an extra chromosome 21 in all cells of the body. The number of chromosomes present in the body cells of individuals with this condition is (1) $n + 1$ (2) $3n$ (3) $2n + 1$ (4) $4n$

45. The graph below shows the relationship between maternal age and the number of children born with Down syndrome per 1000 births.

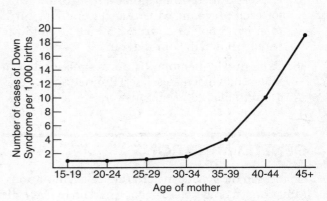

According to the graph, the incidence of Down syndrome (1) generally decreases as maternal age increases (2) is about nine times greater at age 45 than at age 30 (3) stabilized at 2 per 1000 births after age 35 (4) is greater at age 15 than at age 35

46. Ultraviolet rays, x-rays, and certain other forms of radiation can increase the rate of gene mutation. These forms of radiation are said to act as (1) mutagenic agents (2) catalysts (3) enzymes (4) indicators

47. The large size and exceptional vigor of certain varieties of wheat, apples, and zinnias are due to the possession of extra sets of chromosomes, which result from (1) incomplete dominance (2) gene mutations (3) nondisjunction of complete sets of chromosomes (4) nondisjunction of chromosome number 21 only

48. A type of chromosomal alteration in which a segment of chromosome breaks off and does not reattach to any chromosome is called (1) addition (2) inversion (3) deletion (4) translocation

49. Which mutation in a fruit fly can be passed on to its offspring? (1) a mutation in a cell of an eye

that changes the color of the eye (2) a mutation in a sperm cell that changes the shape of the wing (3) a mutation in a leg cell that causes the leg to be shorter (4) a mutation in a cell of the digestive tract that produces a different enzyme

Part B-2

Base your answers to questions 50 through 53 on the following information about an experiment and on your knowledge of biology.

Two groups of 100 lima beans each were used. Group *A* was exposed to natural light for a period of 24 hours and then planted. Group *B* was exposed to microwave energy for 24 hours and then planted under the same conditions as Group *A*. When the seeds germinated, the plants were observed for growth over a period of two weeks. The results are summarized in the table below.

Number of Plants

Group	Normal Growth	Stunted and/or Pale
A	83	17
B	54	46

50. What hypothesis was most likely being tested in this experiment?

51. Describe the results of the experiment.

52. Based on the data, propose a conclusion for the experiment.

53. What are some of the implications of the data?

Part C

54. Explain how it is possible for an individual to inherit an extra chromosome. List two or more human genetic disorders caused by the inheritance of an abnormal number of chromosomes.

55. Mutagens are agents that increase the rate of gene mutations in cells. Identify three types of mutagenic agents and briefly explain how each one causes mutations. Describe how people may reduce their chances of being harmed by these particular agents.

HEREDITY AND THE ENVIRONMENT

The development and expression of inherited traits can be influenced by environmental factors such as nutrients, temperature, sunlight, and so on. The relationship between gene action and environmental influence can be seen in the following examples.

Temperature affects fur color in the Himalayan rabbit. Under normal circumstances, these rabbits are white with black ears, nose, tail, and feet. (The black fur helps the rabbit absorb more heat in its extremities.) However, when some of the white fur on a Himalayan rabbit's back is shaved off and the area kept covered with an ice pack, the new hairs grow in black. The artificial change in temperature produces a change in fur color. Some animals that live in very cold climates change their fur color as summer passes into winter. The Arctic hare and the Arctic fox both have dark fur in summer. However, in winter, the new fur that grows in is white. Temperature affects the genes that control fur color in these mammals. The white coat is a survival adaptation; the animals are well camouflaged against the snow in their winter environment.

Experiments have shown that the production of chlorophyll requires exposure to sunlight. When parts of a leaf are covered with dark paper, chlorophyll production stops in the area that is covered. Only the exposed part produces chlorophyll, is green, and performs photosynthesis.

Stress and nutrition can affect gene expression. For example, someone who has a tall genotype may not develop a tall phenotype if his or her growth is stunted by malnutrition.

PLANT AND ANIMAL BREEDING

Using the principles of genetics, plant and animal breeders have been able to produce, improve, and maintain new varieties of plants and animals. Methods of **selective breeding** include artificial selection, inbreeding, and hybridization.

In *artificial selection,* individuals with the most desirable traits (for example, sheep with thick, soft wool) are crossed or allowed to mate in the hopes that their offspring will show the desired traits.

The offspring of selected organisms may be mated with one another to produce more individuals with the desirable traits. This technique, called *inbreeding,* involves the mating of closely related organisms. (Of course, the risk of inbreeding is that harmful recessive genes are more likely to be inherited and cause disorders in the offspring.)

Two varieties of a species may have different desirable traits. In a technique called *hybridization,* breeders cross two such varieties in the hope of producing hybrid offspring that show the desirable traits of both varieties. For example, if one variety of rose has very large petals and another variety has a very sweet scent, their hybrid might show both desirable traits.

56. If bean plant seedlings are germinated in the dark, the seedlings will lack green color. The best explanation for this condition is that (1) bean plants are heterotrophic organisms (2) bean seedlings lack nitrogen compounds in their cotyledons (3) the absence of an environmental factor limits the expression of a genotype (4) bean plants cannot break down carbon dioxide to produce oxygen in the dark

57. In many humans, exposing the skin to sunlight over prolonged periods of time results in the production of more pigment by the skin cells (tanning). This change in skin color provides evidence that (1) ultraviolet light can cause mutations (2) gene action can be influenced by the environment (3) the inheritance of skin color is an acquired characteristic (4) albinism is a recessive characteristic

58. Identical twins were separated at birth and brought together after 13 years. They varied in height by 5 centimeters and in weight by 10 kilograms. The most probable explanation for these differences is that (1) their environments affected the expression of their traits (2) their cells did not divide by mitotic cell division (3) they developed from two different zygotes (4) they differed in their genotypes

59. A normal bean seedling that had the ability to produce chlorophyll did not produce any chlorophyll when grown in soil that was totally deficient in magnesium salts. Which statement concerning this plant's inability to produce chlorophyll is true? (1) The lack of magnesium prevented the plant's roots from absorbing water. (2) The production of chlorophyll was controlled solely by heredity. (3) The lack of magnesium caused a mutation of the gene that controlled chlorophyll production. (4) The production of chlorophyll was influenced by environmental conditions.

60. To ensure the maintenance of a desirable trait in a particular variety of plant, a farmer would use (1) binary fission (2) mutagenic agents (3) artificial selection (4) natural selection

61. The mating of very closely related organisms in order to produce the most desirable traits is known as (1) inbreeding (2) hybridization (3) karyotyping (4) crossing-over

62. Plant and animal breeders usually sell or get rid of undesirable specimens and use only the desirable ones for breeding. This practice is referred to as (1) vegetative propagation (2) artificial selection (3) natural breeding (4) random mating

63. A single gene mutation results from (1) a change in a base sequence in DNA (2) recombination of traits (3) the failure of chromosomes to separate (4) blocked nerve messages

64. The table below shows relationships between genes, the environment, and coloration of tomato plants. Which statement best explains the final appearance of these tomato plants? (1) The expression of gene A is not affected by light. (2) The expression of gene B varies with the presence of light. (3) The expression of gene A varies with the environment. (4) Gene B is expressed only in darkness.

Inherited Gene	Environmental Condition	Final Appearance
A	Light	Green
B	Light	White
A	Dark	White
B	Dark	White

65. Some mammals have genes for fur color that produce pigment only when the outside temperature is above a certain level. This pigment production is an example of how the environment of an organism can (1) destroy certain genes (2) cause new mutations to occur (3) stop the process of evolution (4) influence the expression of certain genes

66. Identify three environmental factors that can influence phenotype. Give an example of each.

67. Describe the process a breeder would use to produce an organism that has certain desirable traits.

HUMAN HEREDITY

The principles of genetics apply to all organisms. However, specific studies of human genetics are limited because humans are not suitable subjects for experimentation: human generation time is too long; there are only a small number of offspring per generation in a human family; and it is unethical to perform such experiments on humans. Knowledge of human heredity has been gathered indirectly through studies of human pedigree charts and materials obtained in the course of genetics counseling.

Human Pedigree Charts

The patterns of inheritance of certain traits can be traced in families for a number of generations. These patterns can be illustrated in *pedigree charts* that show the presence or absence of certain genetic traits in each generation. The use of a pedigree chart may also make it possible to identify carriers of recessive genes.

Human Genetic Disorders

Some diseases caused by genetic abnormalities are sickle-cell disease, Tay-Sachs disease, and phenylketonuria. These disorders are caused by gene mutations.

Sickle-cell disease is a blood disorder found most commonly in individuals of African descent. The disorder is caused by a gene mutation that results in the production of abnormal hemoglobin molecules and red blood cells. The abnormal hemoglobin and sickle-shaped cells do not carry oxygen efficiently, resulting in anemia. The sickle-shaped red cells also tend to obstruct blood vessels, causing severe pain. Sickle-cell anemia occurs in individuals homozygous for the trait. Both homozygous and heterozygous individuals can be detected by blood tests. Heterozygotes are carriers of the trait and may show minimal or no effects of sickle-cell disease.

Tay-Sachs disease is a recessive genetic disorder in which nerve tissue in the brain deteriorates because of an accumulation of fatty material. The disorder is a result of the body's inability to synthesize a particular enzyme. Tay-Sachs disease, which is fatal, occurs most commonly among Jewish people of Central European descent.

Phenylketonuria (PKU) is a disorder in which the body cannot synthesize an enzyme necessary for the normal metabolism of the amino acid phenylalanine. The disease, which occurs in homozygous recessive individuals, is characterized by the development of mental retardation. Analysis of the urine of newborn infants can detect PKU. If PKU is detected, mental retardation can be prevented by maintaining a diet free of phenylalanine.

Detection of Genetic Disorders

Some human genetic disorders can be detected either before or after birth by the use of one or more of the following techniques.

Advances in genetic research have resulted in the development of simple blood and urine tests that can determine if an individual has certain genetic disorders. Carriers of sickle-cell anemia and Tay-Sachs disease can be identified by these screening techniques.

Karyotyping is a technique in which a greatly enlarged photograph of the chromosomes of a cell is prepared. The homologous pairs of chromosomes are matched together, and the chromosomes are examined to see if there are any abnormalities in number or structure.

Amniocentesis is a technique in which a small sample of amniotic fluid is withdrawn from the amniotic sac of a pregnant woman. The fluid contains fetal cells, which can be used for karyotyping or for chemical analysis. Amniocentesis is used in the identification of sickle-cell anemia, Tay-Sachs disease, and Down syndrome in fetuses. DNA testing is used frequently to identify genes that may have negative consequences.

Genetic Counseling

The various techniques described above are used by *genetics counselors* to inform concerned parents about the possible occurrence of genetic defects in their children. For couples whose families show the presence of a particular genetic disorder, a pedigree chart may be developed to predict the probability of their children's having the disorder. Amniocentesis, followed by karyotyping and chemical tests, may be performed once pregnancy is established.

QUESTIONS
Part A

68. An inherited metabolic disorder known as phenylketonuria (PKU) is characterized by severe mental retardation. This condition results from the inability to synthesize a single (1) enzyme (2) hormone (3) vitamin (4) carbohydrate

69. Which statement best describes amniocentesis? (1) Blood cells of an adult are checked for anemia. (2) Saliva of a child is analyzed for the amino acids. (3) Urine of a newborn baby is analyzed for the amino acid phenylalanine. (4) Fluid surrounding a fetus is removed for chemical and genetic analysis.

70. Which is a genetic disorder in which abnormal hemoglobin leads to fragile red blood cells and obstructed blood vessels? (1) phenylketonuria (2) sickle-cell anemia (3) leukemia (4) Down syndrome

71. Human disorders such as PKU and sickle-cell anemia, which are defects in the synthesis of individual proteins, are most likely the result of (1) gene mutations (2) nondisjunction (3) crossing-over (4) polyploidy

72. Which technique can be used to examine the chromosomes of a fetus for possible genetic defects? (1) pedigree analysis (2) analysis of fetal urine (3) karyotyping (4) blood cell tests

73. Give three reasons why a direct study of the inheritance of human traits is difficult to carry out.

74. Briefly describe the two ways that information about patterns of human heredity is usually obtained.

MODERN GENETICS

Through numerous experiments and the contributions of many scientists, biochemists have learned that DNA is the genetic material that is passed from generation to generation. Genes are sections of DNA (deoxyribonucleic acid) molecules on the chromosomes. DNA controls cellular activities by controlling the production of enzymes and other proteins.

DNA Structure

DNA molecules are very large; each is made up of thousands of repeating units called **nucleotides**. A DNA nucleotide is composed of three parts: a *phosphate group*; a molecule of the 5-carbon sugar *deoxyribose*; and a *nitrogenous base* (Figure 7-8).

There are four different nitrogenous bases found in DNA nucleotides: *adenine, cytosine, guanine,* and *thymine.* Therefore, there are four different kinds of nucleotides, depending on which nitrogenous base is present.

Watson-Crick Model. In the model of DNA developed by James Watson and Francis Crick, the DNA molecule consists of two connected chains of nucleotides forming a ladderlike structure (Figure 7-9). The sides of the "ladder" are composed of alternating phosphate and deoxyribose (sugar) molecules. Each rung of the ladder consists of a pair of nitrogenous bases bonded together by hydrogen bonds. The two chains of the DNA molecule are twisted to form a spiral, or *double helix.*

The DNA model of Watson and Crick was based largely on x-ray pictures of DNA taken in a lab by molecular biologist Rosalind Franklin. The double-helix shape of the DNA molecule was apparently visible in Franklin's photograph.

The four nitrogenous bases of DNA nucleotides

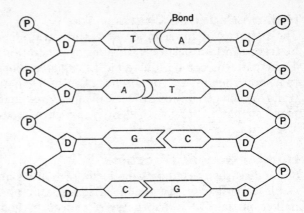

FIGURE 7-9 Structure of the DNA molecule.

bond together in only one way because of their chemical structure: adenine (A) pairs with thymine (T), and cytosine (C) pairs with guanine (G). The bases are held together by a special type of bond known as a *hydrogen bond.* Because the bases pair together in only one way, the two strands of a DNA molecule are always *complementary.* Where there is an adenine nucleotide on one strand, there is a thymine nucleotide on the other; where there is a cytosine on one strand, there is a guanine on the other. If you know the order of bases on one strand, then you also know the order on the second strand.

DNA Replication

DNA, unlike any other chemical compound, can make exact copies of itself—that is, DNA can **replicate.** This process, called DNA *replication,* is a necessary part of the chromosome replication that occurs during mitosis and meiosis.

In replication, the double-stranded DNA helix unwinds; the two strands then separate, or unzip, by breaking the hydrogen bonds between the nitrogenous base pairs. Free nucleotides from the cytoplasm then enter the nucleus, where they bond to their complementary bases on the DNA strands (Figure 7-10). Replication produces two identical DNA molecules that are exact copies of the original molecule. The process of DNA replication is actually carried out by a team of several important, specific enzymes.

Gene Control of Cellular Activities

The unique qualities of an organism are determined by the DNA of its genes. The genes control enzyme synthesis, and the enzymes control cell activities. For example, a dominant gene enables people to produce the enzyme lactase, which digests milk sugar (lactose). People who lack an active copy of this gene cannot digest milk sugar and, thus, are lactose intolerant.

The hereditary information is in the sequence of the nucleotides in DNA molecules. The DNA

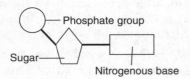

FIGURE 7-8 Structure of a DNA nucleotide unit.

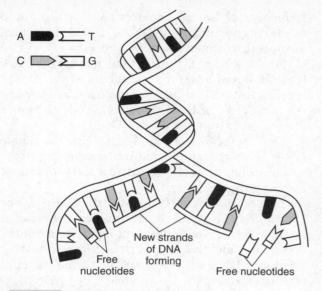

A ■▶ ⊐ T
C ▭▶ ⊐ G

New strands
of DNA
forming
Free
nucleotides   Free nucleotides

FIGURE 7-10 Replication of DNA strands.

nucleotide sequence determines the sequence of amino acids in enzymes and other proteins. The genetic control of protein synthesis involves RNA as well as DNA and many enzymes.

RNA

Molecules of *ribonucleic acid,* or *RNA,* are similar to DNA in that they are also made up of nucleotide units. However, in RNA nucleotides, the 5-carbon sugar *ribose* is substituted for deoxyribose, and the nitrogenous base *uracil* (U) is substituted for thymine. RNA molecules consist of one strand of nucleotides, while DNA molecules have two. There are three kinds of RNA molecules in cells: *messenger RNA* (mRNA), *transfer RNA* (tRNA), and *ribosomal RNA* (rRNA).

Messenger RNA is synthesized in the cell nucleus. Portions of a DNA molecule unwind, and the two strands separate. The RNA nucleotides pair with complementary bases on a DNA strand, forming a strand of messenger RNA that is complementary to the DNA strand. The DNA strand serves as a **template**, or pattern, for the synthesis of messenger RNA. In this way, the hereditary information in the nucleotide sequence of DNA is copied in complementary form into the nucleotide sequence of messenger RNA.

The sequence of nucleotides in messenger RNA contains the genetic code, which determines the amino acid sequence of proteins. The genetic code for each amino acid is a specific sequence of three nucleotides. The three-nucleotide sequence in messenger RNA that specifies a particular amino acid is called a *codon.*

Transfer RNA molecules are found in the cytoplasm. Their function is to carry amino acid

molecules to the *ribosomes,* the sites of protein synthesis. Ribosomes are made up of rRNA and proteins. There are 20 different kinds of amino acids in cells, and there is a different form of transfer RNA for each amino acid. Each kind of transfer RNA has a three-nucleotide sequence, called an *anticodon,* which is complementary to a codon on the messenger RNA.

Protein Synthesis

Protein synthesis begins with the synthesis of messenger RNA molecules, which then move from the nucleus into the cytoplasm. In the cytoplasm, the strand of messenger RNA becomes associated with ribosomes (Figure 7-11). Amino acids are carried to the ribosomes and messenger RNA by the transfer RNAs. The anticodons of the transfer RNAs align with the codons of the messenger RNA. The amino acids carried by the transfer RNAs bond together in a sequence determined by the base sequence of the messenger RNA. The resulting chain of amino acids is a polypeptide. Some proteins consist of a single polypeptide chain, while others include two or more.

One Gene–One Polypeptide Hypothesis

According to the *one gene–one polypeptide hypothesis,* each gene controls the synthesis of a single polypeptide. A modern definition of the gene is the sequence of nucleotides in a DNA molecule necessary to synthesize one polypeptide. However, this hypothesis is seen as overly simplified. It is now known that genes are not necessarily fixed in one place on the chromosomes. Rather, they can move to different locations, or *loci,* on the chromosomes and form new genetic codes when they are positioned next to different segments of DNA. In this way, a limited number of genes can have a much larger

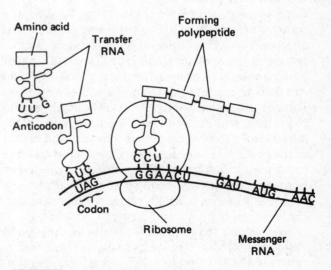

Amino acid   Transfer   Forming
RNA   polypeptide

U U G
Anticodon

C C U
A U G   G G A A C U   G A U A U G A A C
U A G
Codon   Ribosome   Messenger
RNA

FIGURE 7-11 Protein synthesis (at the ribosome).

variety of expression than would be possible if the genes remained in one place. The geneticist Barbara McClintock first proposed the idea of movable, or "jumping," genes in the early 1940s, but other scientists largely dismissed her work at the time. Now known to exist, these movable genes, or transposable genetic elements, are called *transposons*. The recently completed Human Genome Project revealed that we have far fewer genes than had been expected. Now, the large variety of human traits can be better understood because we know about transposons. By "jumping" around the chromosomes, the same gene can be expressed in several different ways.

Gene Mutations

Any change in the sequence of nucleotides in a DNA molecule is a *gene mutation*. If the mutation occurs in the DNA of the sex cells, it may be inherited. Gene mutations may involve the *addition* or *deletion* of bases, or the *substitution* of one base for another. Sickle-cell disease is caused by the substitution of one incorrect nitrogenous base in a gene that controls hemoglobin synthesis. The incorrect base results in the insertion of one incorrect amino acid, which in turn affects the structure and function of the hemoglobin protein.

Cloning

Cloning is the process by which a group of genetically identical offspring is produced from the cells of an organism. The cloning of plants shows great promise for agriculture, where plants with desirable qualities can be produced rapidly from the cells of a single plant. To date, cloning has been achieved in many animals, too, such as frogs, mice, sheep, goats, cows, cats, dogs, and monkeys.

Genetic Engineering

Gene splicing, or **genetic engineering**, involves the transfer of genetic material from one organism to another. This recombining of genes results in the formation of *recombinant DNA*. Using gene-splicing, or **biotechnology**, techniques, genes from one organism can be inserted into the DNA of another organism. Human genes that control the synthesis of insulin, interferon, and growth hormone have been introduced into bacterial cells, where they function as part of the bacterial DNA. In this way, bacterial cells are being used to synthesize these substances needed by humans. Genetic engineering may eventually be able to correct some genetic defects and produce commercially desirable plants and animals. For example, it is now possible to produce genetically modified food crops, such as corn, that are more disease- and insect-resistant. However, many people are reluctant to consume foods that have been genetically altered.

Techniques of Genetic Engineering. The technique of making recombinant DNA (rDNA) molecules involves three important components.

First, a specific enzyme is needed to cut the DNA from the donor genes at a specific site. This enzyme is called a *restriction enzyme*. The enzyme is used to cut out a piece of DNA that contains one or more desired genes from the donor's DNA.

Next, a *vector* is needed to receive the donor DNA. Most frequently, a naturally occurring circular piece of bacterial DNA, called a *plasmid*, is used for this purpose.

Finally, an enzyme is used to "stitch" the donor DNA into the plasmid vector. This enzyme is called *ligase*, and it creates permanent bonds between the donor DNA and the plasmid DNA. The result is that the donor DNA is incorporated into the bacterial plasmid, forming the recombinant DNA (rDNA).

It is important that the donor and the plasmid DNA be cut with the same restriction enzyme. Since each enzyme cuts DNA only at a specific site, the two different DNAs will have matching cut ends known as "sticky ends." The nitrogenous bases exposed at these cut sites can then match up according to the base-pairing rules, A to T and G to C (Figure 7-12).

The rDNA is then inserted into bacteria. When these bacteria reproduce, they copy the rDNA plasmid along with their own DNA. The plasmid is copied thousands of times, forming a clone (a colony having identical genetic material).

In addition to copying the plasmid along with their other DNA, the bacteria *express* the genes that

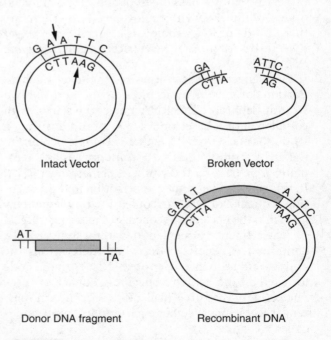

FIGURE 7-12 Use of a restriction enzyme, plasmid vector, and donor DNA to form recombinant DNA.

the plasmid carries, including the donor genes. As they reproduce, the bacteria continue to code for production of the desired protein. In this way, the bacteria can produce human proteins because they carry the genes with the instructions. This technique has made it possible to produce many chemicals that are needed by people who cannot produce them, due to genetic disorders. Two human proteins that have been successfully synthesized by rDNA techniques are the hormone insulin and human growth hormone.

Electrophoresis

We have already learned that DNA molecules can be cut with specific enzymes known as restriction enzymes. These enzymes cleave DNA molecules at highly specific sites that have a certain sequence of bases, such as AAAGGG. Different restriction enzymes have specific restriction sequences that they recognize. Each time the enzyme encounters its unique restriction site, it cuts the DNA molecule between a phosphate and a sugar subunit in the backbone. If DNA is incubated with a specific restriction enzyme, the molecule will be cut into many fragments of varying sizes, depending on where the restriction site is located in the DNA molecule.

DNA fragments can be separated according to size because they are electrically charged. The phosphate group at the end of a DNA fragment carries a negative charge; thus, it will be attracted to an area with a positive charge. To separate DNA fragments by means of electrophoresis, a small chamber or box is connected to an electrical source. DNA samples are loaded into small wells within a medium, called a *gel,* which is prepared so that an electric current can pass through it. When the current is switched on, the DNA fragments begin to move in response to the electrical field that is created in the gel. They move away from the wells (the negative end) toward the opposite (positive) end of the box (Figure 7-13).

The size of a DNA fragment depends on the number of base pairs it contains. The more base pairs, the larger and heavier the fragment. Heavier DNA fragments cannot move as far as smaller DNA fragments can within an electrical field. Thus, the smaller fragments will move the farthest from the wells. The

result is a series of bands of DNA running from the wells to the other end of the gel. These DNA fragments are made visible to the human eye by means of a simple staining technique, a special chemical, and/or ultraviolet light.

Electrophoresis is useful in determining the sizes of DNA fragments as well as in comparing DNA from two or more different sources. If two different DNA samples (from different individuals) are cut using the same restriction enzyme and then run on a gel in separate wells, we can determine how closely matched the two samples are. If the DNA samples are very similar, they will produce similar-sized fragments that will line up next to each other on the gel. If the two samples are very different, they will produce many different-sized fragments and relatively few will match up. If DNA samples are run from identical twins, all the fragments should match up, since the DNA in these individuals is identical.

Gel electrophoresis has been extremely helpful in law enforcement and forensics. Using this technique, often referred to as "DNA fingerprinting," scientists have been able to match DNA collected at a crime scene with the DNA gathered from a suspect. Biologists also use electrophoresis to determine current and evolutionary relationships among living things.

75. Which diagram illustrates the correct structure of a segment of a DNA molecule? (1) 1 (2) 2 (3) 3 (4) 4

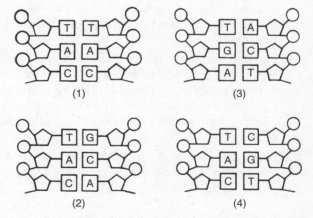

76. DNA and RNA molecules are similar in that they both contain (1) nucleotides (2) a double helix (3) deoxyribose sugars (4) thymine

77. Which series is arranged in correct order according to *decreasing* size of structures? (1) DNA, nucleus, chromosome, nucleotide, nitrogenous base (2) nucleotide, chromosome, nitrogenous

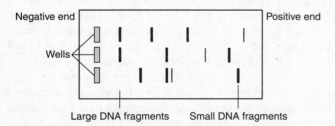

FIGURE 7-13 Gel electrophoresis: The smaller DNA fragments move farthest from the wells.

base, nucleus, DNA (3) nucleus, chromosome, DNA, nucleotide, nitrogenous base (4) chromosome, nucleus, nitrogenous base, nucleotide, DNA

78. Which substances are components of a DNA nucleotide? (1) phosphate, deoxyribose, and uracil (2) phosphate, ribose, and adenine (3) thymine, deoxyribose, and phosphate (4) ribose, phosphate, and uracil

79. Which two bases are present in equal amounts in a double-stranded DNA molecule? (1) cytosine and thymine (2) adenine and thymine (3) adenine and uracil (4) cytosine and uracil

80. Which process can be used to rapidly produce a group of genetically identical plants from the cells of a single plant? (1) screening (2) karyotyping (3) gene splicing (4) cloning

81. In humans, a gene mutation results from a change in the (1) sequence of the nitrogenous bases in DNA (2) chromosome number in a sperm cell (3) chromosome number in an egg cell (4) sequence of the sugars and phosphates in DNA

82. Which set of statements correctly describes the relationship among the terms *chromosomes, genes,* and *nuclei*? (1) Chromosomes are found on genes. Genes are found in nuclei. (2) Chromosomes are found in nuclei. Nuclei are found in genes. (3) Genes are found on chromosomes. Chromosomes are found in nuclei. (4) Genes are found in nuclei. Nuclei are found in chromosomes.

83. The genetic code for one amino acid molecule consists of (1) five sugar molecules (2) two phosphates (3) three nucleotides (4) four hydrogen bonds

84. During the replication of a DNA molecule, separation of the DNA molecule will normally occur when hydrogen bonds are broken between (1) thymine and thymine (2) guanine and uracil (3) adenine and cytosine (4) cytosine and guanine

85. In the diagram, what substance is represented by the letter *x*? (1) ribose (2) deoxyribose (3) phosphate (4) adenine

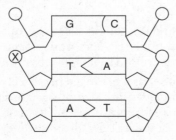

86. Which terms describe gene activities that ensure homeostasis of life processes and continuity of hereditary material? (1) oxidation and hydrolysis (2) enzyme synthesis and DNA replication (3) oxygen transport and cyclosis (4) pinocytosis and dehydration synthesis

87. The formation of recombinant DNA results from the (1) addition of messenger RNA molecules to an organism (2) transfer of genes from one organism to another (3) substitution of a ribose sugar for a deoxyribose sugar (4) production of a polyploid condition by a mutagenic agent

88. The replication of a double-stranded DNA molecule begins when the strands "unzip" at the (1) phosphate bonds (2) ribose molecules (3) deoxyribose molecules (4) hydrogen bonds

89. Which situation is *least* likely to result in new inherited characteristics? (1) altering genetic information (2) producing new individuals by means of cloning (3) changes in the structure of genes (4) changes in the structure of individual chromosomes

90. The diagram below represents a section of a molecule that carries genetic information. The pattern of numbers represents (1) a sequence of paired bases (2) the order of proteins in a gene (3) folds of an amino acid (4) positions of gene mutations

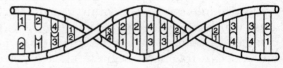

91. Enzymes are used in moving sections of DNA that code for insulin from the pancreas cells of humans into a certain type of bacterial cell. This bacterial cell will reproduce, giving rise to new cells that can produce (1) human insulin (2) antibodies against insulin (3) enzymes that digest insulin (4) a new type of insulin

92. In the human pancreas, acinar cells produce digestive enzymes and beta cells produce insulin. The best explanation for this is that (1) a mutation occurs in the beta cells to produce insulin when the sugar level increases in the blood (2) different parts of an individual's DNA are used to direct the synthesis of different proteins in different types of cells (3) lowered sugar levels cause the production of insulin in acinar cells to help maintain homeostasis (4) the genes in acinar cells came from one parent, while the genes in beta cells came from the other parent

93. A gene that codes for resistance to glyphosate, a biodegradable weed killer, has been inserted into certain plants. As a result, these plants will be more likely to (1) produce chemicals that kill weeds growing near them (2) die when exposed to glyphosate (3) convert glyphosate into fertilizer (4) survive when glyphosate is applied to them

94. Gel electrophoresis is used to separate DNA fragments on the basis of their (1) size (2) color (3) functions (4) chromosomes

Part B-1

To answer questions 95 through 98, select from the list below the type of nucleic acid that is best described by the phrase.

    A. DNA

    B. Messenger RNA

    C. Transfer RNA

95. Genetic material responsible for the traits of an organism, that is passed from parent to offspring (1) A (2) B (3) C

96. Carries genetic information from the cell nucleus out to the ribosomes (1) A (2) B (3) C

97. Contains thymine instead of uracil (1) A (2) B (3) C

98. Carries amino acid molecules to the ribosomes in the cytoplasm (1) A (2) B (3) C

Base your answers to questions 99 through 103 on the following diagram, which represents the process of protein synthesis in a typical cell.

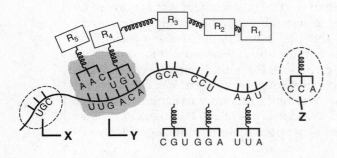

99. The original template for this process is a molecule of (1) DNA (2) messenger RNA (3) transfer RNA (4) ribosomal RNA

100. The units labeled R_1, R_2, and R_3 represent (1) nucleotides (2) RNA molecules (3) DNA molecules (4) amino acids

101. The organelle labeled *Y*, on which this process occurs, is the (1) nucleus (2) ribosome (3) chloroplast (4) mitochondria

102. The circled portion labeled *X* is (1) an amino acid (2) a codon (3) an anticodon (4) a single nucleotide

103. The circled portion labeled *Z* represents a molecule of (1) DNA (2) messenger RNA (3) transfer RNA (4) ribosomal RNA

Part B-2

104. Briefly describe two important functions of DNA.

105. Why is DNA replication critical to the survival of organisms?

Base your answers to questions 106 through 108 on the information and table below and on your knowledge of biology.

    In DNA, a sequence of three bases is a code for the placement of a certain amino acid in a protein chain. The table below shows eight amino acids with their abbreviations and DNA codes.

Amino Acid	Abbreviation	DNA Code
Phenylalanine	Phe	AAA, AAG
Tryptophan	Try	ACC
Serine	Ser	AGA, AGG, AGT, AGC, TCA, TCG
Valine	Val	CAA, CAG, CAT, CAC
Proline	Pro	GGA, GGG, GGT, GGC
Glutamine	Glu	GTT, GTC
Threonine	Thr	TGA, TGG, TGT, TGC
Asparagine	Asp	TTA, TTG

106. Which amino acid chain would be produced by the following DNA base sequence?

    C-A-A-G-T-T-A-A-A-T-T-A-T-T-G-T-G-A

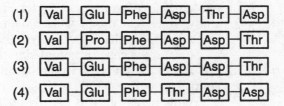

107. Identify one environmental factor that could cause a base sequence in DNA to be changed to a different base sequence.

108. Describe how a protein would be changed if a base sequence mutates from GGA to TGA.

109. Explain the role of each of the following in making recombinant DNA: *restriction enzymes, plasmids,* and *ligase.*

110. How are the techniques of genetic engineering making it possible to treat some diseases caused by genetic disorders? Provide an example.

111. The following is a scrambled list of the techniques used in making recombinant DNA. Write these steps in the correct sequence and, for each step, explain why it is placed in that order.

Steps

Cut open plasmid with restriction enzyme.

Obtain synthesized protein from the bacteria.

Clone bacterial cells with rDNA plasmids.

Insert donor DNA into the open plasmid.

Cut out donor DNA with restriction enzyme.

Add ligase to bond donor DNA and plasmid.

112. Animal cells utilize many different proteins. Discuss the synthesis of proteins in an animal cell. Your answer must include:
- the identity of the building blocks required to synthesize these proteins
- the identity of the sites in the cell where the proteins are assembled
- an explanation of the role of DNA in the process of making proteins in the cell

113. Mike has a pet cat named Jinx. He knows that Smokey is Jinx's mother and he suspects that Sparky is Jinx's father. Mike decides to do DNA testing on Jinx, Smokey, and Sparky to determine the paternity. DNA is collected from all three cats and an electrophoresis is run. Describe the results of the DNA test that would confirm that Sparky is Jinx's father. Draw a diagram of an electrophoresis set-up that shows your results.

LITERACY SKILL: READING FOR COMPREHENSION

Base your answers to questions 114 through 117 on the information below and on your knowledge of biology. Source: Science News *(October 23, 2010): vol. 178, no. 9, p. 15. Reprinted with permission of* Science News.

Heaps of Genes Have Hand in Height: Study Finds Hundreds of Genetic Variants Influencing Stature

Geneticists are getting to the long and short of the genes that control how tall a person will grow. The short answer is that at least 180 common genetic variants are involved; the long, up to a thousand variants may control human height.

Scanning the genetic blueprints of more than 100,000 people, scientists have turned up at least 180 different genetic variants involved in determining human height, the researchers report online September 29 in *Nature.* That may sound impressive, but each of the genes involved has a small effect, and researchers are still able to account for only about 10 percent of the genetic contributions that give rise to the wide diversity seen in height.

"It's a lot more complicated than we originally thought, and there may be thousands of variants with subtle effects," says Michael Weedon, a geneticist at Peninsula College of Medicine & Dentistry in Exeter, England. Weedon is one of 293 coauthors of the new study, which reanalyzed data from more than 50 previous genome-wide association studies to find genes that affect growth in people.

Some of the genes pinpointed in the new study were already known to affect height, but others are involved in biological processes that were not previously suspected to control growth.

While height itself is usually not of great medical significance, the new study may provide insight into the ways that many genes influence the development of some diseases, says Jeffrey Barrett, a statistical geneticist at the Wellcome Trust Sanger Institute near Cambridge, England. "This tells us something about the architecture of other human traits," he says.

Larger studies might uncover even more genetic variants associated with height. Assuming all variants have the same modest effects as the ones in this study—each affecting height by a millimeter or so—the researchers calculate that between 483 and 1,040 different variants may be involved, accounting for almost 20 percent of the genetic components that determine height. Scientists are still debating where the remaining genetic components are likely to be found.

114. Humans show great diversity in height. How does the fact that at least 180 genetic variants are involved support this observation?

115. What implications for studying diseases in humans does this research present?

116. State one fact mentioned in the article that indicates the outcomes of the research are reliable.

117. "The researchers calculate that between 483 and 1,040 different variants may be involved." State one aspect of this research project that remains unanswered.

8 Evolution

VOCABULARY AT A GLANCE

adaptations	dichotomous key	fossils	natural selection
antibiotics	diversity	genetic variations	pesticides
atmosphere	evolution	geologic time	speciation
cladogram	extinction	hominids	variability

Evolution is the process of change over time. The theory of evolution suggests that existing forms of life on Earth have evolved from earlier forms over long periods of time. These earlier forms were usually very different from the related organisms living today. Evolution accounts for the similarities and differences in structure, function, and behavior among all life-forms, as well as for the changes that occur within populations over many generations.

EVIDENCE OF EVOLUTION

Observations and data that support the theory of evolution have been obtained from the study of the geologic record and from studies of comparative anatomy, embryology, cytology, and biochemistry. It is important to understand that the word "theory" in science has a very different meaning from the same word in everyday language. A scientific theory is a concept that is supported by much documented evidence and experimental research. Scientific theories are based on the culmination of years of laboratory work, field observation, and extensive testing in order to validate results.

Geologic Record
Geologists estimate the age of Earth to be around 4.6 billion years old. This estimate is based on *radioactive dating* of the oldest known rocks from Earth's crust. (It is assumed that Earth is at least as old as the oldest rocks and minerals in its crust.)

In studying the geology of the planet, scientists have found many **fossils**, the remains or traces of organisms that no longer exist. From their studies of rocks and fossils, scientists have developed a picture of the changes that have occurred both in Earth itself and in living things on the planet.

Fossils
The earliest known fossils are traces of bacteria-like organisms that are about 3.5 billion years old. (The age of these fossils was determined by radioactive dating of the rocks in which they were found.)

Fossils of relatively intact organisms have been found preserved in ice, tar, and amber (a sticky plant resin that hardens). Mineralized bones, shells, teeth, and other hard parts of ancient organisms are sometimes found intact. (The soft parts generally decay within a short time.)

Other fossils have been formed by *petrifaction,* a process in which the tissues are gradually replaced by dissolved minerals that produce a stone replica of the original material. Imprints, casts, and molds of organisms or parts of organisms are frequently found in *sedimentary* rock. This type of rock is formed from the deposition of thick layers of soft sediments that eventually harden and turn to rock from the weight of

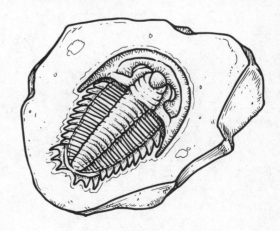

overlying sediments and water. The fossils form when the remains of dead organisms settle to the bottom of a body of water and are quickly covered by sediment. The overlying sediment slows or halts decay. When the layers of sediment harden, traces of the buried organisms are preserved in the rock.

In studying undisturbed sedimentary rock, scientists assume that each layer is older than all the layers, or *strata,* above it. Thus, fossils in the lower strata are older than fossils in the overlying strata. Fossils in the upper strata of a sedimentary rock sample are generally more complex than fossils in the lower strata, but there is often a resemblance between them. This suggests a link between recent forms and older forms of life. The fossil record may also provide evidence of divergent evolutionary pathways of some organisms from a common ancestor (Figure 8-1).

Some fossils in older strata are unlike any organisms living today. This suggests that many previous species have died out, or gone *extinct,* over time; **extinction** means there are no longer any living members of the species. Other fossils have structures that show ancestral connections to present-day life-forms. On the other hand, there are fossils that are quite similar to modern organisms, suggesting that some species have existed for a long time without much evolutionary change.

Comparative Anatomy
Another line of evidence for evolution comes from observations of basic structural, or anatomical, similarities between various organisms. *Homologous structures* are anatomical parts found in different organisms that are similar in origin and structure, although they may differ in function. For example, the flippers of whales, the wings of bats, the forelimbs of cats, and the arms of humans are homologous structures; they serve different functions, but their basic bone structures are similar (Figure 8-2). The

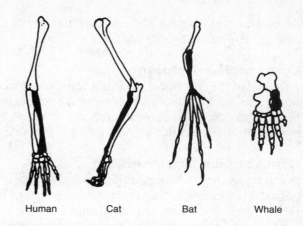

Human   Cat   Bat   Whale

FIGURE 8-2 The presence of homologous structures in their limb bones suggests that these mammals all evolved from a common ancestor.

presence of such homologous structures suggests that these mammals all evolved from a common ancestor.

Comparative Embryology
Although adult organisms of different species may look very different from one another, a comparison of the early stages of their embryonic development may show similarities that suggest a common ancestry. For example, the very early embryos of such vertebrates as fish, reptiles, birds, and mammals show some similarities in structure, such as having a tail and gill pouches (Figure 8-3). As embryonic

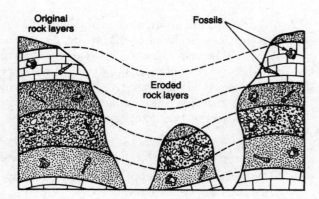

FIGURE 8-1 A resemblance between fossils in the upper and lower rock strata often indicates an evolutionary link between recent and older life-forms.

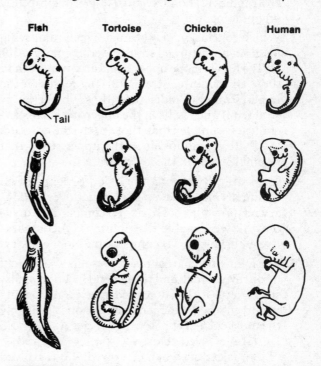

Fish   Tortoise   Chicken   Human

FIGURE 8-3 Similar features, such as a tail, in the early stages of embryonic development point to a common ancestry for these different vertebrates.

development continues, the characteristic traits of each species become more apparent.

Comparative Cytology

As stated in the cell theory, all living things are made up of cells. Cell organelles, including the cell membrane, ribosomes, and mitochondria, are structurally and functionally similar in most living organisms.

Comparative Biochemistry

All living things contain similar biochemical compounds. For example, the structure and function of DNA, RNA, and proteins (including enzymes) are similar in all organisms. The closer the relationship between any two organisms, the greater are their biochemical and genetic similarities. Today, biochemical relationships can be shown by means of gel electrophoresis. If two organisms are closely related, their DNA samples will show very similar banding patterns on the gel. Similarly, the proteins (such as enzymes) of the two organisms would be very similar, since a major function of DNA is the synthesis of proteins.

QUESTIONS
Part A

1. The front legs of a frog and the front legs of a horse are examples of structures that are (1) heterotrophic (2) homozygous (3) hermaphroditic (4) homologous

2. Which conclusion may be made when comparing fossils in undisturbed strata of sedimentary rock? (1) The fossils in the upper strata are younger than those in the lower strata. (2) The fossils in the upper strata are older than those in the lower strata. (3) The fossils in the upper strata are generally less complex than those in the lower strata. (4) There are no fossils in the upper strata that resemble those in the lower strata.

3. The similarity among the blood proteins of all mammals may be taken as evidence of evolutionary relationships based on (1) comparative anatomy (2) geographic distribution (3) comparative embryology (4) comparative biochemistry

4. The following chart above represents a section of undisturbed rock and the general location of fossils of several closely related species. According to current theory, which assumption is probably the most correct concerning species A, B, C, and D? (1) A evolved before the species B, C, and D. (2) B was extinct when C evolved. (3) C evolved more recently than A, B, and D. (4) D was probably the ancestor of A, B, and C.

| Species C & D |
| Species C |
| Species A & B & C |
| Species A & B |
| Species A |

5. Which assumption is a basis for the use of fossils as evidence for evolution? (1) Fossils show a complete record of the evolution of all animals. (2) In undisturbed layers of Earth's surface, the oldest fossils are found in the lowest layers. (3) Fossils are always found deep in volcanic rocks. (4) All fossils were formed at the same time.

6. Many related organisms are found to have the same kinds of enzymes. This suggests that (1) enzymes work only on specific substrates (2) enzymes act as catalysts in biochemical reactions (3) organisms living in the same environment require identical enzymes (4) these organisms probably share a common ancestry

7. Which is an example of evidence of evolution based on comparative biochemistry? (1) Sheep insulin can be substituted for human insulin. (2) The structure of a whale's flipper is similar to that of a human hand. (3) Human embryos have a tail during an early stage of their development. (4) Both birds and bats have wings.

8. The presence of gill pouches in early-stage human embryos is considered to be evidence of the (1) likelihood that all vertebrates share a common ancestry (2) theory that the first organisms on Earth were heterotrophs (3) close relationship between fish and human reproductive patterns (4) close relationship between humans and amphibians

9. The proteins in a chimpanzee's blood are shown, through gel electrophoresis, to be similar to those in a human's blood. This is an example of which type of evidence supporting the theory of evolution? (1) comparative habitat (2) comparative anatomy (3) comparative embryology (4) comparative biochemistry

Part B-2

10. State the five main types of evidence used to support the theory of evolution.

11. The diagram at the top of page 119 represents a cross section of undisturbed rock layers. A

scientist discovers bones of a complex vertebrate species in layers *B* and *C*. In which layer would an earlier, less complex form of this vertebrate most likely first appear? Explain.

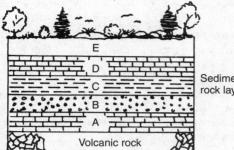

Sedimentary rock layers

Volcanic rock

12. *R, S,* and *T* are three species of birds. Species *S* and *T* show similar coloration. The enzymes found in species *R* and *T* show similarities. Species *R* and *T* also exhibit many of the same behavioral patterns. Show the relationship among species *R, S,* and *T* by placing the letter representing each species at the top of the appropriate branch on the diagram below.

13. Frogs and lizards are very different animals, yet they have many similarities. Provide a brief explanation of why frogs and lizards have many characteristics in common.

THEORIES OF EVOLUTION

Any theory of evolution must attempt to explain the origin and **diversity** (great variety) of life on Earth. Such a theory must also account for the wide variety of *adaptations* found among both living and extinct species. Different theories may account for different aspects of the evolutionary process. However, taken together, they can explain how life on Earth came to be and how it has progressed from the relatively simple and few to the complex and diverse.

THE HETEROTROPH HYPOTHESIS

The *heterotroph hypothesis* is one proposed explanation of how life arose and evolved on the primitive Earth. According to this hypothesis, the first life-forms were heterotrophic and therefore had to obtain organic nutrients from their environment.

The Primitive Earth

It is assumed that during the period preceding the development of the first life-forms, the primitive Earth was an exceptionally hot body consisting of inorganic substances in solid, liquid, and gaseous states.

The **atmosphere**, or air, of primitive Earth is thought to have had no free oxygen; instead, it consisted of hydrogen (H_2), ammonia (NH_3), methane (CH_4), and water vapor (H_2O). As Earth cooled, much of the water vapor condensed and fell as rain, which carried dissolved atmospheric gases (ammonia, methane, and hydrogen) and some minerals into the seas that formed. The seas became rich in these dissolved substances and minerals and are often described by biologists as having been a "hot, thin soup."

The primitive Earth provided an energy-rich environment. In addition to the heat, there was electrical energy in the form of lightning, radiation (x-rays and ultraviolet rays) from the sun, and radioactivity from rocks.

Synthesis of Organic Compounds

The large amount of available energy was the driving force for synthesis reactions on the primitive Earth. In these reactions, the inorganic raw materials in the seas became chemically bonded to form organic molecules, including simple sugars and amino acids. These organic molecules were the building blocks for the first life-forms.

The scientist Stanley Miller devised an apparatus in which he simulated the conditions thought to exist in the primitive environment. His experiments showed that in the presence of heat and electrical energy, dissolved gases could combine to form simple organic compounds.

Formation of Aggregates

In time, the simple organic molecules accumulated in the seas. Eventually, they combined in synthesis reactions to form more complex organic molecules. (Such interactions between organic molecules have been demonstrated in laboratories.) Some of the large, complex molecules formed groupings, or clusters, called *aggregates*. These aggregates developed a membrane that enclosed them, thus forming a barrier between themselves and the surrounding water. This made it possible for the substances inside an aggregate to remain separate from those in the surrounding water. It is thought that aggregates absorbed simple organic molecules from the environment for "food." Thus, they carried on a form of heterotrophic nutrition. Over time, the aggregates became more complex and highly organized. Eventually, they developed the ability to reproduce. At that point, when their ability to reproduce had evolved, the aggregates are considered to have been living cells.

Heterotrophs to Autotrophs

It is thought that these early heterotrophic life-forms carried on a form of anaerobic respiration, or *fermentation* (in which glucose is converted to energy and CO_2 without O_2 being present). As a result of very long periods of fermentation, carbon dioxide was added to the atmosphere. Eventually, as a result of evolution, some heterotrophic forms developed the capacity to use carbon dioxide from the atmosphere in the synthesis of organic compounds. These organisms became the first *autotrophs* (meaning "self-feeders"). Some bacteria are autotrophs, but most of the autotrophs alive today are green plants and algae.

Anaerobes to Aerobes

Autotrophic activity (photosynthesis) added oxygen molecules to the atmosphere. Over time, the capacity to use free oxygen in respiration (aerobic respiration) evolved in both autotrophs and heterotrophs.

There are both autotrophs and heterotrophs on Earth today. Some life-forms still carry on anaerobic respiration; but in most life-forms, respiration is aerobic. This is because aerobic respiration releases much more energy from food than does anaerobic respiration.

QUESTIONS
Part A

14. According to the heterotroph hypothesis, the first living things probably were anaerobic because their environment had no available (1) food (2) energy (3) water (4) oxygen

15. Which is one basic assumption of the heterotroph hypothesis? (1) More complex organisms appeared before less complex organisms. (2) Living organisms did not appear until there was oxygen in the atmosphere. (3) Large autotrophic organisms appeared before small photosynthesizing organisms. (4) Autotrophic activity added oxygen molecules to the environment.

16. The heterotroph hypothesis is an attempt to explain (1) how Earth was originally formed (2) why simple organisms usually evolve into complex organisms (3) why evolution occurs very slowly (4) how life originated on Earth

17. The heterotroph hypothesis states that heterotrophic life-forms appeared before autotrophic forms as the first living things. A major assumption for this hypothesis is that (1) sufficient heat was not available in the beginning for the food-making process (2) the heterotrophic organisms were able to use molecules from the sea as "food" (3) lightning and radiation energy were limited to terrestrial areas (4) moisture in liquid form was limited to aquatic areas

Base your answer to the following question on the chart below and on your knowledge of biology.

A	B	C
The diversity of multicellular organisms increases.	Simple, single-celled organisms appear.	Multicellular organisms begin to evolve.

18. According to most scientists, which sequence best represents the order of biological evolution on Earth? (1) $A \rightarrow B \rightarrow C$ (2) $B \rightarrow C \rightarrow A$ (3) $B \rightarrow A \rightarrow C$ (4) $C \rightarrow A \rightarrow B$

Part B-2

19. Identify the source of oxygen in Earth's early atmosphere; tell how this was important later to the evolution of life.

EVOLUTION BY NATURAL SELECTION

Darwin's Theory of Natural Selection

Darwin's theory was based on the presence of variations among members of a population and their interaction with the process he called **natural selection**. Darwin's theory includes the following main ideas.

Overpopulation: Within a population, there are more offspring produced in each generation than can possibly survive.

Competition: The natural resources, such as food, water, and space, available to a population are limited. Because there are more organisms produced in each generation than can survive, there must be *competition* among them for the resources needed for survival.

Survival of the fittest: Variations among members of a population make some of them better adapted to the environment than others. Such **variability** within populations means that, due to competition, the best-adapted individuals are most likely to survive.

Natural selection: The environment is the agent of natural selection, determining which adaptations or variations are helpful and which are harmful. For example, in an environment that is undergoing a particularly cold period, animals that have thicker fur than most other members of their population are more likely to survive. In this case, their variation—thicker fur—is helpful in terms of surviving the environmental pressure of colder temperature.

Reproduction: Individuals with useful variations tend to survive and reproduce at a higher rate than other members of their population, thus transmitting these **adaptations** to their offspring. Likewise, those individuals that do not have such favorable adaptations tend to die off within the population, so the less favorable traits are not passed on to future generations.

Speciation: The development of new species, a process called **speciation**, occurs as certain variations or adaptations accumulate in a population over many generations.

According to Darwin's theory, environmental pressures act as a force for the natural selection of the best-adapted individuals in a population—those with helpful adaptations that enable them to survive and reproduce successfully. However, Darwin's theory did not explain *how* variations arise in members of a species. (At Darwin's time—in the mid- to late 1800s—the scientific study of genes and mutations had not yet begun.) It is important to understand that *individuals* do not evolve; rather it is the *population* that evolves as the percentage of changes in its gene pool increases over time.

QUESTIONS
Part A

20. Darwin's theory of evolution did *not* contain the concept that (1) genetic variations are produced by mutations and sexual recombination (2) organisms that are best adapted to their environment survive (3) population sizes are limited due to the struggle for survival (4) favorable traits are passed from one generation to the next

21. Natural selection is best defined as (1) survival of the strongest organisms only (2) elimination of the smallest organisms by the largest organisms (3) survival of those organisms best adapted to their environment (4) reproduction of those organisms that occupy the largest area in an environment

22. Although similar in many respects, two species of organisms exhibit differences that make each one well adapted to the environment in which it lives. The process of change that helps account for these differences is (1) evolution by natural selection (2) parthenogenesis (3) comparative embryology (4) inheritance of acquired traits

23. A key idea in Darwin's theory of evolution is that members of a population (1) are always identical (2) compete for limited resources in the environment (3) all get to reproduce and pass on their traits (4) are all equally well adapted to the environment

24. A species that lacks the variation necessary to adapt to a changing environment is more likely to (1) develop many mutated cells (2) begin to reproduce sexually (3) become extinct over time (4) develop resistance to diseases

25. Which characteristics of a population would most likely indicate the lowest potential for evolutionary change in that population? (1) sexual reproduction and few mutations (2) sexual reproduction and many mutations (3) asexual reproduction and few mutations (4) asexual reproduction and many mutations

26. The theory of biological evolution includes the concept that (1) species of organisms found on Earth today have adaptations not always found in earlier species (2) fossils are the remains of present-day species and were all formed at the same time (3) individuals may acquire physical characteristics after birth and pass these acquired characteristics on to their offspring (4) the smallest organisms are always eliminated by the larger organisms within the ecosystem

27. The graph below shows the populations of two species of ants. Ants of species 2 have a thicker outer covering than the ants of species 1. The outer covering of an insect helps prevent excessive evaporation of water. Which statement would best explain the population changes shown in the graph? (1) The food sources for species 1 increased while the food sources for species 2 decreased from January through November. (2) Disease killed off species 1 beginning in May. (3) The weather was hotter and drier than normal from April through September. (4) Mutations occurred from April through September in both species, resulting in their both becoming better adapted to the environment.

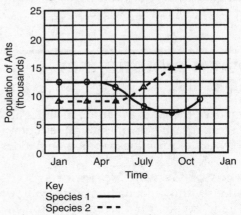

28. When a particular white moth lands on a white birch tree, its light color is beneficial, or *adaptive*, for survival. If the birch trees become covered with black soot, the white color of this particular moth in this environment would most likely (1) remain just as adaptive for survival (2) become more adaptive for survival (3) change to black immediately (4) become less adaptive for survival

29. The diversity of organisms present on Earth today is the result of (1) natural selection (2) homeostasis (3) ecosystem stability (4) selective breeding

30. In order for new species to develop, there *must* be a change in the (1) temperature of the environment (2) migration patterns within a population (3) genetic makeup of a population (4) rate of succession in the environment

31. The diagram below shows the evolution of some different species of flowers. Which statement about the species is correct? (1) Species *A, B, C,* and *D* came from different ancestors. (2) Species *C* evolved from species *B*. (3) Species *A, B,* and *C* can interbreed successfully. (4) Species *A* became extinct.

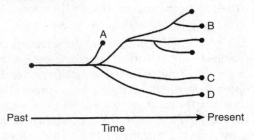

Past ——————————————→ Present
Time

32. State the four main ideas that make up Darwin's theory of evolution by natural selection.

33. Explain what is meant by "the environment is the agent of natural selection."

MODERN EVOLUTIONARY THEORY

The modern theory of evolution includes both Darwin's ideas of variation and natural selection and the genetic basis of variations within populations.

Sources of Genetic Variations
Variations within a population result from two kinds of genetic events. First, recombination of alleles during sexual reproduction is a source of variations. Second, random and spontaneous gene and chromosome mutations produce genetic variations. Mutations may arise spontaneously in organisms, or they may be caused by exposure to *mutagenic* (mutation-causing) chemicals or radiation, such as ultraviolet rays and x-rays. These variations provide the raw material for evolution within a population.

Natural Selection and Genetic Variation
Natural selection involves the struggle of organisms to survive and reproduce in a given environment. In order for natural selection to occur, the mutations in genes or chromosomes must have an effect on the phenotype (outward appearance or behavior) of an organism. This is because natural selection works by "choosing" favorable traits that are expressed. As a result, individuals having favorable **genetic variations** are more likely to survive, reproduce, and pass those traits on to future generations. If a genetic change results in a *silent mutation,* the variation is not expressed in the phenotype; natural selection cannot work on this type of mutation.

Favorable Variations. Favorable characteristics tend to increase in (genetic) frequency within a population. Favorable variations may include physical traits, such as larger muscles and increased speed, or behavioral traits, such as better food-finding or nest-building skills.

If environmental conditions change, traits that formerly had low survival value may come to have greater survival value. Likewise, traits that were favorable may no longer be so adaptive. The survival value of traits that had been neither helpful nor harmful may also change. In all of these cases, those traits that prove to be favorable under the new environmental conditions will increase in frequency within the population.

Unfavorable Variations. Unfavorable characteristics tend to decrease in frequency from generation to generation. Individuals with nonadaptive or unfavorable traits may be so severely selected against that, over time, populations that have unfavorable traits may become extinct. Indeed, the fossil record shows that extinction is a fairly common event, having been the fate of about 99 percent of all species that have ever existed on Earth.

Geographic Isolation
Changes in gene frequencies that lead to the development of a new species are more likely to occur in small populations than in large ones. Small groups may be segregated from the main population by

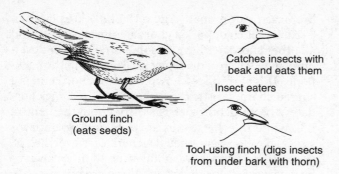

Ground finch
(eats seeds)

Catches insects with
beak and eats them

Insect eaters

Tool-using finch (digs insects
from under bark with thorn)

FIGURE 8-4 These Galápagos finches show a variety of adaptations for getting food in their particular environments.

a geographic barrier, such as a body of water or a mountain range. As a result of this *geographic isolation,* the small population cannot interbreed with the larger, main population. In time, the isolated population may evolve into a new species.

The following factors may be involved in the evolution of a new species: (a) the gene frequencies in the isolated population may already have been different from the gene frequencies in the main population, a difference known as the *founder effect*; (b) different mutations occur in the isolated population and the main population; and (c) different environmental factors exert different selection pressures on each population. Since there is no interbreeding between the two populations, any mutations that occur in one population cannot be transmitted to the other. Over long periods of time, the two populations may become so different that they will no longer be able to interbreed even if direct contact is made. In such a case, two new species have evolved from the one. An example of this is seen in the two populations of Grand Canyon squirrels: the Kaibab and the Abert's squirrel. These two squirrel populations were originally members of one species that became separated, over time, by the formation of the canyon. As a result of natural selection, the divided populations evolved to be the two different species that exist today.

Darwin observed the effect of geographic isolation among the finches he collected on the Galápagos Islands. Darwin hypothesized that the 14 different species he observed had evolved from a single species that had originally migrated to the islands from the mainland of South America. Over time, the different environments on the islands gradually resulted in the evolution of new separate species (Figure 8-4).

Reproductive Isolation

Geographic isolation may eventually lead to *reproductive isolation.* The isolated population becomes so different from the main population that members of the two groups cannot interbreed, even if

the geographic barriers were to be removed. When two populations can no longer interbreed and produce fertile offspring, they have become two distinct species.

Time Frame for Evolution

Although scientists generally agree on the basic factors involved in evolutionary change, there is some disagreement about the time frame in which such change occurs.

According to Darwin's original theory, evolutionary change occurs very gradually and continuously over the course of **geologic time** (millions of years). This theory, called *gradualism,* proposes that new species develop as a result of the gradual accumulation of small genetic variations that eventually, together, cause reproductive isolation and lead to speciation.

The more recent theory of *punctuated equilibrium* proposes that most species have long periods (several million years) of relative stability, or stasis, interrupted by geologically brief periods during which major changes occur, possibly leading to the evolution of new species (Figure 8-5). In this way, drastic environmental changes, for example, a global cooling event, could cause species to evolve—or become extinct.

In the fossil records of some evolutionary lineages, there are transitional forms that support the theory of gradualism. However, in many evolutionary lineages, there is an apparent lack of transitional forms, which better supports the theory of punctuated equilibrium.

Classification and Cladistics

Biologists classify organisms in order to better understand and study them. In the most commonly used *classification* system for grouping organisms, all living things are placed within the following six

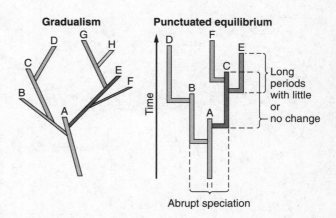

FIGURE 8-5 Two evolutionary processes: gradualism and punctuated equilibrium.

kingdoms: Archaebacteria, Eubacteria, Protists, Fungi, Plantae, and Animalia. Organisms are classified in a group according to their evolutionary relationships and shared characteristics. Similar organisms that are capable of breeding and producing fertile offspring with each other are placed in the smallest classification group, the *species*. Closely related species that most recently evolved from a common ancestor are placed in the same *genus,* and so on up to the most inclusive level, the *kingdom*. Some scientists also classify organisms within three major groups called *domains,* which are based on similarities at the cellular level. These domains are called Bacteria, Archaea, and Eukaryotes.

Cladistics is a tool or method of classifying used by evolutionary biologists to show relationships among these groups of organisms. In the past, organisms were grouped based on how they looked and when and where they lived. This model provided limited information on how the organisms may have been related to one another. In the cladistics model, scientists look for patterns or characteristics forming "nested groups" in which groups of organisms are placed within larger and larger categories. These groupings of organisms are referred to as *clades*. A clade consists of all the descendants of a common ancestor. That is, all organisms that are in the same clade share the same evolutionary features and also those of their ancestors. For example, the dinosaurs are placed in a clade called vertebrates because they and all other vertebrates share a common feature, namely the spinal column and

braincase. Additionally, the vertebrates are placed in a still larger clade called chordates because they and all other chordates have, at some time in their development, a stiff rod made of cartilage along the backbone. This stiff rod is known as a notochord and is a shared characteristic of all chordates. In some chordates, the notochord persists throughout their entire life, while in others, it exists only during embryological development, then degenerates. Nevertheless, possessing a notochord at any time signifies an evolutionary relationship among these organisms.

Currently, the cladistics model is the best method for reconstructing evolutionary relationships. It was developed in the 1960s by a German scientist named Willi Hennig. Cladistics differs from other models of classification in that it uses features called *shared derived characteristics* to look for relationships among organisms. The derived features are represented as branch points or nodes along the branches of a diagram called a **cladogram** (Figure 8-6). All organisms beyond a node point share that particular feature. Derived characteristics closest to the base of the cladogram are considered more primitive (evolved earliest), while those features farther out on the branches are considered to be "advanced" (evolved later). The cladogram illustrates all the advanced feaures the organisms have in common and how they are related to each other. Because the major evolutionary features are shown as branch points or nodes on the diagram, the clades extend outward from these nodes. Organisms on any given branch have the specific feature that evolved at that

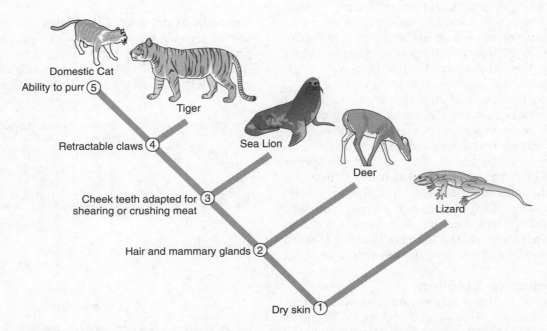

FIGURE 8-6 A cladogram showing evolutionary relationships among different organisms based on shared derived characteristics.

node plus all the features that preceded it; they can be traced back along the branches to their ancestors and thus reveal other evolutionary relationships. Organisms are more closely related when they share a multitude of derived evolutionary features.

The Dichotomous Key

Biologists have developed a precise method to help them classify and identify unknown organisms. This classification tool is called a **dichotomous key**, and it uses a logical step-by-step approach to classify an organism. Each dichotomous key is composed of a list of observable characteristics that leads, in a series of steps, to the correct identification of the organism. The term *dichotomous* refers to the fact that there are always *two* choices to pick from at every step of the key. At each step, one of the two descriptions is eliminated, which narrows the possibilities. For example, at some step in a key for identifying plants, there would be a choice between the types of structures used for reproduction, such as spores versus seeds, and then pinecones versus flowers. The key would also have choices based on whether the plant's stem is soft or woody; the type of leaf structure it possesses, and so on. In this way, an unknown plant can be identified.

Impact of Humans on Natural Selection

It has been found that some insects have a genetic mutation that makes them resistant to the effects of insecticides (the group of **pesticides** developed to kill insect pests). Before the widespread use of insecticides, this trait was of no particular survival value. With the increased use of insecticides, however, this trait developed a very high survival value. Because the insects that are resistant to insecticides have survived and reproduced, the frequency of insecticide resistance has increased greatly in insect populations.

Resistance to **antibiotics** (drugs that fight bacterial infections) in populations of bacteria has followed the same pattern. The frequency of resistant individuals in bacterial populations has increased with the increasing use of certain antibiotics.

It is important to note that resistance to insecticides and antibiotics did not arise as a result of exposure to these substances. The traits were already present in some members of the organisms' populations, and the insecticides and antibiotics simply acted as the selecting agents.

Humans and Artificial Selection

In nature, there is no particular direction in which each species must evolve. Over time, many variations appear within the populations of organisms, similar to the branching of twigs on a tree. Natural selection continuously "prunes" these branches, or lineages, eliminating those with unfavorable adaptations while letting those with favorable adaptations survive.

In contrast, humans can and do have an effect on the inheritance of traits in some populations of organisms. For example, human actions, such as pesticide use, have led to unexpected changes in the genetic makeup of some insect populations. Modern humans have intentionally altered the traits of many plant and animal species as well. In the process of domesticating organisms, people have selectively bred plants and animals for desired traits. In such cases, it is a person, not the environment, that is the selecting agent. Advances in biotechnology, or bioengineering techniques, have also had an impact on the genetic traits of some plant and animal populations.

34. A population of mosquitoes is sprayed with a new insecticide. Most of the mosquitoes are killed, but a few survive. In the next generation, the spraying continues, but still more mosquitoes hatch that are immune to the insecticide. How could these results be explained according to the present concept of evolution? (1) The insecticide caused a mutation in the mosquitoes. (2) The mosquitoes learned how to fight the insecticide. (3) A few mosquitoes in the first population were resistant and transmitted this resistance to their offspring. (4) The insecticide caused the mosquitoes to develop an immune response, which was inherited.

35. What would be the most likely effect of geographic isolation on a population? (1) It has no effect on variations in the species. (2) It favors the production of new species. (3) It prevents the occurrence of mutations. (4) It encourages the mixing of gene pools.

36. Two organisms can be considered to be of different species if they (1) cannot mate with each other and produce fertile offspring (2) live in two different geographical areas (3) mutate at different rates depending on their environment (4) have genes drawn from the same gene pool

37. Certain strains of bacteria that were susceptible to penicillin have now become resistant. The probable explanation for this is that (1) the gene mutation rate increased naturally (2) the strains needed to become resistant for survival (3) a mutation that gave some of them resistance was passed on to succeeding generations because it

had high survival value (4) the penicillin influenced the bacterial pattern of mating

38. The continents of Africa and South America were once a single landmass but have drifted apart over millions of years. The monkeys of both continents, although similar, show several genetic differences from each other. Which factor is probably the most important for causing and maintaining these differences? (1) fossil records (2) comparative anatomy (3) use and disuse (4) geographic isolation

39. When a species includes organisms with a wide variety of traits, it is most likely that this species will have (1) a high proportion of individuals immune to genetic diseases (2) a greater chance to survive if environmental conditions suddenly change (3) less success competing for resources (4) limitless supplies of important resources

40. Modern evolutionary biologists have accepted the main ideas of Darwin's theory of evolution but have added genetic information that gives a scientific explanation for (1) overproduction (2) the struggle for existence (3) the survival of the fittest (4) variations

41. As a result of sexual reproduction, the potential for evolutionary change in plants and animals is greatly increased because (1) the offspring show more variability than those from asexual reproduction (2) characteristics change less frequently than in asexual reproduction (3) environmental changes never affect organisms produced by asexual reproduction (4) two parents have fewer offspring than one parent

42. Populations of a species may develop traits that are different from each other if they are geographically isolated for sufficient lengths of time. The most likely explanation for these differences is that (1) acquired traits cannot be inherited by the offspring (2) the environmental conditions in the two areas are identical (3) mutations and selective forces will be different in the two populations (4) mutations will be the same in both populations

Part B-2

43. State how genetic variations and natural selection in a population can lead to the evolution of a new species.

44. How did Darwin explain the evolution of 14 finch species from one ancestral finch species? Use the terms *geographic isolation* and *reproductive isolation* in your answer.

Part C

Base your answers to questions 45 through 48 on the following information and data table.

A population of snails was living on a sandy beach. The snails' shells appeared in two colors: tan or black. The sand on the beach was a tan color. One day, a nearby volcano erupted, spewing out tons of ash and debris. The ash and debris coated the sand on the beach, blackening it. Biologists had kept careful records of the snail population before and after the volcanic eruption. Their data are presented in the table below.

Time	Number of Tan Snails	Number of Black Snails
Before volcano erupted	6000	50
After volcano erupted (one year later)	400	3000

45. Explain why the numbers of tan snails and black snails changed.

46. How does this event support the idea of evolution by natural selection?

47. Give one reason why the tan snails might disappear within a few years.

48. Using the data in the preceding table, prepare a bar graph that shows the information on snail populations before and after the volcanic eruption.

49. A species of wildflower grows in a meadow. The flowers are of two color varieties: yellow and purple. There are about equal numbers of yellow flowers and purple flowers. A biologist observes that bees frequently visit the yellow flowers but seldom go to the purple ones.

Use the above data and your knowledge of biology to write a brief experimental procedure that addresses the following:

- a question prompted by the information given
- a hypothesis that addresses your question
- a brief experimental procedure that could be used to test your hypothesis
- a description of the main selecting force on the flowers in this meadow
- a prediction of what may happen to this population of wildflowers in 50 years

50. Describe how the continued widespread use of antibiotics may result in the evolution of more resistant strains of bacteria. How does the antibiotic act as a selecting agent? How does this illustrate the concept of natural selection?

HUMAN EVOLUTION

Humans, like all other organisms on Earth, have an evolutionary history. In fact, there was a time in Earth's geologic history when humans did not even exist on the planet. As a group, humans are a relatively recent arrival, having been on Earth for less than 1/1000 of its existence. As noted earlier, Earth is more than four billion years old (4.6×10^9), and the earliest known **hominids** (humans and humanlike ancestors) date back over four million years (4.4×10^6). A common misconception about human evolution is that people evolved from apes such as chimpanzees. This is incorrect. Humans and chimpanzees share a *common ancestor.* The ape lineage that gave rise to modern chimps and humans diverged (split apart) between six and eight million years ago. Thus, the chimpanzee is not an ancestor but rather the closest living relative of modern humans.

In 2009, scientists announced the discovery of an early humanlike fossil they named *Ardipithecus ramidus.* This fossil dates back to 4.4 million years and is, at present, the oldest known hominid fossil. This ancient human ancestor lived in what is present-day Ethiopia. Because the anatomy of this hominid is quite distinct from that of chimpanzees and other apes, it reinforces the concept that humans and apes diverged a very long time ago and evolved separately from one another. Prior to the discovery of *A. ramidus,* the distinction of being the oldest known human ancestor belonged to a fossil named "Lucy" (*Australopithecus afarensis*), discovered in 1974 by paleoanthropologist Donald Johanson of Arizona State University. Lucy has some traits similar to apes but also has a number of clearly human characteristics, such as bone structure that suggests an upright, or bipedal, posture. Lucy dates back about 3.2 million years. Although the australopithecines were important ancestral hominids, all of them eventually became extinct some 1.5 to 2 million years ago.

Early Human Species

Important early human ancestors include *Homo habilis,* which lived about 1.75 million years ago and used primitive stone tools, and its descendant *Homo erectus,* a fully bipedal hominid that lived about 1.5 million years ago. *Homo erectus* had a large brain and used more advanced stone tools, lived in caves, wore clothes, and used fire. A well-known human ancestor is *Homo neanderthalensis* (Neanderthals), which lived between 400,000 and 30,000 years ago (Figure 8-7). These early humans spread across Europe, Russia, and western Asia. They had large braincases and a heavy build. Fossil evidence found at archaeological sites suggests that Neanderthals also used a variety of tools, wore clothing, used fire, and buried their dead. *Homo neanderthalensis* lived simultaneously

FIGURE 8-7 A drawing of how a Neanderthal might have looked. Note that Neanderthals wore clothes and used tools.

alongside the ancestors of modern humans, *Homo sapiens,* for more than 100,000 years. It is not entirely clear why *H. neanderthalensis* became extinct, but it is generally thought that they could not compete with the better adapted *H. sapiens.* There is also the possibility that some interbreeding occurred between Neanderthals and early modern humans, known as Cro-Magnons.

Homo sapiens is the species that comprises Cro-Magnons and modern humans. In fact, the anatomy of the Cro-Magnons and of modern humans is essentially identical. *H. sapiens* evolved about 200,000 years ago, most probably in Africa and then spread out to other parts of the world. Early members of this species wore clothing, used fire, made sophisticated tools, and produced beautiful cave paintings. The only surviving species of humans on Earth is *Homo sapiens.* Most scientists think that we continue to evolve, since evolution is not a static process. For example, *H. sapiens* has shown a 10 percent decrease in average body mass over the past 50,000 years and our teeth and chewing muscles have become smaller.

QUESTIONS
Part A

51. Humans and chimpanzees share a common ancestor that was (1) a type of chimp (2) a type of ape (3) a Neanderthal (4) an australopithecine

52. The ancestors of chimps and humans diverged between (1) one and two million years ago

(2) three and five million years ago (3) six and eight million years ago (4) 10 and 12 million years ago

53. The fossil named Lucy has a bone structure that indicates it (1) had a large brain (2) had an upright posture (3) made stone tools (4) lived in trees

54. Which is the correct hominid sequence in terms of fossil age? (1) *A. ramidus, A. afarensis, H. habilis, H. erectus* (2) *A. afarensis, A. ramidus, H. habilis, H. erectus* (3) *A. afarensis, H. habilis, A. ramidus, H. erectus* (4) *A. ramidus, H. erectus, A. afarensis, H. habilis*

55. *Homo habilis* is important because it is thought to have (1) worn clothes (2) used stone tools (3) lived in caves (4) had a large brain

56. The hominid that is thought to have first used fire was (1) *A. ramidus* (2) *H. habilis* (3) *A. afarensis* (4) *H. erectus*

57. The human ancestor that had a large braincase and a heavy build was (1) *H. habilis* (2) *H. erectus* (3) *H. sapiens* (4) *H. neanderthalensis*

58. The anatomy of modern humans is essentially identical to that of the (1) ancestral apes (2) australopithecines (3) Cro-Magnons (4) Neanderthals

59. Modern humans evolved in (1) Europe and spread to Asia (2) Asia and spread to Europe (3) Africa and spread to Europe and Asia (4) Asia and Europe and spread to Africa

Part B-2

60. Compare the features and behaviors of *Homo erectus* with those of the Neanderthals. How were they similar and how were they different?

Part C

61. You and a friend are discussing human evolution. Your friend insists he has been told that humans arose directly from chimpanzees. You disagree with your friend's concept of human evolution. Present an argument to help your friend obtain a better understanding of human evolution and the origins of humans as a species. Your answer must include references to both humans and apes.

62. Some major advances made by ancient humans included the use of fire, the making and use of tools, and the wearing of clothing. Select *two* of these advances and explain how each one played a role in helping early humans survive.

LITERACY SKILL: READING FOR COMPREHENSION

Base your answers to questions 63 through 66 on the information below and on your knowledge of biology. Source: Science News *(January 15, 2011): vol. 179, no. 2, p. 16. Reprinted with permission of* Science News.

African Elephants Are Two Species: Forest and Savanna Dwellers Prove Distinct in Gene Analysis

Forest-dwelling African elephants are a separate species from Africa's savanna elephants, a genetic analysis shows. The research, published December 21 in *PLoS Biology*, "does a very thorough job of nailing shut the coffin on some of the more heretical theories" about elephant evolution, says Stephen O'Brien, a geneticist at the National Cancer Institute in Frederick, Md., who was not involved in the research.

Forest and savanna elephants evolved into different species from a common ancestor between 2.6 and 5.6 million years ago, the new analysis reveals. Forest elephants are smaller, with more rounded ears and straighter tusks.

In the study, researchers compared nuclear DNA from living elephants as well as from a 43,000-year-old woolly mammoth bone from Siberia and from a 50,000- to 130,000-year-old North American mastodon tooth. The African forest and savanna groups are at least as different as Asian elephants and mammoths, the researchers say.

"I've always argued that they are very different, but that level of difference surprised me," says study coauthor Alfred Roca, a conservation geneticist at the University of Illinois at Urbana-Champaign.

People have debated for a long time whether the big savanna elephants and smaller forest elephants belong to one or two species. "This has been an ongoing debate since before genetics began," Roca says.

The two pachyderms look different but sometimes come together and breed, producing hybrids. Hybrid males are sterile, but females can breed.

The study may not be the final word on the number of elephant species, but many researchers say it is convincing. "It's hard not to agree with this overwhelming amount of genetic data that gives such clear-cut answers," comments Sergios-Orestis Kolokotronis, a conservation geneticist at the American Museum of Natural History in New York City.

63. State three physical differences between forest and savanna elephants.

64. How did the researchers determine that the two groups of elephants belong to two different species?

65. Forest and savanna elephants evolved from a common ancestor about 2.6 to 5.6 million years ago. Speculate on how the two species may have diverged (separated).

66. How is a hybrid elephant produced? Compare and contrast a male hybrid elephant and a female hybrid elephant in terms of reproductive ability.

Humans and the Environment

Humans, more than any other organisms, have the capacity to change the environment. Some human activities have a negative effect on the environment, while other activities have a positive effect. Many other living things can make changes to their environment in order to ensure their survival, such as beavers building dams. Yet no creature can make the dramatic, large-scale changes that humans can, and these changes usually have an effect on other organisms as well.

PEOPLE AFFECT THE ENVIRONMENT

Some human activities have upset the natural balance of ecosystems. These activities have brought about undesirable and lasting changes in one or more of the biotic or abiotic factors in some ecosystems, harming humans and other living things.

Human Population Growth. The human population of Earth is increasing at a rapid rate (Figure 9-1). A major factor in this increase involves medical advances that have increased human survival rates and the average life span. In most parts of the world, population growth is no longer limited by disease to the extent that it was in the past. However, in many places, the population has grown faster than the food-producing capacity, resulting in hunger and starvation. In addition, as the human population grows, more people move into and alter wilderness areas, resulting in a loss of natural habitat for wildlife.

Human Activities. Some human activities have led to the endangerment or extinction of numerous species of plants and animals and also have produced less

favorable living conditions for many species. Such activities include overhunting, importation of organisms, exploitation of wild organisms, poor land-use practices, and technological oversights.

Uncontrolled hunting, fishing, and trapping, which still occur in many parts of the world, have resulted in the extinction of some species and the endangerment of others. Several vertebrate species, such as the passenger pigeon and Steller's sea cow, have been hunted to extinction already; hundreds of other animals are currently listed as threatened or endangered as a result of such human activities.

Humans have both accidentally and intentionally imported species into areas where they have no natural enemies or competition. These imported organisms have increased in numbers, leading to the disruption of existing ecosystems. Imported organisms, or **invasive species**, that have caused serious

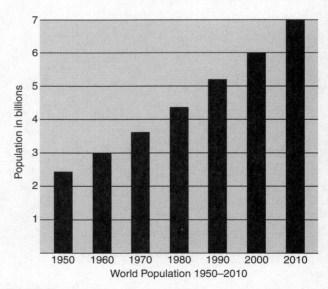

FIGURE 9-1 Human population growth over the past 60 years.

damage include the Japanese beetle, gypsy moth, zebra mussel, and various plant species, such as the purple loosestrife. This plant thrives in the wild because few animals eat it, and it outcompetes native plant species, resulting in a loss of biodiversity.

People have exploited plants and animals for their own use for centuries, often with negative impacts on wild populations. For example, the extensive cutting down, or **deforestation**, of tropical rain forests has led to habitat loss for wildlife and erosion of topsoil; elephants and walrus have been overhunted for their ivory tusks; tropical parrots and monkeys have been captured and sold as pets.

The increased building of cities and suburbs has reduced the amount of farmland and natural habitats, threatening the existence of various native plant and animal species. Overgrazing and poor agricultural practices have caused valuable soil nutrients and topsoil to be lost, or **depleted**.

Some technological developments have contributed to the pollution of air, land, and water. In many areas, chemical wastes from homes, factories, and farmlands have polluted the water. Major chemical wastes include phosphates, heavy metals, and PCBs (an industrial by-product). Radioactive materials have been dumped or have leaked into the water supply from factories and waste-storage areas. Such chemical and radioactive wastes are **toxins** that can cause harm to people and wildlife alike.

The increased temperature, or *thermal pollution*, of river water occurs when water is taken from a river and used for cooling in factories and then returned to the waterway. Untreated sewage, which contains harmful bacteria, has been dumped into rivers and oceans. Water pollutants have killed fish and other animals, as well as plant life.

Global Warming. Exhaust gases from the burning of fossil fuels in factories, automobiles, and other places have polluted the air. The major air pollutants include carbon dioxide, carbon monoxide, hydrocarbons, and particulate matter. The increasing levels of carbon dioxide and other greenhouse gases in the atmosphere have been linked to **global warming** trends. (The destruction of rain forests also adds to an increase in atmospheric carbon dioxide, because there are fewer trees taking in the gas.)

Climate data over the last few decades indicate that the global average (mean) temperature has been increasing. The amount of ice cover at the poles has shown some evidence of decreasing coverage, and some glaciers in colder regions have shrunk in size. Many scientists think that human activities are greatly accelerating the warming of the planet, called the **greenhouse effect**. Some of the negative impacts may include sea-level rise, flooding of coastal cities, and extinction of species not able to adapt quickly enough to the warming temperatures. Among the possible reasons cited for rising temperatures worldwide is an increase in the greenhouse gases such as carbon dioxide. Some scientists and environmentalists claim that an increase in these gases tends to hold heat in Earth's atmosphere. These gases accumulate in the atmosphere as a result of human activities such as burning of fossil fuels, but they are also produced as a result of natural processes such as respiration and volcanic activity.

There are also some scientists who disagree with the idea that people have caused global warming because there is not enough scientific evidence to support it as a theory. They believe that the increase in global temperatures is merely due to natural cyclic changes in Earth's climate patterns. As evidence, they cite the fact that during its long history, Earth has undergone many cycles of warming and then cooling as a by-product of naturally occurring events. For example, the last Ice Age was caused not by any human activities but by a decrease in the total amount of solar energy reaching Earth. The idea of global warming remains a very controversial topic today with scientists and environmentalists on both sides of the issue.

Other Pollutants. Compounds used in aerosol sprays have weakened Earth's **ozone shield**, allowing more ultraviolet radiation to penetrate the atmosphere, causing harm to both plants and animals. Nitrogen oxides and sulfur dioxides are gaseous pollutants that combine with water vapor in the atmosphere, forming acids (Figure 9-2 on page 132). Precipitation of these acids, called *acid rain,* kills plants and lowers the pH of lakes and ponds, thereby harming and killing aquatic wildlife.

Several *biocides* (pesticides and herbicides) that are used to kill insects and to prevent the growth of weeds have had negative effects on the environment. Biocides have contaminated the soil, air, and water supplies. The **residue**, or chemical remains, of their use has also entered food chains and caused harm to some organisms, thereby disrupting whole food webs. For example, the pesticide DDT was linked to reproductive failure and subsequent population decrease among bald eagles and peregrine falcons. Its use has been banned in the United States, and eagle and falcon populations are now on the increase.

Technological developments have resulted in the increased production of solid, chemical, and nuclear wastes. Disposal of these wastes, many of them highly toxic, is a major problem. In addition, disposal of household garbage is becoming a problem, as more landfills are filled to capacity and shut down.

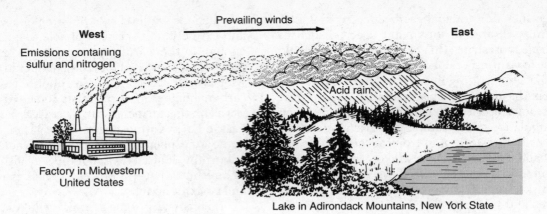

West   Prevailing winds   East

Emissions containing
sulfur and nitrogen

Acid rain

Factory in Midwestern
United States

Lake in Adirondack Mountains, New York State

FIGURE 9-2 Nitrogen oxides and sulfur dioxides combine with water vapor in the atmosphere, forming acid rain.

QUESTIONS
Part A

1. An increased burning of coal would cause additional tons of sulfur dioxide to be released into the atmosphere, which could increase environmental problems associated with (1) acid rain (2) PCBs (3) DDT (4) dioxin

2. One possible reason for the rise in the average air temperature at Earth's surface is that (1) decomposers are being destroyed (2) deforestation has increased the levels of oxygen in the atmosphere (3) industrialization has increased the amount of carbon dioxide in the air (4) growing crops is depleting the ozone shield

3. Recent evidence indicates that lakes in large areas of upstate New York are being affected by acid rain. The major effect of acid rain in these lakes is the (1) increase in game fish population levels (2) stimulation of a rapid rate of evolution (3) elimination of various species of aquatic wildlife (4) increase in local agricultural productivity

4. Compared to other organisms, humans have had the greatest ecological effect on the biosphere due to their (1) internal bony skeleton (2) homeostatic regulation of metabolism (3) adaptations for respiration (4) ability to modify the environment

5. The rapid increase in the human population over the past few hundred years has been due mainly to (1) increasing levels of air and water pollution (2) depletion of topsoil from farmable lands (3) medical advances that increase survival rates (4) increasing resistance levels of insect species

6. When plant and animal species are introduced into a new area, they often become pests in the new habitat, even though they were not pests in their native habitats. The most probable reason for this is that in their new habitat they (1) have fewer natural enemies (2) have a much lower mutation rate (3) develop better resistance to the new climate (4) learn to use different foods

7. Recent studies have found traces of the insecticide DDT accumulated in the fat tissue of many wild animals. A correct explanation for this accumulation is that (1) fat tissue absorbs DDT directly from the air (2) fat tissue cells secrete DDT (3) DDT is needed for proper metabolic functioning (4) DDT is passed along in many food chains

8. Which factor is considered a major cause of global warming? (1) increased burning of fuels (2) increased number of green plants (3) decreased mineral availability (4) decreased carbon dioxide in the atmosphere

9. If humans remove carnivores such as wolves and coyotes from an ecosystem, what will probably be the first noticeable result? (1) The natural prey will die off. (2) Certain plant populations will increase. (3) Certain herbivores will exceed carrying capacity. (4) The decomposers will fill the predator niche.

10. Many farmers plant corn and then harvest the entire plant at the end of the growing season. One negative effect of this action is that (1) soil minerals used by the corn plants are not recycled (2) corn plants remove acidic compounds from the air all season long (3) corn plants may replace renewable sources of energy (4) large quantities of water are produced by the corn plants

11. The Susquehanna River, which runs through the states of New York, Pennsylvania, and Maryland, received the designation "America's Most Endangered River" in 2005. One of the river's problems results from the large number of sewage overflow

sites that are found along the course of the river. These sewage overflow sites are a direct result of an increase in (1) global warming (2) human population (3) recycling programs (4) atmospheric changes

12. One environmental problem caused by the use of nuclear power as an energy source is the (1) destruction of the ozone shield (2) disposal of toxic wastes (3) production of acid rain (4) accumulation of CO_2 in the atmosphere

13. The importation of organisms such as the Japanese beetle and gypsy moth to areas where they have no natural enemies best illustrates (1) the use of abiotic factors to reduce pest species (2) the selection of species to mate with each other to produce a new variety (3) attempts by humans to protect rare species (4) a human activity that disrupts existing native ecosystems

Part B-2

14. A farmer has been growing only corn in his fields for several years. Each year the corn stalks were cut off near the ground and processed as food for cattle. The farmer observed that with each passing year, corn production in his fields decreased. Explain why removing the dead corn stalks reduced corn production in these fields.

Base your answers to questions 15 through 17 on the following information and on your knowledge of biology.

A group of ranchers was very concerned about a local wolf population that they thought was preying on their livestock. After several attempts, they persuaded a court to authorize a hunt in order to eliminate the wolf population in their area. The court set a quota of 200 wolves, to be eliminated over the course of six months.

15. State a negative effect that the removal of these wolves might have on the habitat.

16. How would this hunt affect the biodiversity of the area's natural ecosystem?

17. Suppose that you are a local environmental official in the area. Propose a plan that would preserve the wolves yet keep them away from the ranchers' livestock.

Part C

Base your answers to questions 18 and 19 on the following information and graph.

Reducing toxic chemicals released into the environment often requires laws. When making

decisions about whether to support the passing of such laws, individuals must weigh the benefits against the potential risks if the law is not passed.

The amounts of toxic chemicals released into the environment of New York State over a ten-year period are shown in the graph below.

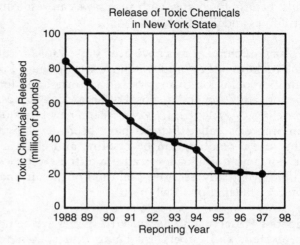

18. State one possible negative effect of passing a law to reduce the release of toxic chemicals.

19. State one possible explanation for why the amount of toxic chemicals released remained relatively constant between 1995 and 1997.

PEOPLE PROTECT THE ENVIRONMENT

People are becoming increasingly aware of the negative effects of some of their activities on the environment. As a result, they are making many efforts to correct past damage and avoid future harmful effects.

Population Control. Methods for limiting the high rate of human population growth have been, and continue to be, developed. For example, in some countries, policies have been adopted to limit family size. Also, many people make their own choice to limit the number of offspring they have by using birth-control methods to prevent conception. In many communities, professional organizations such as Planned Parenthood assist people in deciding how large a family to have.

Conservation of Resources. Measures have been taken to conserve water, fossil fuels (oil, coal, and natural gas), and other natural resources (such as trees and wildlife). Reforestation projects help prevent further loss of trees. This is good for the environment because trees hold topsoil in place and take in excess carbon dioxide from the atmosphere.

Planting of cover crops helps conserve topsoil, too. People are now realizing the economic and environmental benefits of recycling various materials, such as paper, metals, glass, and plastic. Most cities have enacted laws to make people recycle household items that used to be thrown away and dumped into landfills. Failure to comply with such laws can result in stiff fines and penalties.

Pollution Control. Laws have been passed to control the pollution of air and water. New techniques for limiting pollution from cars and factories, and for better sanitation and disposal of hazardous wastes, have been developed. In recent years, new types of automobiles called *hybrids* have been developed that use a combination of gasoline and electricity for power. The widespread use of these vehicles could eventually decrease pollution of the air and our dependence on fossil fuels.

Species Preservation. *Endangered species* are being protected, and efforts are being undertaken to increase their populations in the wild and in captivity. This is accomplished through captive-breeding programs, protection of wild habitats, and the establishment of wildlife refuges and national parks. Management of various forms of wildlife also includes laws that regulate hunting and fishing.

Examples of animals that are, or were, endangered but are now increasing in numbers include the American bison, alligator, whooping crane, fur seal, and bald eagle (Figure 9-3). However, the future of many species is still very much in doubt.

FIGURE 9-3 Bald eagle populations are now on the increase due to protective measures.

Biological Control. Biological control of insect pests reduces the need for chemical pesticides. One method of biological control involves the use of sex hormones to attract and trap insect pests. Another method of biological control involves the use of natural parasites that kill harmful insects. Biological control methods are less likely than chemical methods to affect species that are beneficial to humans, disrupt food webs, or contaminate the land.

The Green Revolution. In recent years, people have become much more aware of the negative impact we have had on our environment. As a result, many people have decided to take real action to preserve the environment for the present and future generations. These ideas and activities have come to be known as "thinking green." Some examples of the ways people are helping to preserve the environment and possibly reverse some of the harm already caused include the following:

- The growing use of hybrid vehicles, which greatly reduce gasoline consumption by utilizing a combination of electricity and gasoline.

- The use of organic food, which is grown without using any chemicals or pesticides that might ultimately end up in the environment as pollutants.

- Carrying reusable bags to the grocery store instead of taking plastic or paper bags from the store. These reuseable bags are themselves made from recycled materials. It is estimated that every reuseable bag saves about 100 plastic grocery bags from ending up in landfills.

- Extension of exisiting recycling laws to include used oil and electronic devices such as cell phones, computers, and rechargeable batteries. Businesses that sell these items are mandated by law to accept them back for recycling.

- Gradually replacing standard incandescent light-bulbs with more energy-efficient CFL (compact fluorescent lamp) bulbs. In fact, incandescent bulbs will eventually be totally phased out of manufacturing, beginning with the 100-watt bulb. The CFLs use much less electricity and can last up to ten times longer than incandescent bulbs.

- Efforts by manufacturers to use less material in packaging goods for sale. For example, water bottles are being made using much less plastic than in previous years.

- Energy Star-rated appliances, which are designed to run efficiently using much less electricity.

- The increasing introduction of consumer goods manufactured from recyled materials.

The Future

A greater awareness of ecological principles and careful use of energy and other natural resources will help to ensure a suitable environment for future generations. There are many environmental organizations that are involved in the effort to conserve wilderness areas, protect threatened and endangered species, and reduce environmental pollution. It is the responsibility of every person who can, to try to help in the preservation of the planet—for now and for the future.

QUESTIONS
Part A

20. Which accomplishment by people has had the most positive ecological effect on the environment? (1) the importation of organisms such as the starling and Japanese beetle into the United States (2) reforestation efforts and planting of cover crops to prevent soil erosion (3) the extinction or near extinction of many predators to protect prey animals (4) the use of pesticides and other chemical compounds to reduce the insect population

21. When a garden became infested with a large population of aphids, some ladybird beetles were introduced into the community as predators on the aphids. The resultant decrease in the aphid population was due to (1) biological control (2) parthenogenesis (3) vegetative propagation (4) chemical control

22. Gypsy moth infestations in rural areas of New York State may pose a potentially serious threat to many forested areas. Which would probably be the most ecologically sound method of gypsy moth control? (1) widespread application of DDT (2) introduction of a biological control (3) removal of its forest habitat (4) contamination of its food sources

23. Which illustrates the human population's increased understanding of, and concern for, ecological interrelationships? (1) importing organisms in order to disrupt existing ecosystems (2) allowing the air to be polluted only by those industries that promote technology (3) removing natural resources from Earth at a rate equal to or greater than the needs of an increasing population (4) developing wildlife game laws that limit the number of organisms that may be hunted each year

24. Some homeowners mow their lawns during the summer, collect the cut grass, then dispose of it in a landfill. Instead of taking the cuttings to a landfill, it might be better for the environment if they (1) left the cuttings to decompose in the lawn and form materials that enrich the soil (2) sprayed the cuttings in the lawn with imported microbes that use them for food (3) burned the cuttings and added the ashes to the soil (4) threw the cuttings into a stream or river to provide extra food for organisms living there

25. In most states, automobiles must be inspected every year to make sure that the exhaust fumes they emit do not contain high levels of pollutants such as carbon monoxide. This process is a way humans attempt to (1) control the water cycle (2) recycle nutrients from one ecosystem to another (3) control energy flow in natural ecosystems (4) maintain the quality of the atmosphere

26. The ivory-billed woodpecker, long thought to be extinct, was recently reported to be living in a southern swamp area. The most ecologically appropriate way to ensure the natural survival of this potential population of birds is to (1) feed them daily with corn and other types of grain (2) destroy their natural enemies and predators (3) move the population of birds to a zoo (4) limit human activities in the habitat of the bird

Part B-2

27. State two positive and two negative effects that humans have had on the natural environment.

28. Describe two benefits of recycling materials rather than throwing them away. In your response, be sure to discuss the
    • effect on the environment
    • costs involved
    • effect on people

Part C

29. Carbon dioxide is known to be a greenhouse gas that contributes to global warming. Due largely to human activity, such as the burning of fossil fuels, the amount of carbon dioxide in the atmosphere continues to increase significantly. Discuss how planting more trees could help reduce the amount of carbon dioxide in the atmosphere. How might this slow down the rate of global warming?

30. Tropical rain forests around the world are being cleared at an alarming rate to make room for the increasing human population and its needs.

Describe two reasons why the remaining tropical forests must be preserved. Suggest a plan by which people might be able to both protect and utilize tropical rain forests in a way that is sustainable.

31. The graph below shows the percentage of solid wastes recycled in New York State between 1987 and 1997. Discuss the effects of recycling. In your answer be sure to state:

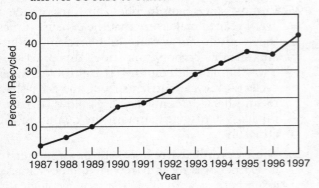

- what recycling is and give *one* example of a material that is often recycled
- *one* specific positive effect that recycling has on the environment
- *one* specific reason the percentage of solid wastes recycled increased between 1987 and 1997

32. Human activities continue to place strains on the environment. One of these strains is the loss of biodiversity. Explain what this problem is, and describe some ways that humans are involved in both the problem and the possible solutions. In your answer be sure to state:
- the meaning of the term *biodiversity*
- *one* negative effect on humans if biodiversity continues to be lost
- *one* practice that could be used to preserve biodiversity in New York State

33. Explain how replacing all the incandescent bulbs in a house or school with CFL bulbs can have a positive impact on the environment. Give two reasons to support your response.

34. Evaluate the truth of this statement and give a reason for your answer: Many people do not take the time to be bothered with protecting the environment because they do not fully understand how their actions impact the natural world.

35. Suppose grocery stores and supermarkets began charging a nickel for every plastic or paper bag used by customers to package their groceries. How might this affect people's decision to bring reusable bags with them when they shop? Would you support this policy? Explain your answer.

LITERACY SKILL: READING FOR COMPREHENSION

Base your answers to questions 36 through 39 on the information below and on your knowledge of biology. Source: Science News (May 7, 2011): vol. 179, no. 10, p. 11. Reprinted with permission of Science News.

How the Moth Lost Its Speckles: Tracing the Genetic Roots of a Classic Evolutionary Tale

The molecular mechanics behind an example of evolution dating back to Darwin's time may soon be revealed.

As soot from coal-fired factories blackened trees and buildings in 19th-century England, naturalists noted that peppered moths in polluted regions blended in by sporting a sleek, all-black look known as the *carbonaria* form instead of the usual lightly speckled wings. Within a few decades the black moths made up 90 percent or more of the population in urban areas.

Now, researchers led by Ilik Saccheri, a geneticist at the University of Liverpool in England, report online April 14 in *Science* that they have traced the mutation responsible for the funereal look to one region of a chromosome that in butterflies contains genetic instructions for creating color patterns. This region is an adaptation hot spot, where mutations produce hundreds of different wing color patterns in many species.

"Presumably it takes hundreds of genes to make a wing pattern," says Robert D. Reed of the University of California, Irvine. "So why does this [relatively small] region appear over and over again?"

No one has found the precise DNA changes that lead to the many different color patterns, but scientists are scouring the region.

Likewise, Saccheri and his colleagues don't yet know the exact nature of the *carbonaria* mutation. They do know that black moths collected from 80 sites in the United Kingdom share some key genetic signposts, suggesting that the *carbonaria* mutation involves only one spot in the genome and happened just once, probably shortly before the first reported sightings in 1848 near Manchester.

36. Describe what caused the population of black peppered moths to rise dramatically in urban areas of 19th-century England. What role did humans play in this event?

37. Where have scientists located the mutation that caused the black wing color in moths?

38. Why is this gene locus (location) called an "adaptation hot spot"?

39. What evidence suggests that the mutation involves only one genome locus and probably occurred only once?

10 Laboratory Skills and Part D Labs

As part of the Living Environment course, students are expected to master a number of specific science-related skills. Some of these skills involve application of the scientific method, while others are actual laboratory techniques and procedures.

Skills Using the Scientific Method

- Formulate a question or define a problem for investigation, and develop a hypothesis to be tested in an investigation.
- Distinguish between controls and variables in an experiment.
- Collect, organize, and graph data.
- Make predictions based on experimental data.
- Formulate generalizations or conclusions based on the investigation.
- Apply the conclusion to other experimental situations.

Skills Involving Laboratory Procedures

- Given a laboratory problem, select suitable lab materials, safety equipment, and appropriate observation methods.
- Demonstrate safety skills in heating materials in test tubes or beakers, using of chemicals, and handling dissection equipment.
- Identify the parts of a compound light microscope and their functions. Use the microscope correctly under low power and high power.
- Determine the size of microscopic specimens in micrometers.
- Prepare wet mounts of plant and animal cells and apply stains, including iodine and methylene blue.
- With the use of a compound light microscope, identify cell parts, including the nucleus, cytoplasm, chloroplasts, and cell walls.
- Use indicators, such as pH paper, Benedict solution (or Fehling solution), iodine solution (or Lugol solution), and bromthymol blue. Interpret changes shown by the indicators.
- Use measurement instruments, such as metric rulers, Celsius thermometers, and graduated cylinders.
- Dissect plant or animal specimens, exposing major structures for examination.

THE SCIENTIFIC METHOD

Defining a Problem and Developing a Hypothesis. Scientists do research to answer a question or to solve a problem. The first step in planning a research project is to define the problem to be solved; this is usually stated in the form of a question. The next step is to develop a possible solution to the problem. This proposed explanation, or *hypothesis,* is the statement that identifies the factor to be tested in the experiment.

For example, a scientist interested in studying the enzyme amylase might want to measure the rate of enzyme action at various temperatures. The basic hypothesis for such an experiment would be that the rate at which amylase hydrolyzes, or breaks down, starch is affected by temperature.

Designing and Conducting an Experiment. Biologists use controlled experiments when doing research. In a controlled experiment, there are two setups: an experimental setup and a control setup. The experimental and control setups are identical except for the single factor, or *variable,* that is being tested. Any changes observed during the experiment can then be explained in terms of the variable factor. In an experiment to determine the effect of temperature on the rate of action of the enzyme amylase, temperature is the variable.

A basic controlled experiment would use two setups—one containing a starch solution only, the other containing exactly the same amount of the same starch solution plus the enzyme amylase. Both setups would then be tested at various temperatures to determine how much starch had undergone hydrolysis. The setup with no enzyme is the control; the setup with the enzyme is the experimental one. The control can show that no hydrolysis occurs without the enzyme. In the experimental setup, all conditions are kept constant except temperature. Thus, the scientist knows that changes in the rate of hydrolysis are caused by the effects of temperature on the enzyme amylase.

Temperature (°C)	Grams of starch hydrolyzed per minute
0	0.0
10	0.2
20	0.4
30	0.8
40	1.0
50	0.3
60	0.2

FIGURE 10-1 A data table.

Collecting, Organizing, and Graphing Data.

During an experiment, the scientist collects data. These data are the results of the experiment. The data may be recorded in a log in the form of a diagram or data table. Sometimes the results are plotted on a graph. Scientists also use computers to record and organize experimental results.

In an experiment to determine the rate of action of amylase at various temperatures, the data collected might be written in a table, as shown in Figure 10-1.

The relationship between two varying factors can also be shown clearly on a line graph. The graph in Figure 10-2 shows the same information as the data table in Figure 10-1.

Making Predictions Based on Experimental Data.

Scientists may make predictions based on experimental data. The validity of these predictions can then be tested by further experimentation.

For example, on the basis of the data shown in Figure 10-1, a scientist might predict that the number of grams of starch hydrolyzed at normal body temperature (37°C) would be between 0.8 and 1.0 gram/minute. Further measurements might show that the prediction was correct, or they might show that at 37°C the rate was higher than 1.0 gram/minute. Scientists must be extremely careful not to make any assumptions that are not supported by the data.

Making Generalizations and Drawing Conclusions.

The results of an experiment are collected and analyzed. For a conclusion to be valid, the experiment must be repeated many times and obtain similar results, and all the results must be included in the analysis. The conclusion is based solely on the experimental data.

In the experiment on the effect of temperature on the rate of action of amylase, the data in the table show that the enzyme functions most efficiently at 40°C. However, if measurements were made only at 10° intervals, you could not say definitely that 40°C is the optimum temperature for amylase without making measurements at other intermediate temperatures. Still, it is probably safe to conclude that the optimum temperature is close to 40°C.

QUESTIONS
Multiple Choice

1. The diagram below represents a setup at the beginning of a laboratory investigation.

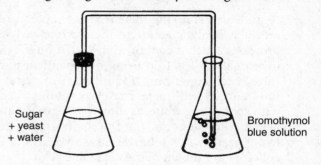

Sugar + yeast + water

Bromothymol blue solution

Which hypothesis would most likely be supported by observing and collecting data from this investigation? (1) The fermentation of a yeast-sugar solution results in the production of carbon dioxide. (2) Yeast cells contain simple sugars. (3) Oxygen is released when a yeast-sugar solution is illuminated with green light. (4) Yeast cells contain starches.

Base your answers to questions 2 and 3 on the information and data table below.

Distance of light from plant (cm)	Number of bubbles per minute
10	60
20	25
30	10
40	5

A green plant was placed in a test tube, and a light was placed at varying distances from the plant. The bubbles of oxygen given off by the

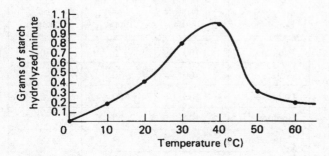

FIGURE 10-2 A line graph.

plant were counted. The table shows the data collected during this experiment.

2. A variable in this investigation is the (1) color of the light used (2) distance between the light and the plant (3) size of the test tube (4) type of plant used

3. Which conclusion can be drawn from this investigation? (1) As the distance from the light increases, the number of bubbles produced decreases. (2) As the distance from the light increases, the number of bubbles produced increases. (3) As the distance from the light decreases, the number of bubbles produced decreases. (4) There is no relationship between the number of bubbles produced and the distance of the plant from the light.

Base your answers to questions 4 through 6 on the following information, diagram, and data table, and on your knowledge of biology.

A student is studying the effect of temperature on the hydrolytic action of the enzyme gastric protease, which is contained in gastric fluid. An investigation is set up using five identical test tubes, each containing 40 milliliters of gastric fluid and 20 millimeters of glass tubing filled with cooked egg white, as shown in the diagram below. After 48 hours, the amount of egg white hydrolyzed in each tube was measured. The data collected are shown in the data table below.

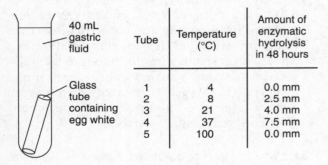

Tube	Temperature (°C)	Amount of enzymatic hydrolysis in 48 hours
1	4	0.0 mm
2	8	2.5 mm
3	21	4.0 mm
4	37	7.5 mm
5	100	0.0 mm

4. Which is the variable in this investigation? (1) gastric fluid (2) length of glass tubing (3) temperature (4) time

5. If an additional test tube were set up identical to the other test tubes and placed at a temperature of 15°C for 48 hours, what amount of hydrolysis might be expected? (1) less than 2.5 mm (2) between 2.5 mm and 4.0 mm (3) between 4.0 mm and 7.5 mm (4) more than 7.5 mm

6. Which set of axes in the next column would produce the best graph for plotting the data from the results of this investigation? (1) 1 (2) 2 (3) 3 (4) 4

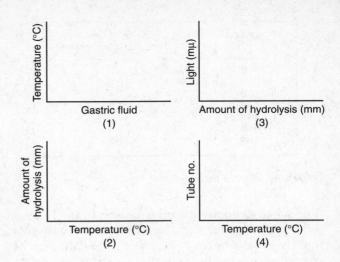

Base your answers to questions 7 through 11 on the information and two charts below and on your knowledge of biology.

Chart I shows the percentages of certain materials in the blood entering the kidney and the percentages of the same materials in the urine leaving the body. Chart II shows the number of molecules in the beginning and at the end of the kidney tubule for every 100 molecules of each substance entering the glomerulus.

Chart I

Substance	% of blood	% of urine
Protein	7.0	7.0
Water	91.5	96.0
Glucose	0.1	0.0
Sodium	0.33	0.29
Potassium	0.02	0.24
Urea	0.03	2.7

Chart II

Substance	Number of Molecules		
	In blood entering glomerulus	Beginning of tubule	End of tubule
Protein	100	0	0
Water	100	30	1
Glucose	100	20	0
Sodium	100	30	1
Potassium	100	23	12
Urea	100	50	90

7. According to chart I, which substance is more highly concentrated in the urine than in the blood? (1) water (2) sodium (3) protein (4) glucose

8. According to charts I and II, which substance enters the tubules but does *not* appear in the urine leaving the body? (1) protein (2) water (3) glucose (4) potassium

9. According to the data, which substance did *not* pass out of the blood into the tubule? (1) water (2) urea (3) glucose (4) protein

10. The data in the two charts would best aid a biologist in understanding the function of the (1) heart of a frog (2) nephron of a human (3) nerve cell of a fish (4) contractile vacuole of a paramecium

11. Which substances enter the tubule and then are reabsorbed back into the blood as they pass through the tubule? (1) urea and potassium (2) water and sodium (3) urea and protein (4) protein and glucose

Base your answers to questions 12 through 14 on the information provided by the graph below. The graph shows the average growth rate for 38 pairs of newborn rats. One member of each pair was injected with anterior pituitary extract. The other member of each pair served as a control.

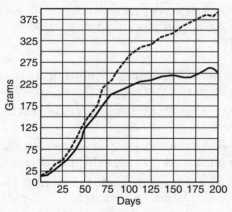

— Average growth of 38 untreated littermates (control)

---- Average growth of 38 rats injected with anterior pituitary extract (experimental)

12. At 75 days, what was the average weight of the rats injected with pituitary extract? (1) 65 grams (2) 125 grams (3) 200 grams (4) 225 grams

13. Based on the graph, it can be correctly concluded that the pituitary extract (1) is essential for life (2) determines when a rat will be born (3) affects the growth of rats (4) affects the growth of all animals

14. The graph shows the relationship between the weight of treated and untreated rats and the (1) age of the rats (2) sex of the rats (3) size of the rats' pituitary glands (4) type of food fed to the rats

Base your answers to questions 15 and 16 on the following information, diagrams, and data table, and on your knowledge of laboratory procedures used in biology.

Diagrams *A* through *E* show the general appearance of five tree fruits that were used by a science class in an experiment to determine the length of time necessary for each type of fruit to fall from a second-floor balcony to the lobby floor of their school. One hundred fruits of each type were selected by the students, and the average time of fall for each type of fruit is shown in the table below.

Fruits (not drawn to scale)

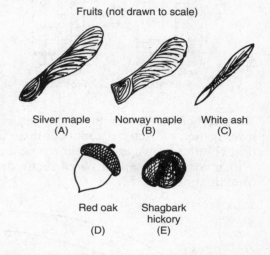

Silver maple (A)   Norway maple (B)   White ash (C)

Red oak (D)   Shagbark hickory (E)

Tree type	Average fall time of 100 fruits
Silver maple	3.2 sec
Norway maple	4.9 sec
White ash	1.5 sec
Red oak	0.8 sec
Shagbark hickory	0.8 sec

15. Based on this experimental evidence, what inference seems most likely to be true concerning the distribution of these fruits during windstorms in nature? (1) Silver maple fruits would land closer to the base of their parent tree than would shagbark hickory fruits. (2) White ash fruits would land farther from the base of their parent tree than would silver maple fruits. (3) White ash fruits would land closer to the base of their parent tree than would shagbark hickory fruits. (4) Norway maple fruits would land farther from the base of their parent tree than would silver maple fruits.

16. Which graph best shows the average fall time for each fruit type tested during this experiment? (1) 1 (2) 2 (3) 3 (4) 4

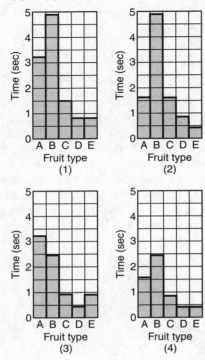

17. The graph below was developed as a result of an investigation of bacterial counts of three identical cultures grown at different temperatures. Which conclusion might be correctly drawn from this graph?

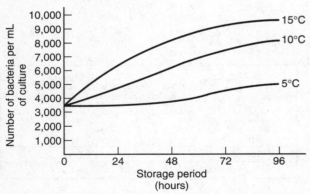

(1) The culture contains no bacteria. (2) Refrigeration retards bacterial reproduction. (3) Temperature is unrelated to the bacteria reproduction rate. (4) Bacteria cannot grow at a temperature of 5°C.

Base your answers to questions 18 through 20 on the following graphs above, which show data on some environmental factors affecting a large New York lake.

18. Which relationship can be correctly inferred from the data presented? (1) As sewage waste

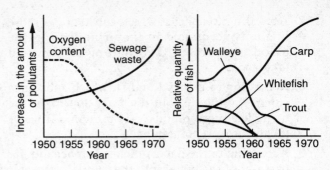

increases, oxygen content decreases. (2) As sewage increases, oxygen content increases. (3) As oxygen content decreases, carp population decreases. (4) As oxygen content decreases, trout population increases.

19. The greatest change in the lake's whitefish population occurred between which years? (1) 1950 and 1955 (2) 1955 and 1960 (3) 1960 and 1965 (4) 1965 and 1970

20. Which of the fish species appears able to withstand the greatest degree of oxygen depletion? (1) trout (2) carp (3) walleye (4) whitefish

LABORATORY PROCEDURES

Selecting Suitable Lab Equipment. Knowledge of the correct lab equipment is essential for planning and carrying out an experiment. Figure 10-3 illustrates some basic laboratory equipment that you should know.

Safety in the Laboratory. Following are some safety precautions that you should practice in the laboratory.

- Do not handle chemicals or equipment unless you are told by your teacher to do so.
- If any of your lab equipment appears to be broken or unusual, do not use it. Report it to your teacher.
- Report any personal injury or damage to clothing to your teacher immediately.
- Report any unsafe activities to your teacher immediately.
- Wear appropriate safety equipment, such as goggles and apron. Tie back long hair; secure dangling jewelry and loose sleeves.
- Never taste or directly inhale unknown chemicals. Never eat or drink in the lab.
- Never pour chemicals back into stock bottles; never exchange bottle stoppers.
- When heating a liquid in a test tube, always wear safety goggles and point the opening away from yourself and all others.

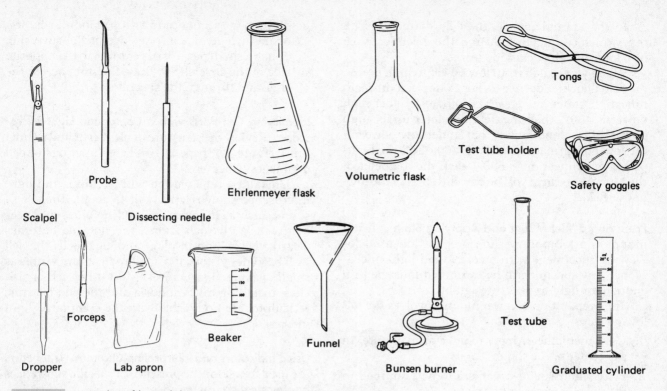

FIGURE 10-3 Examples of basic laboratory equipment (not drawn to scale).

- Handle all sharp instruments with care, moving slowly and deliberately.

Using a Compound Light Microscope. Review the parts of the compound light microscope and their functions by studying Figure 2-2 and Table 2-1 (pages 22–23) in Chapter 2.

In using the compound microscope, begin by viewing the specimen with the low-power objective, focusing first with the coarse adjustment, then with the fine adjustment. The objectives can then be switched from low power to high power. All focusing under high power should be done with the fine adjustment. The field appears dimmer under high power than under low power. Opening the diaphragm allows more light to reach the specimen.

The image of an object seen under the microscope is enlarged, reversed (backward), and inverted (upside down). When viewed through the microscope, an organism that appears to be moving to the right is actually moving to the left. An organism that appears to be moving toward the observer, or up, is actually moving away from the observer, or down.

Determining the Size of Microscopic Specimens. To determine the size of a specimen being examined under a microscope, you must know the diameter of the microscope field. You can measure the field diameter with a clear plastic centimeter ruler. Place the ruler over the opening in the stage of the microscope, as shown in Figure 10-4. Focus on the ruler markings and adjust the position of the ruler so that a millimeter marking is at the left.

Once you have estimated the field diameter under low power, you can estimate the size of specimens observed under low power by how much of the field they cover. For example, if the diameter of the field is 1.5 mm and a specimen is about one-third the diameter of the field, the specimen is about 0.5 mm in length.

The unit most commonly used in measuring microscopic specimens is the *micrometer*, symbol µm, which is one-thousandth of a millimeter. (The micrometer is also referred to as a *micron*.)

$$1 \text{ mm} = 1000 \text{ µm} \quad 1 \text{ µm} = 0.001 \text{ mm}$$

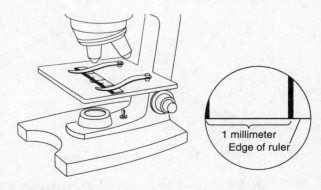

1 millimeter
Edge of ruler

FIGURE 10-4 Measuring with a microscope.

In the example above, the field diameter is 1.5 mm, which is equal to 1500 μm. The specimen is 0.5 mm long, which equals 500 μm.

When you switch from low power to high power, the field diameter decreases. For example, if the magnification under low power is 100× and under high power is 400×, then the field diameter under high power will be one-fourth that under low power. If the low-power magnification is 100× and the high-power magnification is 500×, then the diameter of the high-power field will be one-fifth that of the low-power field.

Preparing a Wet Mount and Applying Stains. A wet mount is a temporary slide preparation used for viewing specimens with a compound light microscope. Any specimen to be examined must be thin enough for light to pass through it.

The preparation of a wet mount involves the following steps:

1. Use a medicine dropper to put a drop of water in the center of the slide.

2. Place the tissue or organism to be examined in the drop of water on the slide.

3. Cover the specimen with a coverslip, as shown in Figure 10-5 below.

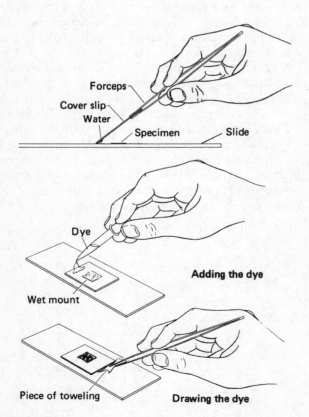

FIGURE 10-5 Making a wet mount (above) and staining a specimen.

4. To stain the section, add a drop of iodine solution or methylene blue at one edge of the coverslip. Touch a small piece of paper towel to the opposite side of the coverslip to draw the stain across the slide and through the specimen.

Identifying Cell Parts with a Compound Light Microscope. Review the structure of plant cells and animal cells (Figure 2-1, page 20) and the functions of cell organelles (Chapter 2).

Unstained cells viewed with a compound light microscope show relatively little detail. The use of stains, such as iodine or methylene blue, enhances contrast. With such stains, the nucleus becomes clearly visible, and in plant and algal cells the cell wall becomes visible, too. Chloroplasts are visible as small oval green structures. Most other cell organelles, including mitochondria and the endoplasmic reticulum, are not visible with the compound light microscope.

Using Indicators and Interpreting Changes. Indicators are used to test for the presence of specific substances or chemical characteristics.

Litmus paper is an indicator used to determine whether a solution is an acid or a base. An acid turns blue litmus paper red. A base turns red litmus paper blue.

pH paper is an indicator that is used to determine the actual pH of a solution. When a piece of pH paper is dipped into a test solution, it changes color. The color of the pH paper is then matched against a color chart, which shows the pH.

Bromothymol blue is an indicator used to detect carbon dioxide. In the presence of carbon dioxide, bromothymol blue turns to bromothymol yellow. If the carbon dioxide is removed, the indicator changes back to bromothymol blue.

Benedict solution is an indicator used to test for simple sugars. When heated in the presence of simple sugars, Benedict solution turns from blue to yellow, green, or brick red, depending on the sugar concentration. *Fehling solution* also may be used to test for simple sugars.

Lugol, or *iodine, solution* is an indicator used to test for starch. In the presence of starch, Lugol solution turns from red to blue-black.

Biuret solution is an indicator used to test for protein. In the presence of protein, Biuret solution turns from light blue to purple.

Using Measurement Instruments. The following tools are used for making scientific measurements.

- *Metric ruler.* The basic unit of length in the metric system is the meter, abbreviated m. One meter

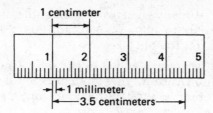

FIGURE 10-6 A centimeter ruler.

contains 100 centimeters (cm). As shown in Figure 10-6, metric rulers are generally calibrated in centimeters and millimeters (mm). Each centimeter contains 10 millimeters; thus, each meter is equal to 1000 mm.

- *Celsius thermometer.* In the metric system, temperature is commonly measured in degrees Celsius. On the Celsius scale, 0°C is the freezing point of water, 21°C is room temperature, and 100°C is the boiling point of water. Figure 10-7 shows a thermometer calibrated in degrees Celsius. Note that each degree is marked by a short line (such as 37°C), and every tenth degree is labeled with the number (such as 30°C and 40°C).

- *Graduated cylinder.* The basic unit used for measuring the volume of a liquid in the metric system is the liter, abbreviated L. A liter contains 1000 milliliters (mL). Most laboratory measurements involve milliliters rather than liters.

The volume of a liquid is frequently measured in graduated cylinders, which come in many sizes. When you need an accurately measured amount of liquid, use a graduated cylinder of appropriate size—that is, to measure 5 mL of liquid, use a 10-mL graduated cylinder, not a 1000-mL graduated cylinder.

The surface of water and similar liquids curves upward along the sides of a cylinder. This curved surface, or *meniscus,* is caused by the strong attraction of liquid molecules to the glass surface (Figure 10-8). For an accurate measurement, the reading should be done at eye level, and the measurement should be read at the bottom of the meniscus. With other types of liquids, the meniscus curves the other way (that is, downward); in such cases, the measurement should be read across the top of the meniscus.

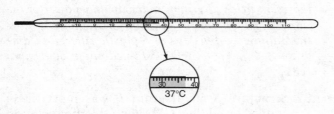

FIGURE 10-7 A Celsius thermometer.

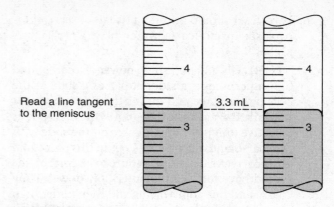

Read a line tangent to the meniscus   3.3 mL

FIGURE 10-8 Measuring with a graduated cylinder.

Dissecting Plant and Animal Specimens. Dissections are done to expose major structures for examination. The specimen is generally placed in a dissection pan and fastened down with pins. While doing a dissection, you should be very careful with the dissection instruments, which are sharp. Scalpels, forceps, scissors, and stereomicroscopes are used. You should also be careful in cutting into and handling the specimen so that you do not damage important structures. Follow all instructions and record your observations by making labeled diagrams as you proceed with the dissection.

QUESTIONS
Multiple Choice

Base your answers to questions 21 through 23 on the four sets of laboratory materials listed below and on your knowledge of biology.

Set A	Set B	Set C	Set D
Light source	Droppers	Scalpel	Compound microscope
Colored filters	Benedict solution	Forceps	Glass slides
Test tubes	Iodine	Scissors	Water
Test-tube stand	Test tubes	Pan with wax bottom	Forceps
	Test-tube rack	Stereo-microscope	
	Heat source	Pins	
	Goggles	Goggles	

21. Which set should a student select to test for the presence of a carbohydrate in food? (1) Set A (2) Set B (3) Set C (4) Set D

22. Which set should a student select to determine the location of the ovules in the ovary of a flower? (1) Set A (2) Set B (3) Set C (4) Set D

23. Which set should a student use to observe chloroplasts in elodea (a water plant)? (1) Set A (2) Set B (3) Set C (4) Set D

24. To view cells under the high power of a compound light microscope, a student places a slide of the cells on the stage and moves the stage clips over to secure the slide. She then moves the high-power objective into place and focuses on the slide with the coarse adjustment. Two steps in this procedure are incorrect. For this procedure to be correct, she should have focused under (1) low power using coarse and fine adjustments and then under high power using only the fine adjustment (2) high power first, then low power using only the fine adjustment (3) low power using the coarse and fine adjustments and then under high power using coarse and fine adjustments (4) low power using the fine adjustment and then under high power using only the fine adjustment

Base your answers to questions 25 and 26 on the following diagram of a compound light microscope.

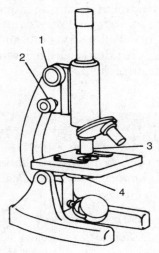

25. The part labeled 1 is used to (1) increase the amount of light reaching the specimen (2) focus with the high-power objective (3) hold the lenses in place (4) focus with the low-power objective

26. To adjust the amount of light reaching the specimen, you would use the part labeled (1) 1 (2) 2 (3) 3 (4) 4

Base your answers to questions 27 through 29 on the information below and on your knowledge of biology.

A student prepares a wet mount of onion epidermis and observes it under three powers of magnification with a compound light microscope (40×, 100×, and 400×).

27. An adjustment should be made to allow more light to pass through the specimen when

the student changes the magnification from (1) 100× to 400× (2) 400× to 100× (3) 400× to 40× (4) 100× to 40×

28. Iodine stain is added to the slide. Under 400× magnification, the student should be able to observe a (1) mitochondrion (2) nucleus (3) ribosome (4) centriole

29. A specimen that is suitable for observation under this microscope should be (1) stained with Benedict solution (2) moving and respiring (3) alive and reproducing (4) thin and transparent

30. A microscope is supplied with 10× and 15× eyepieces, and with 10× and 44× objectives. What is the maximum magnification that can be obtained from this microscope? (1) 59× (2) 150× (3) 440× (4) 660×

31. Under low power (100×), a row of eight cells can fit across the field of a certain microscope. How many of these cells could be viewed in the high power (400×) visual field of this microscope? (1) 1 (2) 2 (3) 8 (4) 32

32. A compound light microscope has a 10× ocular, a 10× low-power objective, and a 40× high-power objective. A student noted that under high power, four cells end to end extended across the diameter of the field. If the microscope were switched to low power, approximately how many cells would fit across the field? (1) 1 (2) 8 (3) 16 (4) 4

33. The diagram below shows a section of a metric ruler scale as seen through a compound light microscope. If each division represents 1 millimeter, what is the approximate width of the microscope's field of view in micrometers (μm)? (1) 3700 (2) 4200 (3) 4500 (4) 5000

Base your answers to questions 34 through 37 on your knowledge of biology and on diagrams A and B, which represent fields of vision under the low power of the same compound microscope (100×). Diagram A shows the millimeter divisions of a plastic ruler, and diagram B shows a sample of stained onion epidermal cells.

34. Structure X in diagram B was most likely stained by adding (1) water (2) iodine solution (3) Benedict solution (4) bromothymol blue

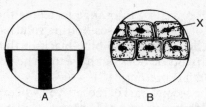

35. Structure *X* in diagram *B* indicates (1) a nucleus (2) a mitochondrion (3) the cell wall (4) the cytoplasm

36. The diameter of the field of vision in diagram *A* is approximately (1) 500 μm (2) 1000 μm (3) 1500 μm (4) 2000 μm

37. What is the approximate length of each onion epidermal cell in diagram *B*? (1) 200 μm (2) 660 μm (3) 1000 μm (4) 2500 μm

38. Iodine solution is used to test for the presence of (1) proteins (2) simple sugars (3) oxygen (4) starch

39. In the presence of carbon dioxide, bromothymol blue (1) shows no color change (2) turns yellow (3) turns blue-black (4) turns red-orange

40. Benedict solution is used to test for (1) disaccharides (2) oxygen (3) starch (4) simple sugars

41. Which piece of equipment should be used to transfer a protist onto a microscope slide? (1) scissors (2) dissecting needles (3) medicine dropper (4) forceps

42. While a student is heating a liquid in a test tube, the mouth of the tube should always be (1) corked with a rubber stopper (2) pointed toward the student (3) allowed to cool off (4) aimed away from everybody

Base your answer to question 43 on the diagram of a peppered moth and the metric ruler below.

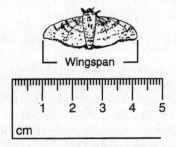

Wingspan

43. Which row in the table below best represents the ratio of body length to wingspan of the peppered moth? (1) 1 (2) 2 (3) 3 (4) 4

Row	Body Length : Wingspan
1	1 : 1
2	2 : 1
3	1 : 2
4	2 : 2

PART D MANDATED LABORATORIES

On Part D of the Living Environment (Biology) Regents, you will be assessed on your knowledge and understanding of four mandatory lab exercises. These investigations are based on the learning standards contained in the Living Environment Core Curriculum and test a variety of skills. Below is a description of each of the mandated labs.

Lab 1: Relationships and Biodiversity

In this lab, you will be performing a number of tests to determine evolutionary relationships between an environmentally important but endangered plant, *Botana curus,* and three related plants. The goal is to identify the plant most closely related to *B. curus.* The tests you will perform include structural and molecular evidence for relationship. They are:

- comparison of the four plants' structures, including types of leaves and stems
- comparison of the four plants' seeds in terms of size and appearance
- microscopic examination of the plants' stem cross sections
- paper chromatography of pigment extracts from the four plants
- chemical test for the presence of an important enzyme in each plant
- simulation of a gel electrophoresis of DNA from the four plants
- translating the DNA from each plant into the corresponding protein product, using a Universal Genetic Code Chart

The plant most closely related to *B. curus* will show many similarities to it in the tests you will perform. Therefore, the more "matches" between the unknown relative and *B. curus*, the more closely related the two plants are. The most significant tests are those for genetic relationships; thus, the plant most closely related to *B. curus* will have DNA very similar to it.

Lab 2: Making Connections

In this activity, you will learn how to measure and record your normal pulse rate and how it may change under certain circumstances, such as exercising. These data will then be graphed and analyzed. You will also explore the effect of repeated exercise on muscle fatigue by squeezing a clothespin as many times as you can in one minute and then repeating the procedure a second time. The purpose of this part of the lab is to determine the effect of exercise on muscles. The second part of the lab exercise involves analyzing two opposing views about the effect of exercise on muscle fatigue. Two students make the following claims: one states that exercise causes a reduction in muscle activity and that rest is necessary before muscles can work effectively again; the second claims that exercise actually enhances the function of muscles. For this part, you will take one of the positions and design a scientific investigation to support or refute the claim. In addition, you may be asked by your teacher to present an oral report of your findings to the class.

Lab 3: The Beaks of Finches

This lab explores adaptations for survival (natural selection). In the activity, you will use some type of common household or lab equipment that has occluding parts (that is, parts that come together) to simulate the beak of a finch. Examples of these tools are pliers, forceps, test-tube holders, hair clips, and salad tongs. These devices represent the different types of finch beaks. They will be used to pick up as many seeds as possible, just one at a time, in a 30-second time period and then transfer them to a storage dish (representing the bird's stomach). You will run trials both with and without competition. During the lab, it also may be necessary for your finch to switch to a different type of food if it was not successful in eating enough of the first type of seed. Survival of your finch depends on picking up and storing at least 13 seeds in the 30-second interval. As the lab is run, you will become aware that some beaks are more adaptive than others, thus allowing their "owners" to survive (i.e., eat enough seeds). This activity is meant to simulate what occurs in natural selection; that is, those organisms having the most adaptive traits for their environment survive, while those with less adaptive traits tend to die out. In some cases, in order to survive, organisms may migrate to a different environment in which they are better adapted for survival.

Lab 4: Diffusion Through a Membrane

In this lab activity, you will explore the permeability of a membrane and the process of diffusion. You will create an artificial cell using dialysis tubing or a thin plastic bag. This "cell" will contain a mixture of a glucose and starch solution. The "cell" will be placed in a water bath that contains starch indicator (iodine solution). After the "cell" has been in the water for at least 20 minutes, you will use chemical indicators to check for diffusion of molecules into and out of the "cell." The chemical indicators include one that tests for glucose (blue Benedict solution) and one that tests for starch (iodine solution). Recall that Benedict solution, when heated in the presence of simple sugars such as glucose, will change from blue

to green to yellow to orange to red as the concentration of sugar increases. Iodine solution changes from yellow (amber) to blue-black in the presence of starch. Iodine does not have to be heated to show that starch is present.

In the second part of the lab, you will examine the effects of osmosis on a red onion cell. By preparing a wet mount of onion tissue and surrounding it with 10% salt solution, you should be able to observe and explain the effect this solution has on the cells. Next, replacing the salt solution on the slide with distilled water should produce another effect on the cells. You will observe these effects on the onion cells through a microscope and draw them.

QUESTIONS
Multiple Choice and Constructed Response

Base your answer to question 44 on the following information and data table.

To determine which colors of light are best used by plants for photosynthesis, three types of underwater green plants of similar mass were subjected to the same intensity of light of different colors for the same amount of time. All other environmental conditions were kept the same. After 15 minutes, a video camera was used to record the number of bubbles of gas (oxygen) each plant gave off in a 30-second time period. Each type of plant was tested six times. The average of the data for each plant type is shown in the table below.

Average Number of Bubbles Given Off in 30 Seconds			
Plant Type	Red Light	Yellow Light	Green Light	Blue Light
Plant 1	35	11	5	47
Plant 2	48	8	2	63
Plant 3	28	9	6	39

44. Which statement is a valid inference based on the data? (1) Each plant carried on photosynthesis best in a different color of light. (2) Red light is better for photosynthesis than blue light. (3) These types of plants make food at the fastest rates with red and blue light. (4) Water must filter out red and green light.

Base your answers to questions 45 through 48 on the information below and on your knowledge of biology.

Three students each added equal volumes of pond water to four beakers and placed each beaker in a different water bath. Each student maintained the water baths at temperatures shown in the data table. The students then added an equal number of water fleas to each of their four beakers. After one hour, the students used microscopes to determine the average heart rate of the water fleas. The procedure was repeated for a total of three trials at each temperature. The results of the investigation are summarized in the data table below.

Water Flea Heart Rate

Water Temperature (°C)	Average Heart Rate (beats/minute)
5	40
15	119
25	205
35	280

45. Use the information in the data table to construct a line graph on the grid provided below. Mark an appropriate scale on each labeled axis.

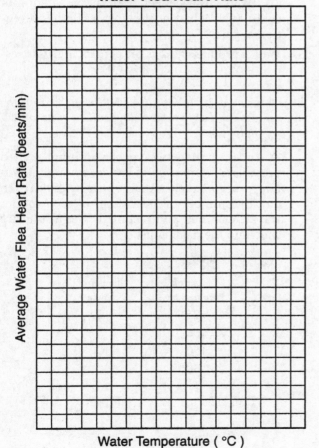

The Effect of Temperature on Water Flea Heart Rate

Average Water Flea Heart Rate (beats/min)

Water Temperature (°C)

46. Plot the data for the average heart rates on the grid; surround each point with a small circle and connect the points.

47. The independent variable in this investigation is the (1) number of trials (2) number of water fleas (3) temperature of the water (4) average heart rate

48. State the relationship between temperature and heart rate in water fleas.

Base your answers to questions 49 through 52 on the following information and diagram and on your knowledge of biology.

The diagram shows the results of a test that was done using DNA samples from three bears of different species. Each DNA sample was cut into fragments using a specific enzyme and placed in the wells as indicated below. The DNA fragments were then separated using gel electrophoresis.

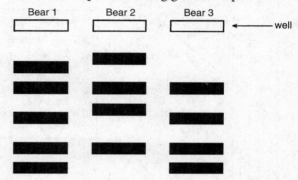

49. Which *two* bears are most closely related? Support your answer with data from the test results.

50. Identify one additional way to determine the evolutionary relationship of these bears.

51. Gel electrophoresis was used to separate the bears' DNA fragments on the basis of their (1) size (2) color (3) functions (4) chromosomes

52. Identify one procedure, other than electrophoresis, that is used in the laboratory to separate the different types of molecules in a liquid mixture.

53. On a television talk show, a guest claims that people who exercise vigorously for 15 minutes or more every day are able to solve math problems more rapidly than people who have no vigorous exercise in their daily routine. Describe a controlled experiment that could be conducted to test this claim. In your description be sure to state:

- the purpose of the experiment
- why the sample to be used should be large
- how the experimental group and the control group will be treated
- the specific data to be collected during the experiment
- *one* way to determine if the results support the claim

Base your answer to question 54 on the following information.

A student measures his pulse rate while he is watching television and records it. Next, he walks to a friend's house nearby and, when he arrives, measures and records his pulse rate again. He and his friend then decide to run to the mall a few blocks away. On arriving at the mall, the student measures and records his pulse rate once again. Finally, after sitting and talking for a half hour, the student measures and records his pulse rate one last time.

54. Which graph below best illustrates the expected changes in the student's pulse rate according to the activities described above? (1) 1 (2) 2 (3) 3 (4) 4

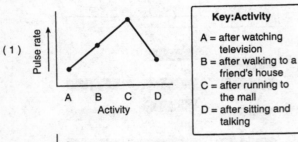

Key: Activity

A = after watching television
B = after walking to a friend's house
C = after running to the mall
D = after sitting and talking

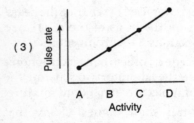

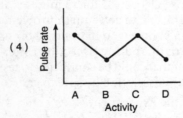

Base your answers to questions 55 through 57 on the following information and table and on your knowledge of biology.

It has been hypothesized that a chemical known as BW prevents colds. To test this hypothesis, 20,000 volunteers were divided into four groups (of 5000 each). Each volunteer took a small pill every morning for one year. The contents of the pill taken by the members of each group are shown in the chart.

Group	Number of Volunteers	Contents of Pill	% Developing Colds
1	5000	5 grams of sugar	20
2	5000	5 grams of sugar 1 gram of BW	19
3	5000	5 grams of sugar 3 grams of BW	21
4	5000	5 grams of sugar 9 grams of BW	15

55. Which factor most likely had the greatest influence on these experimental results? (1) color of the pills (2) amount of sugar added (3) number of volunteers in each group (4) health history of the volunteers

56. Which statement is a valid inference based on the results? (1) Sugar reduced the number of colds. (2) Sugar increased the number of colds. (3) BW is always effective in the prevention of colds. (4) BW may not be effective in the prevention of colds.

57. Which group served as the control in this investigation? (1) 1 (2) 2 (3) 3 (4) 4

Base your answers to questions 58 through 61 on the information and data table below and on your knowledge of biology.

A student added two species of single-celled organisms, *Paramecium caudatum* and *Didinium nasutum,* to the same culture medium. Each day, the number of individuals of each species was determined and recorded. The results are shown in the data table below.

Culture Population

Day	Number of Paramecium	Number of Didinium
0	25	2
1	60	5
2	150	10
3	50	30
4	25	20
5	0	2
6	0	0

58. Use the information in the table to construct a line graph on a copy of the grid on page 151. Mark a scale on the axis labeled "Number of Individuals" that is appropriate for the plotted

Didinium population and for plotting the *Paramecium* population.

Culture Population

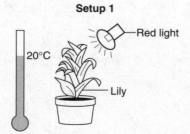

59. Plot the data for *Paramecium* on the grid. Surround each data point with a small triangle and connect the points.

60. What evidence in the data indicates that *Didinium* could be a predator of the *Paramecium*?

61. State *two* possible reasons why the two populations died off between days 4 and 6.

62. Molecules *A* and *B* are both organic molecules found in many cells. When tested, it is found that molecule *A* cannot pass through a cell membrane, but molecule *B* easily passes through. State one way the two molecules could differ that would account for the differences in their ability to pass through the cell membrane.

63. If vegetables become wilted, they can often be made crisp again by soaking them in water. However, they may lose a few nutrients during this process. Using the concept of diffusion and concentration, state why some nutrients would leave the plant cell.

Base your answer to the following question on the information and diagram below.

Elodea is a plant that lives in freshwater. The diagram represents one Elodea leaf cell in its normal freshwater environment.

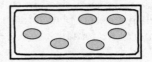

Elodea cell in freshwater

64. Predict how the contents of the Elodea cell would change if the cell were placed in salt water for several minutes by completing, in your notebook, a copy of the diagram "Elodea cell in salt water," shown below. Label the location of the cell membrane.

Elodea cell in salt water

65. A scientist conducted an experiment in which he fed mice large amounts of the amino acid cysteine. He observed that this amino acid protected mouse chromosomes from damage by toxic chemicals. The scientist then claimed that cysteine, added to the diet of all animals, would protect their chromosomes from damage. State whether or not this is a valid claim. Support your answer.

Base your answers to questions 66 through 68 on the information and diagram below.

An investigation was carried out using the two setups shown below. Other than the difference shown in the diagram, all other conditions were identical.

66. State one possible hypothesis that could be tested using these two setups.

67. What data should be collected in order to test the hypothesis you stated for question 66?

68. Describe one change that could be made in the investigation to improve it.

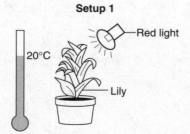
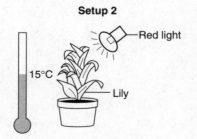

Base your answer to question 69 on the following information.

An experiment was designed to see what effects ibuprofen would have on laboratory mice. Large numbers of male mice and an equal number of female mice were used in this investigation. The male mice were placed in an area with food and water. The female mice were placed in a separate area of the same size and also given food and water. The males were each given 100 milligrams of ibuprofen each day, mixed with their food, and the females were each given 50 milligrams of ibuprofen each day, mixed with their food.

69. Identify *two* errors that were made in the design of this investigation.

Appendix

Living Environment Part D— Sample Lab Questions

Living Environment Part D: Sample Questions

Beginning with the June 2004 administration, the Regents Examination in Living Environment will include a new section, Part D. The questions on Part D will consist of a combination of multiple-choice and open-ended questions related to at least three of the four required living environment laboratory activities and will comprise approximately 15% of the examination.

These sample questions are provided to help teachers and students become familiar with the format of questions for this part of the examination. They provide examples of ways the required laboratory experiences may be assessed. A rating guide is also included.

Sample Items Related to Lab Activity #1: *Relationships and Biodiversity*

1   In the *Relationships and Biodiversity* laboratory activity, students were instructed to use a clean dropper to place each of four different samples of plant extracts on the chromatography paper. A student used the same dropper for each sample without cleaning it between each use. State one way this student's final chromatogram would be different from a chromatogram that resulted from using the correct procedure.   [1]

2   State one reason that safety goggles were required during the indicator test for enzyme *M*.   [1]

Base your answers to questions 3 through 6 on the information and data table below and on your knowledge of biology.

A student was told that three different plant species are very closely related. She was provided with a short segment of the same portion of the DNA molecule that coded for enzyme X from each of the three species.

Information Regarding Enzyme X

DNA sequence from plant species *A*	CAC	GTG	GAC
Amino acid sequence for enzyme *X* coded for by that DNA	Val	His	Leu
DNA sequence from plant species *B*	CAT	GTG	CAA
Sequence of bases in mRNA produced by that DNA	___	___	___
Amino acid sequence for enzyme *X* coded for by the DNA	Val	His	Val
DNA sequence from plant species *C*	CAG	GTA	CAG
Sequence of bases in mRNA produced by that DNA	GUC	CAU	GUC
Amino acid sequence for enzyme *X* coded for by the DNA	___	___	___

3   The correct sequence of mRNA bases for plant species *B* is

(1) GUA CAC GUU
(2) GTA CAC GTT
(3) CAU GUG CAA
(4) TCG TGT ACC

4   Use the mRNA Codon Chart on the next page to determine the amino acid sequence for enzyme *X* in plant species *C* and record the sequence in the appropriate place in the data table. [1]

5   Is it possible to determine whether species *B* or species *C* is more closely related to species *A* by comparing the amino acid sequences that would result from the three given DNA sequences? Support your answer. [1]

6   Determine whether species *B* or species *C* appears more closely related to species *A*. Support your answer with data from the data table. (*Base your answer only on the DNA sequences provided* for enzyme *X* in these three plant species.) [1]

Universal Genetic Code Chart

Messenger RNA codons and the amino acids they code for.

		SECOND BASE			
	U	**C**	**A**	**G**	
U	UUU UUC } PHE UUA UUG } LEU	UCU UCC UCA UCG } SER	UAU UAC } TYR UAA UAG } STOP	UGU UGC } CYS UGA } STOP UGG } TRP	U C A G
C	CUU CUC CUA CUG } LEU	CCU CCC CCA CCG } PRO	CAU CAC } HIS CAA CAG } GLN	CGU CGC CHA CGG } ARG	U C A G
A	AUU AUC AUA } ILE AUG } MET or START	ACU ACC ACA ACG } THR	AAU AAC } ASN AAA AAG } LYS	AGU AGC } SER AGA AGG } ARG	U C A G
G	GUU GUC GUA } VAL GUG	GCU GCC GCA GCG } ALA	GAU GAC } ASP GAA GAG } GLU	GGU GGC GGA } GLY GGG	U C A G

FIRST BASE (left side)   THIRD BASE (right side)

Sample Items Related to Lab Activity #2: *Making Connections*

Base your answers to questions 7 through 9 on the information and data table below and on your knowledge of biology.

In the Making Connections laboratory activity, a group of students obtained the following data:

Student Tested	Pulse Rate at Rest	Pulse Rate After Exercising
1	70	97
2	75	106
3	84	120
4	60	91
5	78	122

7   Explain how this change in pulse rate is associated with homeostasis in muscle cells.   [1]

8   Identify the system of the human body whose functioning is represented by this data.   [1]

9   Identify *one* other system of the human body whose functioning would be expected to be altered as a direct result of the exercise. Describe how this system would most likely be altered.   [1]

Base your answers to question 10 and 11 on the information below and on your knowledge of biology.

A biology class performed an investigation to determine the influence of exercise on pulse rate. During the investigation, one group of twelve students, Group A, counted how many times they could squeeze a clothespin in a 1-minute period, then exercised for 4 minutes, and repeated the clothespin squeeze for an additional 1 minute. Another group of twelve students, Group B, also counted how many times they could squeeze a clothespin in a 1-minute period, but then they rested for 4 minutes, and repeated the clothespin squeeze for an additional 1 minute. The data table below shows the average results obtained by the students.

Effect of Exercise on Number of Clothespin Squeezes

Groups of Student	Average Number of Clothespin Squeezes During First Minute	Average Number of Clothespin Squeezes During Second Minute
Group A (exercise)	75	79
Group B (rest)	74	68

10 State *two* specific examples from the description of the investigation and the data table that support this investigation being a well-designed experiment. [2]

11 The chart below shows relative blood flow through various organs during exercise and at rest.

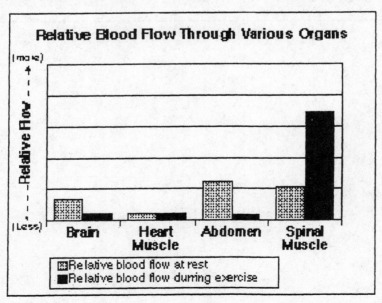

Using information from both the data table and the chart, explain how muscle fatigue and blood circulation could account for the results the students obtained. [2]

Sample Items Related to Lab Activity #5: *Diffusion Through a Membrane*

Base your answers to questions 12 and 13 on the diagrams below and on your knowledge of biology.

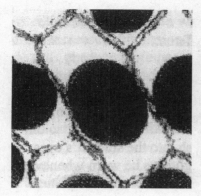 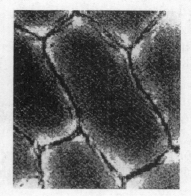

Diagram 1: red onion cells   Diagram 2: red onion cells

12 Describe how to prepare a wet-mount slide of red onion cells with the cell membrane shrinking away from the cell wall, as shown in diagram 1. The following materials are available: microscope slide, pipettes, cover slips, paper towels, water, salt solution, and red onion sections. [3]

13 List the laboratory procedures to follow that would cause the cells in diagram 1 to resemble the cells in diagram 2.   [2]

---

14 A student places an artificial cell, similar to the one used in the laboratory activity *Diffusion Through a Membrane*, in a beaker containing water. The artificial cell contains starch and sugar. A starch indicator is added to the water in the beaker. Explain how the student will know if the starch is able to diffuse out of the artificial cell.   [1]

Scoring Guide for Sample Part D Questions

1 Allow 1 credit for stating one way the student's final chromatogram would be different from a chromatogram that resulted from using the correct procedure. Acceptable responses include, but are not limited to:

— The number of bands could be different.
— The size of the spots would differ.

2 Allow 1 credit for stating one reason that safety goggles were required during the indicator test for enzyme *M*. Acceptable responses include, but are not limited to:

— Some of the chemicals might splash into the student's eyes.
— It is a laboratory requirement that goggles be worn whenever chemicals are used in the lab.

3 **1**

4 Allow 1 credit for **Val   His   Val**

5 Allow 1 credit for indicating that it is not possible to determine whether species *B* or species *C* is more closely related to species *A* by comparing the amino acid sequences, and providing an explanation that supports this response. Acceptable responses include, but are not limited to:

— The amino acid sequences do not make it possible to determine whether species *B* or species *C* is more closely related to species *A*, because both *A* and *B*, and *A* and *C* only differ by one amino acid.

Allow credit for an answer that is consistent with the student's response to question 4.

6 Allow 1 credit for using data from the data table to indicate whether species *B* or species *C* appears to be more closely related to species *A*. Acceptable responses include but are not limited to:

— Species *A* and *B* are the closest because they have only three differences in their DNA code, while species *A* and *C* have four differences.
— Species *A* and *B* are more closely related because there are not as many differences between their DNA sequences as there are between species *A* and *C*.

7   Allow 1 credit for explaining how this change in pulse rate is associated with homeostasis in muscle cells. Acceptable responses include but are not limited to:

— Muscle cells produce more carbon dioxide when they are active than when they are not very active. The increased blood flow carries away the extra carbon dioxide to the lungs, where it can be excreted.
— Muscle cells use more oxygen when they are active than when they are not very active. An increased circulation rate brings more oxygen to the muscle cells.
— Muscle cells produce more heat when they are active than when they are not very active. The increased blood flow helps carry away the excess heat to the skin, where it is lost to the surroundings.

8   Allow 1 credit for indicating that the functioning of the circulatory system is represented by the data.

9   Allow 1 credit for identifying one other system of the human body whose functioning would be expected to be altered as a direct result of the exercise *and* how it would be most likely be altered. Acceptable responses include, but are not limited to:

— respiratory system – increase the intake of oxygen
— respiratory system – increase the exhalation of carbon dioxide
— excretory system – increased sweating

10 Allow a maximum of 2 credits, 1 credit for each of two specific examples that support this investigation being a well-designed experiment. Acceptable responses include but are not limited to:

— It has two groups for comparison (experimental and control).
— It is a controlled experiment.
— Each group did exactly the same thing except for the exercise/rest part.
— Each group contained the same number of students.

11 Allow a maximum of 2 credits, 1 credit for indicating that muscle fatigue and/or waste buildup was the reason for group *A*'s results, and 1 credit for indicating that increased circulation from exercise was the reason for group *B's* results.

Example of a 2-credit response:

The squeezing caused the muscles to become tired as waste products of muscle activity built up. The increased circulation shown in the second table (blood flow to skeletal muscle during exercise) helped the students in group *B* carry the wastes away from their muscle cells so they could continue to function efficiently. Students in group *A* did not increase their circulation rate, so the wastes interfered with the ability to keep squeezing the clothespin.

12 Allow a maximum of 3 credits for correctly describing how to prepare a slide showing red onion cells with the cell membrane shrinking away from the cell wall. The responses must include:

- a simple description of how the onion cells will be obtained
- a description of how a wet-mount slide is made
- an indication that salt solution must be used

Acceptable 3-credit responses include, but are not limited to:

— Break the onion piece and peel off the skin. Put it on a slide and add water. Add a coverslip. Place a piece of paper towel on the edge of the coverslip and add salt solution to the other side. After adding a few drops of salt solution, use a microscope to observe the slide.

— From the onion section obtain a piece of onion skin and put it on a slide. Use a pipette to add some salt solution, then add a coverslip on the onion skin.

13 Allow a maximum of 2 credits for listing the procedures that should be followed to cause the cells in diagram 1 to resemble the cells in diagram 2. The responses must include:

- adding water to the slide[1]
- using a technique that will cause the salt to be rinsed away and replaced with water [1].

Acceptable 2-credit responses include, but are not limited to:

— Remove the slide from the microscope then place a piece of paper towel on the edge of the coverslip and add distilled water (or just water) to the other side. After adding many drops of water put the slide back on the microscope to observe the change. If necessary, repeat the process adding even more water.

— Remove the slide from the microscope, remove the coverslip and carefully rinse the onion skin with water to remove the salt, put the coverslip back on the slide.

14 Allow 1 credit for explaining how the student will know if the starch is able to diffuse out of the artificial cell. Acceptable responses include but are not limited to:

— If the starch diffuses out, the indicator solution will turn black or blueblack.

— If the starch is able to diffuse out, the starch indicator will change color.

Readings
in Science,
Engineering,
Technology,
and Society

Grizzlies at the Door: Can We Bear It?

Montana is known as "big sky" country. It is also big bear country, home to many hundreds of grizzlies. Just a few decades ago, the grizzlies were listed as threatened because there were only a few hundred left in the West. Now they are increasing their population and, as a result, extending their range from the mountains to the plains, along an area called the Rocky Mountain Front. (They are also abundant in parks in Wyoming and Idaho.) The human population has increased in Montana as well.

As you might expect, this can lead to more conflicts between bears and people. Imagine opening your door one day to see a grizzly standing in your yard. Well, it has happened. Even worse, grizzlies have killed some people's chickens and sheep. So a potential conflict now exists between protecting the recovering grizzlies and protecting the people and livestock that live in the same area. Prime bear habitat—containing berry shrubs and other plants that grizzlies love—is found right next to busy towns, as well as in wilderness areas.

Because grizzlies are a protected species, it is illegal to shoot them (except in self-defense). Yet this sometimes occurs when the grizzlies make a nuisance of themselves by preying on people's livestock or destroying property. Most offending bears are "trapped, drugged, and moved" away when they are caught killing livestock or threatening people's safety. However, repeat offenders may be trapped and euthanized to avoid future incidents. People at the U. S. Fish and Wildlife Service are working on the bears' recovery and trying to reduce their mortality.

They want to keep the grizzly population on the rise. Ranchers, in contrast, would like to see the bears' protected status lifted, so that they can be shot on sight when near human property. Christopher Servheen, the Fish and Wildlife Service's recovery coordinator for grizzlies, is working to avoid such conflicts, so that someday no grizzlies have to be killed.

Fish and Wildlife Service scientists are using modern technology to help protect the bears—and the people who live near them. Previously, some bears had radio collars that let the scientists track them from the air about twice a week. Now dozens of bears are collared with GPS units that track and record their movements by satellite as often as every hour, 24 hours a day, enabling scientists to study their locations much more precisely. In this way, researchers can determine when the grizzlies are

too near people's homes, assess what kinds of situations attract the bears, and learn how best to prevent harmful interactions. Just bringing pet food indoors at night and using garbage cans that are bear-proof can help prevent encounters, making the habitat safer for both people and bears. Scientists are also trying to determine what corridors the bears use to move between wilderness areas, so that those areas can be conserved.

Scientists now use modern electronic technology to assess the grizzlies' body fat, figuring that leaner bears might be hungrier bears, which could get into more trouble around people. In fact, when the bears' natural food resources are in shorter supply, conflicts between people and bears increase. The bears seek out other food sources, such as people's garbage, grain, and livestock. Measures that have been undertaken to safeguard people and their property include electric fences, wire fences, and guard dogs. Last—and perhaps not least—there's always that can of pepper spray that should be carried as extra protection against unforeseen grizzly encounters at the door!

The return of the grizzly to the Great Plains is part of a natural process as the bears reclaim their ancestral lands. More people choosing to live *near* the returning bears is another matter altogether.

QUESTIONS

1. Why has the grizzly population increased in the past few decades?

2. Write about some ways that grizzly bears have conflicts with people.

3. How are scientists using technology to study the grizzly bears?

4. Take the position of a Fish and Wildlife Service researcher or a sheep rancher and argue either for or against the protection of the increasing grizzly population. Use evidence from the text to support your argument.

Cool Uses for *E. Coli*: Are They Safe?

Imagine you are at a ball game. Your team is winning and you get hungry and decide to buy a hamburger. You're in a rush to get back to your seat, so you ask the person who is cooking the hamburger to please hurry; you don't want to miss any of the action. You take your hamburger, which was not cooked very long, back to your seat and are eating it happily. However, a couple of hours later you find yourself in the bathroom sick to your stomach—even though your team won the game! What happened? You suddenly realize that you got sick from eating the undercooked meat.

Many cases of food-related illness and death have been reported from around the world in recent years. There were outbreaks that sickened and killed numerous people in the United States, Europe, and Japan during the 1990s. What caused these outbreaks? It turns out that strains of toxin-producing bacteria—*Escherichia coli* (*E. coli*)—had tainted undercooked meat and/or raw vegetables, causing stomach cramps and diarrhea. In 2011, the largest outbreak occurred in Germany and then spread to 11 other European countries. The culprit was a new strain of the same common bacterium.

A normal inhabitant of our gut (and that of other animals), *E. coli* helps in the process of digestion. In that setting, *E. coli* strains are normally harmless. But if a toxic strain gets into other parts of the body, such as the bloodstream and kidneys, it can cause dangerous infections. In the case of the recent European outbreak, a severe strain of the bacterium called enterohemorrhagic *E. coli* (EHEC) was responsible for the illness of thousands and death of dozens of people. In some cases, the EHEC bacterium also led to development of hemolytic uraemic syndrome (HUS), a potentially fatal infection of the kidneys. Europeans were advised to avoid eating raw cucumbers, tomatoes, and lettuce, which were thought to be tainted with the new mutated strain of *E. coli*.

So, depending on the strain, *E. coli* can be either a friend or a foe to people. Most *E. coli* infections are not fatal, and people usually survive, even without medical attention. In the new field of bioengineering called *synthetic biology*, scientists are manipulating harmless *E. coli* for our benefit by engineering strains with helpful traits. The applications for these microscopic organisms include human health to environmental health, among others.

The biochemical engineer Matthew Chang and his team in Singapore are working to produce specially engineered *E. coli* that can kill the antibiotic-resistant bacterium *Pseudomonas aeruginosa*, which can cause deadly infections in people. It turns out that *P. aeruginosa* produces toxic proteins called pyocins that can kill certain strains of its own species. So microbiologists are giving the genes that produce pyocins to *E. coli* and using them to kill the strain of *P. aeruginosa* that infects people. By using a specific protein that targets the lethal bacterium, scientists can avoid the use of broad-spectrum antibiotics, thus reducing the chance for more antibiotic resistance to develop. The pyocin kills only particular strains of *P. aeruginosa* bacteria, so it would not harm the helpful bacteria that live in the body. In addition, the *E. coli* are designed so that they burst open to release the pyocins when they pick up on the chemical signals that *P. aeroginosa* bacteria send to each other. The *E. coli* would therefore be harmless to the human body since they would not survive and reproduce.

For now, this work has been carried out only in laboratories, not in humans. The technology is new and some people are nervous about using one type of bacteria to fight another kind in the human body. The fear is that the bacteria could mutate and become harmful rather than helpful. One microbiologist thinks that it would be best to restrict its use to infections in the human gut, where *E. coli* is normally found.

Another use for engineered *E. coli* that is under development is to fight mercury pollution in the environment. This technique, known as *bioremediation*, would be used to clean up this toxic chemical when it enters water and soil as a result of factory spills and mining practices. The scientist Oscar Ruiz and his team in Puerto Rico have inserted two "mercury-friendly" genes in *E. coli* that bind to toxic metals such as mercury. The proteins coded for by the genes are metallothionein and polyphosphate kinase, which protect cells from mercury. In laboratory tests, the bacteria with genes for these proteins not only survived but thrived in solutions with high mercury concentrations. The bacteria would not only be able to take mercury out of the environment—and hence out of food chains—but might even be able to extract the mercury from them electrochemically to be recycled.

Similar to concerns about the antibacterial *E. coli*, some people view this new *E. coli* strain with suspicion. They fear that the new mercury-absorbing genes in the bacteria could spread to other life-forms, possibly causing harm to humans or the environment. But Ruiz said that these *E. coli* are harmless to the environment and would be used within controlled settings.

So, what do you think? Are *E. coli* friends or foes? Are they safe to use in these special situations?

QUESTIONS

1. Where are harmless strains of *E. coli* normally found?

2. Write about the cause of the 2011 *E. coli* outbreak in Germany.

3. Why might you be concerned about the use of *E. coli* to fight infections? Cite specific textual evidence to support your analysis.

4. How can *E. coli* be used in bioremediation of soil and water?

Spider Silk: Is It the Skin of the Future?

Severe injuries to the skin are both painful and dangerous. The skin forms a barrier between the body and the world, protecting it from dehydration and bacteria. When a person loses skin, due to a burn, bedsore, or other serious injury, doctors try to replace it with grafts of healthy skin. However, this is not always possible. So, scientists have been researching other methods of regrowing skin to place on open wounds.

One proposed method of replacing lost skin is to take a patient's own skin cells, genetically modify them to be resistant to bacteria, and grow them in a test tube. The cells are then placed on a collagen mesh, to which they adhere and grow. The artificial skin is then placed as a graft onto the injured skin. These sheets of mesh encourage growth of the bottom layer of skin (dermis), to which doctors add small pieces from the patient's top layer of skin (epidermis). This then grows and spreads over the new dermis.

Collagen gives skin its structure and elasticity, but it is not the strongest material available. Scientists have discovered that spider silk is a strong and suitable material for forming the matrix of new skin cells. A tissue engineer, Hanna Wendt, at Medical School Hannover in Germany, has suggested that spider silk is stronger than collagen and helps skin tissue to regrow within a matter of weeks. In fact, scientists have referred to it as the "toughest known natural material." In addition, unlike other tissue transplants, the spider silk does not cause an immune response from the recipient's body.

Wendt and her colleagues obtained the material from the silk glands of golden silk orb-weaver spiders. The silk has stretchiness as well as strength, which makes it suitable for tissue replacement. The silk is woven in meshes onto steel frames. Human skin cells placed on these meshes grow very well, as long as they are supplied with nutrients and suitable growing conditions. As with the collagen technique, the scientists were able to grow both the dermis and epidermis layers of skinlike material on top of the silk mesh. The human cells recreated the structures normally found in the layer of dermis, such as capillaries, sweat glands, and nerve endings.

Unfortunately it is not yet possible to harvest large enough quantities of spider silk for medical uses. Wendt thinks that synthetic silk fibers will have to be developed to fill the need for human skin replacement. As a result, many researchers are now trying to find ways to grow synthetic spider silk.

Another option is to produce more spider silk

3

by other means. One way that is being developed is the production of spider silk in goat's milk! Nigerian dwarf goats at a Montreal-based biotechnology company have been genetically enhanced (with the spider's silk-producing gene) to produce spider silk protein within their milk. This silk is skimmed off when the goat is milked. In laboratory experiments, this silk has been mixed with human skin cells, forming a matrix composed of dermis and epidermis. The skin produced is both resilient and strong. In fact, the fibers produced in the goat's milk are so strong that they are referred to as BioSteel. So, besides the use of spider silk in artificial skin, there are other potential applications, such as in prosthetic devices, bulletproof vests, and fishing line. All of these products have less of an environmental impact than synthetic materials such as Kevlar and Polypropylene, since silk is a natural protein that biodegrades over time.

It is hoped that materials made from spider silk will be available for medical and industrial uses within the next few years.

QUESTIONS

1. How does skin normally protect the rest of the human body?
2. What is one way that artificial skin is produced with collagen?
3. Identify three properties of spider silk that make it useful in a skin replacement. Determine the central ideas and provide an accurate summary of the text.
4. How might goats be used to help produce artificial skin? Do Internet research to learn more about this technology.

The Food Groups: Is a Plate Better than a Pyramid?

Two students are discussing their diets. One student says that he tries to follow the U.S. Department of Agriculture's MyPyramid food guidelines. The other student points out that it is now outdated; there is a new set of guidelines to follow. She explains that the food groups are no longer divided into sections of a pyramid. Now the main food groups are reorganized as portions on a plate. As of 2010, the USDA's new diagram, called MyPlate, replaces MyPyramid, which was proposed in 2005.

MyPyramid had six colored stripes of varying widths, each representing a food group. The six groups were grains, vegetables, fruits, oils, dairy, and meat/beans. A figure was shown running up the side of the pyramid to represent physical activity. In contrast, the round MyPlate has four sections labeled to indicate each major food group, plus a side section for dairy products (formerly the milk group). The relative size of each portion is also represented on the plate. Fruits and vegetables are two sections that together make up half the plate; the grains and protein sections make up the other half of the plate. The plate is meant to be a clearer representation of what one's meals should actually look like. It is much easier to understand than MyPyramid, which had no labels in its color-coded sections.

The vegetables group is larger than the fruits group and the grains group is larger than the protein group. The dairy side portion is the smallest section. There is no longer a separate group for fats, oils, and sweets. These items are distributed between the other categories. Although it is not expected that a person will always include food from each group at every meal, MyPlate is an overall guide for a balanced diet.

Some major changes have been made to the kinds of foods included in each category of MyPlate. The grains group now has an emphasis on whole grains such as brown rice, oatmeal, and whole wheat products. It is suggested that fruits and vegetables be consumed fresh and in season as much as possible. The protein group now includes soy, peas, seafood, eggs, nuts, seeds, and poultry, in addition to red meats and beans. The dairy group suggests fat-free or low-fat products that include milk, yogurt, cheese, and soy milk.

Unlike MyPyramid, the new MyPlate does not explicitly show a section for exercise, but it is understood that exercise is important to good health, along with a balanced diet. It is also understood that specific dietary needs depend on an individual's age, gender, height, weight, and activity level. While everyone needs to eat a balanced diet, the exact amount of nutrients required varies by the individual. The suggestions for physical activity can be found in the government's *Dietary Guidelines for Americans, 2010.*

The ideas behind the food portions are that more fruits and vegetables will provide plenty of vitamins, minerals, and fiber plus fewer calories than from the other groups. Grains

also provide fiber, which helps people feel full, so they might eat fewer fatty or empty calorie foods. Proteins are used to build and maintain tissues in the body, but this section is smaller than that of grains because the body does not need as much protein every day.

Although MyPlate might not be an exact guideline for every meal of the day, it gives a general idea of how one should eat to maintain a balanced, healthful diet. The USDA hopes that MyPlate will be more successful than MyPyramid in combating the rise in obesity in this country. While the two students who are discussing their diets at the beginning of this feature might not be obese, teenage obesity rates have more than doubled in the past 20 years. In fact, it is estimated that 35 percent of U.S. teens are overweight or obese. This is mostly due to poor dietary habits. So it is hoped that the new MyPlate will help teens eat a better diet and lead healthier lives. In addition, some high schools are now offering a new course (based on a curriculum developed by FoodFight, a nonprofit group) that teaches students to evaluate food labels, prepare nutritious meals, learn about the economics and politics of the food industry, and keep a food journal.

QUESTIONS

1. Why should people include a variety of food groups in their diet every day? Determine the central idea or conclusion of this article.

2. Name two ways that the USDA's MyPlate is different from MyPyramid.

3. Why is half of MyPlate taken up with the fruits and vegetables sections?

4. According to the MyPlate suggestions, how much of the grains consumed should be whole grains? Cite evidence from the text to support the reason for this.

Malaria: Can We Stop the "Bad Air" Disease?

magine you are planning a trip to a sub-Saharan country in Africa. You would have to be inoculated against a variety of tropical diseases, such as yellow fever. But there is one disease for which a vaccine does not yet exist and it's a potential killer: malaria. The word *malaria* comes from the Italian for "bad air" because it was originally thought to come from swamp gases. But malaria is transmitted by the *Anopheles* mosquitoes that live and breed in swampy areas, not by the air.

Each year more than half a million people (mostly children in Africa) die from malaria and more than 250 million people are infected by malaria in tropical and subtropical regions around the world. Malaria is not caused by the mosquito itself; it is caused by a parasite that is carried in the mosquito's saliva. When a person is bitten by an infected mosquito, the parasite travels to the liver, where it matures; from there it infects the bloodstream. The most common parasites responsible for causing malaria are in the genus called *Plasmodium*, such as *P. falciparum, P. vivax, P. knowlesi,* and *P. ovale.* Typically, an infected person exhibits flulike symptoms, with recurrent chills, fever, muscle pain, and headaches. A severe *P. falciparum* infection can cause vomiting, diarrhea, bleeding and anemia, and even liver or kidney failure.

There are preventive medicines and treatments for malaria, such as artemisinin, quinine, quinidine, doxycycline, and chloroquine, but a vaccine is the desired goal of researchers worldwide. Besides taking anti-malarial drugs, people can use certain techniques to minimize their exposure to infected mosquitoes. These include spraying the walls in a home with an insecticide, spraying skin and clothing with insecticides, and sleeping under a bed net treated with an insecticide. Compared to some other treatments, the insecticide-treated bed nets are a very low-tech and cost-effective way to prevent malaria transmission. Unlike drugs and vaccines, the nets have no need for refrigeration, and they cost about $10 each, so they are less expensive than drug treatments.

The United Nations World Health Organization has approved the production of insecticide-treated bed nets from several countries. The insecticides are actually woven into the fabric of the nets, but their effectiveness lasts for only about three years. An organization called Nothing But Nets buys and distributes the treated nets throughout Africa, where they work by reducing the number of mosquitoes that enter houses that have them. Several organizations send volunteers to actually install the nets in villagers' homes, since donated nets do not always get used by the people who receive them.

However, development of a malaria vaccine is still a high priority for medical researchers because many of the malaria parasites are now immune to the common medicines used to treat or prevent the infection. Selecta Biosciences, a biopharmaceutical company in Massachusetts, is developing so-called targeted Synthetic Vaccine Particle (*t*SVP) products to fight infectious diseases. The company has been awarded a subcontract to develop a "synthetic nanoparticle vaccine" specifically for malaria. The agency supporting the study is part of the National Institutes of Health (NIH). The newly developed *t*SVP products have an effect on the cellular pathways of the immune system, which causes an antigen-specific immune response to the parasite. The *t*SVP vaccine for malaria that Selecta develops will be tested in preclinical studies through a division of the NIH.

A group of researchers at the University of Edinburgh has developed a vaccine that combines multiple versions of a protein found in the various malaria parasites. The protein is known to trigger the formation of antibodies. Thus the vaccine can cause production of a range of antibodies that can give protection against different parasites. This approach is important because more than one malarial parasite can infect a person over time. The scientists still have to conduct trials in humans to see how effective the vaccine is.

Another group of researchers is taking a different approach to developing a malaria vaccine. Scientists at the University of California, San Francisco and Stanford Medical School are involved in research that would test a weakened version of the malaria parasite as a vaccine. The researchers have identified a particular chemical (isopentenyl pyrophosphate, or IPP) that the parasite produces, which gives it the ability to survive in its host's bloodstream. This chemical is produced by a tiny organelle within the parasite, called an apicoplast. Their thinking is that if they could stop the parasite from producing the chemical in this organelle, the parasite would die, since it needs the IPP to make other molecules. The researchers have succeeded in growing the parasite *P. falciparum* in a test tube with red blood cells by giving it the IPP chemical it needs. At the same time,

they are treating the parasite with drugs that stop its own ability to produce IPP (by destroying the apicoplast), ensuring its eventual demise. The idea is to inoculate people in high-risk areas with this weakened form of the parasite, one that could no longer make the necessary chemical. The vaccine would not make people sick; it would give them resistance to the *Plasmodium* pathogen if they are exposed to it later. Like the anti-malarial drugs, which target the parasite while it is in the human bloodstream, this new vaccine would target the parasite during that phase of its life cycle, making it unable to survive in a person.

QUESTIONS

1. What part of the human body does the malaria parasite infect?

2. Write about some of the treatments and/or preventive measures that one can take against malaria.

3. Compare the effectiveness of insecticide-treated bed nets with the potential usefulness of malaria vaccines. What are some pros and cons of each technology?

4. Describe one type of vaccine that is being developed for fighting malaria. Do Internet research to find out more about this type of vaccine.

5. Would you be willing to be vaccinated with a new vaccine that prevents malaria? Why or why not? Write a concluding statement to support your argument.

The Flap over Fluoride: Should It Be in Our Water?

For more than 60 years, the element fluoride has been added to the drinking water supplies of many cities in the United States. In fact, nearly three quarters of the U.S. population drinks fluoridated water. Fluoride compounds, which are mostly a waste product from fertilizer plants, are even added to some toothpastes and mouthwashes. The reason for this is that fluoride is thought to function as a tooth-decay preventive. In particular, fluoride is targeted to prevent tooth decay in children, although it can also protect the teeth of adults.

While children's teeth have improved since the 1940s, it is debatable whether this is due to better diet and health care or to fluoride in the public water system. People who are in favor of fluoridation claim that the addition of fluoride has improved dental health. Those who are opposed maintain that fluoride is a toxic substance that can actually harm the teeth and bones of children and adults. In fact, they want to see fluoride removed from the public's water supplies.

The first studies that claimed fluoride's success in combating cavities were performed in the 1940s in several U.S. and Canadian cities. Since then, there has been conflicting proof of its success. Early studies showed a 60 percent reduction in tooth decay among youth in fluoridated areas. Yet some recent studies have shown no significant differences in cavity rates between children in fluoridated and non-fluoridated cities. In fact, one study has even shown results to the contrary, that children in non-fluoridated cities had less tooth decay than those in fluoridated cities.

Most countries do not add fluoride to their public water supplies. There are several reasons why so many people are cautious about its use. One reason is that fluoridation has been shown, on rare occasions, to cause permanent discoloration in children's teeth, a condition known as dental fluorosis. But this condition may not be the worst problem.

There are those who believe that (based on animal studies) fluoridation can lead to a variety of ill effects in people, such as lower IQ in children. Other possible ill effects that have been attributed to fluoridation include bone cancer; changes in bone structure (leading to more hip fractures); osteoarthritis; birth defects and infant deaths; increased lead and arsenic exposure; an increase in dental cavities; impaired immune system (causing chronic disorders); adverse reactions such as joint pains, headaches, and fatigue;

inhibition of many key enzymes; suppression of thyroid function; acute poisoning; and "severe skeletal fluorosis" when exposure levels are high. Yet none of these effects have been scientifically proven to occur.

There is another major objection to fluoridation of public water supplies: Some people consider it unethical to "mass medicate" the public without their consent, especially when the health benefits have not been proven and there could even be adverse effects. Most recently, a county in Florida voted to stop adding fluoride to its public water supply; this was done for health reasons and as a cost-cutting measure. About 200 other cities in the United States have chosen to stop fluoridation in the past five years, partly due to doubts about its benefits. Although scientists, doctors, and dentists have been among those making these decisions, there are still many who favor the fluoridation of water. The U.S. Public Health Service and the Centers for Disease Control and Prevention continue to support the practice, claiming that the benefits outweigh the risks. In particular, they claim that fluoridation benefits the many people who cannot afford dental care, and at least this way they get some dental protection through their water supply.

QUESTIONS

1. What are some pros and cons of adding fluoride to public water supplies? Support your discussion with evidence from the text and be sure to examine competing views.

2. Does fluoridated water always lead to lower rates of dental decay? Explain.

3. Why do some people find it unethical to fluoridate public water supplies?

GM Foods: What's Cropping Up?

Recent headlines show the increased importance of biotechnology in our everyday lives. These topics include the planting of genetically modified (GM) crops. Some people worry about the possible impact of genetically modified crops on regular and organic crops, on people and other organisms, and on the environment. But that does not stop this technology from advancing and affecting our lives. In fact, according to one source, "biotech crops now cover 10 percent of the world's farmland," whereas 20 years ago there were no GM crops planted. By 2010, over 250 million acres of GM crops were being grown by millions of farmers in nearly 30 countries. More than 50 percent of the GM crops are being grown in the United States, and it is estimated that between 70 and 85 percent of the foods we eat contain ingredients that have been genetically modified. As a result, most Americans have eaten GM foods without realizing it, because there are no laws in this country requiring that GM foods be labeled as such.

Since the start of agriculture, people have been selectively breeding desirable traits in their crops. However, the use of genetic engineering to create GM foods allows scientists to add genes from any other organism to a particular crop. GM foods are given traits that will benefit farmers by helping them increase their yield. Crops are most often modified to be more resistant to insects, viruses, and chemical herbicides.

Genetically modified crops are produced through the use of recombinant DNA technology, in which genes from different organisms are combined. Genes from an organism with a desirable trait, such as having a natural pesticide, are inserted into the genome of the specific crop. Plants can have new genes added through the use of a bacterial species called *Agrobacterium tumefaciens*. This bacterium is used because it has the ability to change the DNA of plant cells. Scientists splice the desired gene for the food plant into the DNA of *A. tumefaciens* bacterial cells. Next they place these cells in a petri dish with undifferentiated plant cells; the bacteria then transfer their modified genes into the plant cells.

The most common crops that have had their DNA changed are corn and soybeans. In fact, 93 percent of the soy that is planted in the United States is genetically modified. Other crops that have been modified include alfalfa, canola, cotton, rice, sugar beets, potatoes, tomatoes, squash, papaya, and flax.

Making plants resistant to insects is helpful to farmers because they do not have to spray their crops with insecticides. These chemicals can be dangerous to handle, so farmers appreciate being able to avoid working with them. This is also beneficial to consumers, since they do not have to eat plants that have been sprayed with these dangerous chemicals. One example of such a crop is the genetically modified corn called "Bt corn." This corn now contains a gene from the soil bacterium *Bacillus thuringiensis*, which produces a toxin to a specific insect, the corn borer. The Bt toxin is harmful only to the insects, not to the people who eat the corn. However, according to one study, Bt toxin has been found in the bloodstream of consumers, raising some safety concerns. The Bt trait is now being put into other crops, such as cotton, rice, and potatoes.

Farmers also benefit from growing crops with a gene that makes them tolerant of herbicides (chemicals that are used to kill weeds but can also harm crops). Herbicides are not selective and can hurt all plants, but if the GM plants are tolerant or made resistant to the herbicides, then they can be sprayed without being damaged. One example of this is the herbicide called Roundup. Strains of soybean, canola, corn, and cotton have been engineered that are resistant to this herbicide, thus making them easier to grow.

Also, efforts are under way to tackle two major health problems in developing nations using GM crops. One plan is to engineer a type of banana that has a gene for a hepatitis B vaccine; the other plan is to grow a variety of rice, called "golden rice," that has a high vitamin A content, to help prevent blindness in Africa and South East Asia.

Some people think that by creating GM foods, we are tampering with nature. Environmental groups in Europe and Japan have limited the sale of GM foods in those regions. Other people are concerned that a GM crop could cause a bad reaction when eaten if it has a gene from a different food to which a person is allergic. Yet a report by scientists in 2005 stated that no GM foods had caused any allergic reactions.

QUESTIONS

1. What are the possible benefits of GM food crops (to consumers and farmers)?

2. What are some possible concerns about genetically modified foods? Do Internet research and cite evidence from the text to support your answer.

3. Do you agree or disagree with the development of new types of GM crops? Write a concluding statement to support your argument.

The Great Bat Die-Off: Can It Be Stopped?

According to a news article in 2008, surveys showed that bats in upstate New York caves were "mysteriously dying off by the thousands," and scientists were not sure why. The problem was first noticed during the winter of 2005–2006. By 2007, biologists discovered caves that had thousands of dead and dying bats. The only telltale sign of illness appeared to be what they called "white-nose syndrome"—a condition marked by a white fungus on the bats' faces. The wildlife experts were not sure if the fungus caused the bats' illness and death, or was just a symptom of their as-yet-unknown illness. By 2008, scientists had confirmed that this was a new species of fungus and named it *Geomyces destructans*.

The biologists at first thought the die-off might be caused by any number of other factors—bacteria,

a virus, changes in weather, a toxin, or some contaminant brought in by a cave explorer from another region. But by 2011, scientists from the U.S. Geological Survey had performed numerous experiments and gathered enough information to be certain of the cause of the huge bat die-off, which by then had spread 2,000 kilometers across the eastern United States and into Canada. More than five million bats have died across this area. The cause was indeed the *Geomyces* fungus, which attaches to living bats in the middle of the winter when they are most vulnerable during hibernation.

The bats typically gather in groups of hundreds and thousands, in areas known as *hibernacula,* where they cluster for warmth as their body temperatures decrease. The fungus thrives in the cold and is passed between the closely packed bats. It attacks the wings and other tissues of such species as the little brown bat, *Myotis lucifugus,* digesting and replacing the healthy tissue with fungal cells. Once numbering in the hundreds of thousands, the little brown bat has had a more than 90 percent drop in its population since it was hit by the fungus. There are five other bat species that have also been affected in North America, but not to the extent of the little brown bats.

What had puzzled scientists at first is that the same white-nose fungus condition is seen among European bats, but they are not killed by the infection. Experiments have indicated that while the North American bats are susceptible to fatal infection by the fungus, the European bats must have built up immunity to it over many thousands of years of exposure. Scientists are looking for clues to the

European bats' ability to survive the fungus to find ways that they may be able to save the American bats. They are also investigating the genetics of the fungus to see how it kills and thus how it might be stopped.

There are many antifungal medications that are used for people and other animals. One of these, called terbinafine, has been tried on the bats, but the bats did not survive being disturbed during the treatment; they are sensitive to capture and handling. The researchers still hope they can find a way to use terbinafine to cure the bats, without disturbing them while they are roosting in the hibernacula. Scientists are studying the genetic variation in the few bats that have been surviving to see if they have some special genetic resistance to the fungus that most other bats are missing. Sadly, the few bats that survive might not be able to maintain their body heat during hibernation, making them more vulnerable to infection. It may take many decades for the surviving bats to recover their population, if they do at all, since even the surviving bats have been weakened by infection and may have trouble reproducing.

Some scientists fear that this epidemic could lead to the extinction of bat species before a cure can be found. And why should anyone, besides scientists, care about bats dying off? For one thing, bats have a huge impact on the environment because they consume millions of insects that are agricultural pests. This could have terrible economic as well as ecological consequences. In addition, this sudden die-off is similar to the recent massive die-off of another important agricultural friend: honeybees, which pollinate countless crops. So the question becomes even larger: What is happening in our environment that is causing such sudden epidemics among wildlife populations? How will this ultimately affect our lives? Fortunately, the U.S. Fish and Wildlife Service is allocating $1 million for research into the white-nose syndrome in a desperate attempt to save bats from extinction.

QUESTIONS

1. Is the white-nose fungus the cause or the effect of the fatal bat infections in North America? Support your answer with evidence from the text.

2. When does the infection spread among the bats? How is it spread? Cite specific textual evidence to support your analysis of the issue.

3. What is the likely reason that European bats are not killed by the infection?

4. Why is it a problem for people that bats are dying off in huge numbers?

From Algae to Oils: The New Green Fuel?

You have probably heard about fossil fuel-related problems such as high gasoline prices and environmentally damaging crude oil spills. Because of problems such as these, biochemists are working on alternative fuel sources to power our cars, ships, and planes. Corn-based ethanol is one such source, but it takes a lot of corn to produce this fuel. The production of just one liter of ethanol from corn requires thousands of liters of water, and takes up land that could be used to grow food crops. Several bioengineering companies are now engaged in producing various types of fuel from blue-green algae—the unicellular organisms that produce much of the world's oxygen. This is truly a "green" technology!

Algae can be used to produce oil, ethanol, and diesel fuels. At the Massachusetts-based biotech company Joule Unlimited, scientists genetically engineer the algae to excrete tiny drops of fuel as they carry out photosynthesis. All that is needed are sunlight, seawater, fertilizer, and carbon dioxide to support the process. And that's the good part—the plan is to try to use waste carbon dioxide from nearby power plants to produce this new biofuel. Using up excess carbon dioxide is a plus, since it is considered a greenhouse gas that contributes to global warming. The fuel produced by the algae is said to burn cleaner than gasoline, so that's another benefit for the environment.

Most of the work is being done in laboratories at present, with many varieties of algae being grown in beakers in conditions that simulate the outside environment. In a pilot project in Texas, the oil-producing algae are housed in structures that resemble solar panels. Some algae have to be harvested to obtain the oil inside their cells. However, other algae have been engineered so that they basically "ooze" the oil into the water. Water that flows through the panels carries off the liquid fuel, which is then separated and collected. The algae continue to produce the fuel for two months before being replaced by a fresh batch of genetically engineered algae.

A company called Sapphire Energy is also using algae to make crude oil, considering it the "most economical" substitute for petroleum. Even Exxon Mobil is getting involved in the business by investing in a genetic-engineering company that can produce the algae-based fuel. Clearly, "big oil" sees that this could be the fuel of the future for all forms of transportation and they do not want to miss out on the moment—or the potential money.

Another good thing about algae as a fuel producer is that unlike corn, the organisms do not need to be grown on good farmland. Vats of algae can be set out in the desert to grow and make fuel. The algae are more productive than corn, producing nearly eight times as much fuel per unit of biomass. And the oil that the algae produce is a pure, high-quality fuel.

It remains to be seen if the algae being grown in the open fields produce as well as those in the laboratories. Some data show that the algae may need more fertilizer per hectare than crops such as corn. Also, a commercial algae fuel plant would require thousands of cubic meters of carbon dioxide every day. So the problem of getting enough waste carbon dioxide gas from power plants to the algae farms has to be solved, too. In addition, although the algae could be grown in desert environments, the facilities would still require large areas of land to produce enough fuel to compete with current gasoline supplies. Fortunately,

it is thought that the same pipelines that are used by the oil industry could be used for pumping the algae-based fuel. Nevertheless, a complete switch to the algae-derived fuel will take some time, since it is still in the pilot phase of development.

QUESTIONS

1. Write about the environmental benefits of producing fuel from algae. Cite evidence from the text.

2. What kind of land can be used to develop algae fuel plants? How might this be an improvement over growing corn for ethanol?

3. Discuss the pros and cons of using waste carbon dioxide to grow algae for fuel. Support your discussion with evidence from the text and be sure to examine competing views.

Glossary

abiotic describes the nonliving parts of an organism's environment

acidity describes a low pH level due to dissolved acids, such as in acid rain

acquired immunity occurs when a person develops antibodies to a disease

active immunity occurs when a person is exposed to pathogen directly

active transport movement of substances across a membrane from an area of lower concentration to an area of higher concentration; requires energy

adaptations special characteristics that make an organism well suited for a particular environment

AIDS (acquired immunodeficiency syndrome) an immunodeficiency disease, caused by HIV in humans

algae plantlike organisms, often single-celled, that carry out photosynthesis

alleles the two different versions of a gene for a particular trait

allergic reactions conditions caused by an overreaction of the immune system

amino acids organic compounds that are the building blocks of proteins

antibiotics chemicals that kill specific microorganisms; frequently used to combat infectious diseases

antibodies molecules that individuals produce as a defense against foreign objects in the body; antibodies bind to specific antigens

antigens proteins on a foreign object that stimulate the immune system to produce antibodies

asexually describes reproduction that requires only one parent to pass on genetic information; e.g., budding and fission

atmosphere the blanket of gases that covers Earth; commonly called "air"

atoms the smallest units of an element that can combine with other elements

ATP (adenosine triphosphate) the substance used by cells as an immediate source of chemical energy for the cell

autoimmune disease condition in which the immune system accidentally targets some of the body's own cell proteins as antigens

autotrophic describes a self-feeding organism that obtains its energy from inorganic sources; e.g., plants and algae (producers)

bacteria single-celled organisms that have no nuclear membrane to surround and contain their DNA molecule

biodiversity the variety of different species in an ecosystem or in the world

biome a very large area characterized by a certain climate and types of plants and animals

biotechnology describes new procedures and devices that use discoveries in biology; usually refers to recombinant DNA technology

biotic describes the living parts of an organism's environment

cancer a disease that results from uncontrolled cell division, which damages normal tissues

carbon one of the six most important chemical elements for living things; carbon atoms form the backbone of nearly all organic compounds

carbon dioxide the inorganic molecule from which plants get carbon for photosynthesis; waste product of cellular respiration; a greenhouse gas

carnivores animals that obtain their energy by eating other animals; see also *consumers* and *heterotrophic*

carrying capacity the size of a particular population that an ecosystem can support

catalysts substances that increase the rate of a chemical reaction, but are not changed during the reaction

cell membrane a selectively permeable plasma membrane that separates and regulates substances that pass between the inside and the outside of a cell

cells the smallest functioning units of an organism; all living things are made up of at least one cell

cellular respiration the process that uses oxygen to create ATP for energy use

chloroplasts the organelles within plant cells that contain the pigment chlorophyll and carry out photosynthesis

chromosomes structures composed of DNA that contain the genetic material

circulation the movement of blood throughout the body of an animal

cladogram a diagram that shows evolutionary relationships among organisms

cloning the production of identical individuals (i.e., clones) from the cell of another individual

community populations of different species that interact within an area

competition the struggle between organisms for limited resources such as food and space

consumers organisms that obtain their energy by feeding on other organisms; heterotrophic life-forms

coordination the means by which body systems work together to maintain homeostasis; a property of living things

cytoplasm the watery fluid that fills a cell, surrounding its organelles

decomposers heterotrophic organisms that obtain their energy by feeding on decaying organisms

deforestation the cutting down and clearing away of forests; clear-cutting

deplete to use up natural resources that cannot be replaced within our lifetimes

development the changes in an organism that occur from fertilization until death

deviations changes in the body's normal functions that are detected by control mechanisms, which maintain a balanced internal environment

dichotomous key the method by which biologists classify and identify unknown organisms

differentiation the creation of specialized cells from less specialized parent cells through controlled gene expression

diffusion the movement of molecules from an area of higher concentration to an area of lower concentration

digestion the process of breaking down food particles into molecules small enough to be absorbed by cells

diversity the variety of different traits in a species or different species in an ecosystem

DNA (deoxyribonucleic acid) the hereditary material of all organisms, which contains the instructions for all cellular activities

dynamic equilibrium in the body, a state of homeostasis in which conditions fluctuate yet always stay within certain limits

ecology the study of the interactions of living things with their environment

ecosystem an area that contains all living and non-living parts that interact

egg the female gamete that supplies half the genetic information to the zygote

embryo an organism in an early stage of development before it is hatched, born, or germinated

energy pyramid describes the flow of energy through an ecosystem; most energy is at the base (producers) and decreases at each higher level (consumers)

enzymes protein compounds that act as catalysts for biological reactions

equilibrium in ecosystems, an overall stability in spite of cyclic changes

estrogen in females, along with progesterone, a major sex hormone that affects secondary sex characteristics and reproduction

evolution the change in organisms over time due to natural selection acting on genetic variations that enable them to adapt to changing environments

excretion the removal of metabolic wastes from the body

expression the use of genetic information in a gene to produce a particular characteristic, which can be modified by interactions with the environment

extinction the death of all living members of a species

feedback mechanisms systems that reverse an original response that was triggered by a stimulus; also, *negative feedback mechanisms* or *feedback loops*

fertilization in sexual reproduction, process by which an egg cell and a sperm cell unite to form a zygote

fetus a developing embryo after the first three months of development

food chain the direct transfer of energy from one organism to the next

food web the complex, interconnecting food chains in a community

fossils the traces or remains of dead organisms, preserved by natural processes

fungi (*singular,* fungus) heterotrophic organisms that obtain their energy by feeding on decaying organisms; e.g., yeast and mushrooms

gametes the male and female sex cells that combine to form a zygote during fertilization

gene expression see *expression*

genes the segments of DNA that contain the genetic information for a given trait or protein

genetic engineering recombinant DNA technology, i.e., the insertion of genes from one organism into the genetic material of another

genetics the study of heredity, or how the characteristics of living things are transmitted from one generation to the next

genetic variations see *variability*

genotype the genetic makeup of an organism, either homozygous or heterozygous

geologic time Earth's history divided into vast units of time by which scientists mark important changes in Earth's climate, surface, and life-forms

global warming an increase in the average global atmospheric temperature due to more heat-trapping CO_2 and greenhouses gases in the air

glucose a simple sugar that has six carbon atoms bonded together; a subunit of complex carbohydrates

greenhouse effect the warming of the planet

habitat the place in which an organism lives; a specific environment that has an interacting community of organisms

herbivores animals that obtain their energy by eating plants; see also *consumers* and *heterotrophic*

hereditary describes the genetic information that is passed from parents to offspring

heterotrophic describes an organism that obtains its energy by feeding on other living things; e.g., animals (consumers)

heterozygous occurs when the two genes of a pair of alleles are different, or hybrid

homeostasis in the body, the maintenance of a constant internal environment

hominids any of the modern or extinct members of the human and humanlike family of bipedal primates

homozygous occurs when the two genes of a pair of alleles are the same, or pure

hormones chemical messengers that bind with receptor proteins to affect gene activity, resulting in long-lasting changes in the body

host the organism that a parasite uses for food and shelter by living in it or on it

hydrogen one of the six most important chemical elements for living things

immune system recognizes and attacks specific invaders, such as bacteria, to protect the body against infection and disease

immunity the ability to resist or prevent infection by a particular microbe

infectious diseases caused by factors outside the body and can be passed from one organism to another

inheritance the process by which traits are passed from one generation to the next

innate immunity is present at birth and is determined genetically

inorganic in cells, substances that allow chemical reactions to take place; in ecosystems, substances that are cycled between living things and the environment

insulin substance secreted by the pancreas that maintains normal blood sugar levels

internal development describes an embryo's development within the female's body

internal fertilization describes the sperm fertilizing the egg cell within the female's body

invasive species

kingdoms the major groupings into which scientists categorize all living things

lipids the group of organic compounds that includes fats, oils, and waxes

malfunction when an organ or body system stops functioning properly, which may lead to disease or death

meiosis the division of one parent cell into four daughter cells; reduces the number of chromosomes to one-half the normal number

membrane see *cell membrane*

metabolic describes the chemical reactions (building up and breaking down) that take place in an organism

microbes microscopic organisms that may cause disease when they invade another organism's body; e.g., microorganisms such as bacteria and viruses

mitochondria the organelles at which the cell's energy is released

mitosis the division of one cell's nucleus into two identical daughter-cell nuclei

molecules the smallest unit of a compound, made up of atoms

movement the flow of materials between the cell and its environment; a property of living things, i.e., locomotion

multicellular describes organisms that are made up of more than one cell

mutations errors in the linear sequence (gene) of a DNA molecule that can affect gene expression

natural selection the process by which organisms having the most adaptive traits for an environment are more likely to survive and reproduce

nerve cells in animals, the cells that transmit nerve impulses to other nerve cells and to other types of cells

niche an organism's role in, or interaction with, its habitat and ecosystem

nitrogen one of the six most important chemical elements for living things

nucleotides the building blocks, or subunits, of DNA; they include four types of nitrogen bases, which occur in two pairs

nucleus the dense region of a (eukaryotic) cell that contains the genetic material

nutrients important molecules in food, such as lipids, proteins, and vitamins

nutrition the life process by which organisms take in and utilize nutrients

omnivores animals that eat both plants and animals; see also *consumers* and *heterotrophic*

organ describes a level of organization in living things, i.e., a structure made up of similar tissues that work together to perform the same task; e.g., the liver

organelles structures within a cell that perform a particular task; e.g., the vacuole

organic relating to compounds that contain carbon and hydrogen (in living things)

organisms living things; life-forms

organ system a group of organs that works together to perform a major task; e.g., the respiratory system

ovaries the female reproductive organs that produce the mature egg cells

oxygen one of the six most important chemical elements for living things; released as a result of photosynthesis; essential to cellular (aerobic) respiration

ozone shield the layer of ozone gas that surrounds Earth high in the atmosphere and blocks out harmful ultraviolet (UV) radiation

pancreas gland that secretes pancreatic juice (containing enzymes that aid digestion) and insulin (maintains normal blood sugar levels)

parasite an organism that lives in or on another organism (the host), deriving nutrients from it and usually causing it harm

passive immunity when antibodies are transferred from another source to the person

passive transport movement of substances across a membrane; requires no use of energy

pathogens microscopic organisms that cause diseases, such as certain bacteria and viruses; see also *microbes*

pesticides chemicals used to kill agricultural pests, mainly insects, some of which have evolved resistance to the chemicals

pH a measurement (on a scale of 0 to 14) of how acidic or basic a solution is

phenotype the physical appearance that results from an organism's genetic makeup

photosynthesis the process that, in the presence of light energy, produces chemical energy (glucose) and water, and releases oxygen

placenta the organ that forms in the uterus of mammals to nourish a developing embryo and remove its waste products

pollination the transfer of pollen grains from an anther to a stigma

population all of the individuals of the same species that live in the same area

predators organisms that feed on other living organisms (the prey); see also *carnivores, consumers,* and *heterotrophic*

pregnancy in animals, the condition of having a developing embryo within the body

prey an organism that is eaten by another organism (the predator)

producers organisms on the first trophic level, which obtain their energy from inorganic sources (i.e., by photosynthesis); autotrophic life-forms such as plants and algae

progesterone in females, along with estrogen, a major sex hormone; see *estrogen*

proteins the group of organic compounds made up of chains of amino acids

radiation a form of energy that can cause genetic mutations in sex cells and cancer in body cells

receptors molecules that play an important role in the interactions between cells; e.g., molecules that bind with hormones

recombination the formation of new combinations of genetic material due to crossing-over during meiosis or due to genetic engineering

regeneration the process of replacement, or regrowth, of lost or damaged body parts

replicate the process by which DNA makes a copy of itself during cell division and protein synthesis

reproduction the production of offspring (i.e., the passing on of hereditary information), by either sexual or asexual means

residue the remains of dead organisms, which are recycled in ecosystems by decomposers; also, the remains of chemicals in the soil, air, and water

respiration in the lungs, the process of exchanging gases; in cells, the process that releases the chemical energy stored in food; see also *cellular respiration*

response an organism's reaction to an internal or external stimulus

ribosomes the organelles at which protein synthesis occurs, and which contain RNA

RNA (ribonucleic acid) a nucleic acid that is generally single stranded (double stranded in some viruses) and plays a role in transferring information from DNA to protein-forming system of the cell.

scavengers animals that eat the remains of a kill, rather than hunt the living animals selective breeding the process by which humans encourage the development of specific traits by breeding only the plants or animals that have those traits

sex cell the male or female gamete; it has one-half the normal chromosome number as a result of meiosis

sexually describes reproduction that requires two parents to pass on genetic information

simple sugars single sugars that have six carbon atoms; e.g., glucose

solar energy radiant energy from the sun that is a renewable resource

speciation the development of new species

species a group of related organisms that can breed and produce fertile offspring

sperm the male gamete that supplies half the genetic information to the zygote

stability the ability of an ecosystem to continue and to remain healthy; usually, the greater the species diversity, the more stable the ecosystem; see also, *homeostasis*

starch a complex carbohydrate made up of many glucose molecules; used for energy storage in plants

stimulus (*plural,* stimuli) any event, change, or condition in the environment that causes an organism to make a response

subunits the four types of nucleotide bases that make up the DNA molecule; also, the components (i.e., amino acids) that make up a protein molecule

succession the gradual replacement of one ecological community by another until it reaches a point of stability

symbiosis a close relationship between two or more different organisms that live together, which is often but not always beneficial

synthesis the building of compounds that are essential to life; e.g., protein synthesis

system describes a level of organization in living things; e.g., in an ecosystem, the living and non-living parts that function together, and, in a body, the groups of organs that work together to perform the same task; see also *organ system*

template in DNA replication, the original molecule that is used to make copies

testes the pair of male reproductive organs that produces the sperm cells

testosterone in males, the main sex hormone that influences secondary sex characteristics and reproduction

tissues describes a level of organization in living things, i.e., groups of similar cells that work together to perform the same function; e.g., muscle tissue

toxins chemicals that can harm a developing fetus if taken in by the mother during pregnancy; harmful chemicals that may get passed from one energy level to the next as they move up the food chain

uterus in female mammals, the reproductive organ that holds the developing embryo

vaccination a medical substance (usually an injection) that prepares the immune system to better fight a specific disease in the future

vacuoles organelles that store materials, e.g., food or wastes, for plant and animal cells

variability the differences that exist among offspring in their genetic makeup

virus a particle of genetic material that can replicate only within a living host cell, where it usually causes harm

white blood cells several types of cells that work to protect the body from disease-causing microbes and foreign substances

zygote the fertilized egg cell that is formed when the nuclei of two gametes (a male and a female) fuse

Index

A

Abiotic factors of ecosystems, 2
ABO blood group system, 54
Accessory organs, 49
Accessory pigments, 33
Acidity, 28
Acid rain, 131
Acquired immunity, 74
Active acquired immunity, 74
Active immunity, 54, 74
Active site, 27
Active transport, 37
Adaptations, 32, 119, 121
Addition, 103–104
Adenine, 108
Adenosine diphosphate (ADP), 41
    conversion of adenosine triphosphate
        (ATP) to, 41
Adenosine triphosphate (ATP), 18, 41
    conversion of, to adenosine diphosphate
        (ADP), 41
Adrenal cortex, 66
Adrenal glands, 66
Adrenaline, 66
Adrenal medulla, 66
Aerobes, 120
Aerobic cellular respiration, 10
Aerobic respiration, 41, 120
Agents, mutagenic, 104, 122
Aggregates, formation of, 119–120
Aging, 91
Algae, 2, 11–12, 32, 43, 180–181
Algal cells, 3
Alleles, 97
Allergic reactions, 54, 74–75
Altitude, 14
    effects of, on terrestrial biomes, 14
Alveoli, 58
Alzheimer's disease, 64
Ameba, 35–36, 43, 81
Amino acids, 25, 50, 109
    essential, 51
    structure of, 25–26
Ammonia, 43
Amniocentesis, 107
Amnion, 90
Amylase, 49
Anaerobes, 120
Anaerobic respiration, 41, 57, 120
Anal pore, 36
Anaphylactic shock, 75
Anatomy, comparative, 117
Ancestor, common, 127
Anemia, 56
Angina pectoris, 56
Animal hormones, 46
Animals
    cells in, 21
    multicellular, 36
    simple, 45
    transport in, 40
Anther, 93
Antibiotics, 125

Antibodies, 53, 73–74
Anticodon, 109
Antigens, 53, 73
Aorta, 55
Appendicitis, 51
Aquatic biomes, 15
Arctic fox, 105
Ardipithecus ramidus, 127
Arteries, 54
Arthritis, 69
Artificial selection, 105
    humans and, 125
Asbestos, 104
Asexual reproduction, 79
    types of, 81–82
Asthma, 59
Atmosphere, 119
Atoms, 25
Atria, 55
Australopithecus afarensis, 127
Autoimmune deficiency syndrome (AIDS),
        26, 72, 75
Autoimmune diseases, 75
Autonomic nervous system, 63
Autosomes, 101–102
Autotrophic nutrition, 32–33
Autotrophs, 2, 32, 120
    photosynthetic, 2
Axons, 44–45

B

Bacteria, 32
    denitrifying, 11
    nitrifying, 11
    nitrogen-fixing, 3
Ball-and-socket joints, 68
Barnacles, 3
Bats, die-off of, 178–179
Behavior, nervous system and,
        63
Benedict solution, 144
Benzene, 104
Biceps, 69
Bile, 50
Binary fission, 81
Biochemistry, 25–26
    comparative, 118
Biocides, 131
Biodiversity, 12
    relationships and, 147
Biological control, 134
Biology
    human
        endocrine system in, 65–66
        excretion in, 60–61
        locomotion in, 68–69
        nervous system in, 62–64
        nutrition in, 49–51
        respiration in, 57–59
        transport in, 53–56
        synthetic, 166
Biomass, 5–6
Biomass pyramid, 5–6

Biomes, 14
    aquatic, 15
    freshwater, 15
    marine, 15
    terrestrial, 14
Bioremediation, 167
Biosphere, 1
BioSteel, 169
Biotechnology, 110
Biotic factors of ecosystems, 2–3
Birth canal, 89
Births, 90–91
    multiple, 90
Biuret solution, 144
Blastula, 86, 90
    formation of, 86
Blood, 53
Blood cells
    red, 53
    specialized, 73–74
    white, 53
Blood clotting, 53
Blood pressure, 55
Blood transfusions, 54
Blood-typing, 54
Bolus, 50
Bonds
    chemical, 25
    covalent, 25
    hydrogen, 108
    ionic, 25
    peptide, 26
Bones, 68
Bone tissue, 68
Bovine spongiform encephalopathy, 72
Bowman's capsule, 61
Brain, 63
Breathing, 58–59
Breathing center, 59
Breathing rate, 59
Breeding, selective, 105
Bromthymol blue, 144
Bronchi, 58
Bronchioles, 58
Bronchitis, 59
Brown, Robert, 20
Bud, 81
Budding, 81

C

Calcium, 25
Cambiums, 94
Cancer, 72
Capillaries, 54
Carbohydrates, 25, 49, 51
    complex, 25
Carbon dioxide, 2, 18, 33, 42
Carbon hydrogen, 25
Carbon-hydrogen-oxygen cycle, 10
Carcinogens, 72
Cardiac muscle, 68, 69
Cardiovascular diseases, 56
Carnivores, 2

Energy flow relationships, 4
Energy pyramid, 5
Environment, 32
    effect of people on, 130–131
    heredity and, 105
    role of people in protecting, 133–135
Enzymes, 27
    factors influencing action, 27–28
    induced fit model of, 27
    models of action, 27
    role of, 27
    structure of, 27
    substrate concentration and, 28
Epicotyl, 94
Epidermis, 34
Epiglottis, 58
Equilibrium, 37
Escherichia coli, 166–167
Esophagus, 50
Essential amino acids, 51
Estrogen, 66, 89
Evaporation, 10
Evolution
    defined, 116
    evidence of, 116
    human, 127
    by natural selection, 120–121
    theories of, 119
    time frame for, 123
Evolutionary theory, modern, 122–123
Excretion, 43–44, 60–61
    adaptations for, 43
Exhalation, 58
Experiment, designing and conducting, 138
Experimental data, making predictions based
    on, 139
External development, 87
External fertilization, 86
Extinction, 12, 117
Extracellular, 35
Eyepiece, 22

F
Fallopian tube, 89
Fats, 26, 51
    saturated, 51
    trans, 51
    unsaturated, 51
Fatty acids, 26, 50
Favorable variations, 122
Feces, 50
Feedback, 71
    negative, 66, 71, 90
Fehling solution, 144
Female reproductive system, 89
Fermentation, 41, 120
Fertilization, 83, 93
    external, 86
    internal, 86
Fetus, 91
Fiber, 51
Fibrin, 53
Fibrinogen, 53
Filament, 93
Filtrate, 61
Filtration, 61
Finches, beaks of, 148
First filial (F_1) generation, 98
Flagella, 46
Flowering plants, sexual reproduction in,
    93–94
Flowers, structure of, 93
Fluid mosaic model, 37
Flu (influenza), 74

Fluoride, 174–175
Follicle, 89
Follicle-stimulating hormone (FSH), 66, 90
Food chains, 4–5
Food groups, 170–171
Foods, genetically modified, 176–177
Food webs, 5
Formaldehyde, 104
Fossils, 116–117
    evidence of, 127
Founder effect, 123
Freshwater biomes, 15
Fructose, 25
Fruits, 93, 94
Fungi, 35

G
Galactose, 25
Gallbladder, 49, 50, 51
Gallstones, 51
Gametes, 83
Gametogenesis, 84–85
Gas exchange, 58
Gastric glands, 50
Gastrointestinal (GI) tract, 49
Gastrula, 87
Gastrulation, 87, 90
Gene-chromosome theory, 97
Gene control of cellular activities, 108–109
Gene expression, 97–98
    effect of stress and nutrition on, 105
Gene mutations, 104, 110
Generalizations, making, and drawing con-
    clusions, 139
Genes, 97
    sex-linked, 102
Genetically modified (GM) crops, 176–177
Genetic counseling, 107
Genetic disorders, detection of, 107
Genetic engineering, 110
    techniques of, 110–111
Genetic mutations, 103–104
Genetics, 97
    foundations of, 97–98
    major concepts in, 98
    Mendelian, 97
    modern, 108–111
Genetic variations
    natural selection and, 122
    sources of, 122
Genotype, 98
Genus, 124
Geographic isolation, 122–123
Geologic record, 116
Geologic time, 123
Germinates, 93
Germination, seed, 94
Germ layers, 87
Gestation period, 90–91
Glands, sweat, 60
Global warming, 131
Glomerulus, 61
Glucagon, 66
Glucose, 18, 25, 33, 50, 57
Glycerol, 26, 50
Goiter, 66
Gonads, 66, 84
Gout, 61
Gradualism, 123
Graduated cylinder, 145
Green fuel, 180–181
Greenhouse effect, 131
Green revolution, 134
Grizzlies, 164

Growth, 18, 87
Growth-stimulating hormone, 66
Guanine, 108

H
Habitat, 9
Habits, 63
Haploid, 84
Heart, 55
    circulation through, 55
    structure of, 55
Helper T cells, 75
Hemoglobin, 40, 42
Hemolytic uraemic syndrome (HUS), 166
Hemophilia, 102
Hennig, Willi, 124
Hepatitis, 74
Herbivores, 2
Heredity, 97
    environment and, 105
    human, 106–107
Hermaphrodites, 84
Heterotroph hypothesis, 119–120
Heterotrophic nutrition, 32, 35–36
    adaptations for, 35–36
Heterotrophs, 2, 35, 120
Heterozygous, 98
High blood pressure, 56
Himalayan rabbit, 105
Hinge joints, 68
Histamine, 54
Homeostasis, 19, 37, 71
    failure of, 71–72
Hominids, 127
Homo erectus, 127
Homo habilis, 127
Homologous pairs, 83–84
Homologous structures, 117
Homo neanderthalensis, 127
Homo sapiens, 127
Homozygous, 98
Hooke, Robert, 19
Hormones, 45, 65
    animal, 46
    plant, 46
    production of, 89
Human activities, 130–131
Human biology
    endocrine system in, 65–66
    excretion in, 60–61
    locomotion in, 68–69
    nervous system in, 62–64
    nutrition in, 49–51
    respiration in, 57–59
    transport in, 53–56
Human circulatory system, 40
Human digestive system, 36, 49–50
Human evolution, 127
Human genetic disorders, 107
Human Genome Project (HGP), 110
Human heredity, 106–107
Human immunodeficiency virus (HIV), 26,
    75
Human pedigree charts, 107
Human population growth, 130
Human respiratory system, 57–58
Humans
    artificial selection and, 125
    central nervous system in, 45
    excretion in, 44
    impact of, on natural selection, 125
    locomotion in, 47
    respiratory gases in, 42
Hybridization, 105

Hybrids, 134
Hydra, 45, 46, 81
Hydrochloric acid (HCl), 25, 50
Hydrogen bond, 108
Hydrogen sulfide, 2
Hydrolysis, 50
Hypertension, 56
Hypocotyl, 94
Hypothalamus, 65
Hypothesis, 138

I
Immovable joints, 68
Immune response, 53, 54
    to transplants, 75
Immune system, 54, 73–75
    damaged or weakened, 75
    functions of, 73–74
    problems in, 74–75
Immunity, 54, 74
    acquired, 74
    active, 54, 74
    active acquired, 74
    innate, 74
    passive, 54, 74
    types of, 74
Immunodeficiency disease, 75
Immunosuppressant drugs, 75
Impulses, 44–45, 63
Inbreeding, 105
Independent assortments, 97
Indicators, 144
Induced fit model of enzyme, 27
Infectious diseases, 72
Ingestion, 18
Inhalation, 58
Inheritance, 97
Innate immunity, 74
Inorganic compounds, 25
Insulin, 66
Intercellular circulation, 38
Intercellular fluid, 54–55
Internal development, 87
Internal fertilization, 86
Interneurons, 63
Intestine
    large, 50
    small, 50
Intracellular, 35
Intracellular circulation, 38
Invasive species, 130–131
In vitro fertilization, 90
Iodine, 25, 66
Iodine solution, 144
Ionic bond, 25
Ions, 25
Iron, 25
Islets of Langerhans, 66
Isolation
    geographic, 123
    reproductive, 123

J
Johanson, Donald, 127
Joints, 68

K
Karyotyping, 107
Kidneys, 61
Kingdoms, 20, 124
Kuru, 72

L
Laboratory
    procedures in, 142–145
        skills involving, 138
    safety in, 142–143
    selecting suitable equipment, 142
Lactase, 108
Lacteal, 50
Lactic acid, 57
Lactose, 108
Lactose intolerant, 98
Large intestine, 50
Larynx, 58
Latitude, 14
    effects of, on terrestrial biomes, 14
Leaves, 40
    structure of, 34
Leeuwenhoek, Anton van, 19
Leukemia, 56
Lichens, 3, 11–12
Life
    concept of, 18–19
    functions of, 18–19
Ligaments, 69
Ligase, 110
Limiting factors, 2
Linkage, 100
Lipids, 26, 49
Litmus paper, 144
Liver, 49, 50, 60
Living things, cellular structure of, 19–21
Lock-and-key model, 27
Locomotion, 46–47, 68–69
    adaptations for, 46–47
    disorders of, 69
Locus, 97
Lucy (fossil), 127
Lugol solution, 144
Lungs, 58, 60
Lupus erythematosus, 75
Luteinizing hormone (LH), 90
Lymph, 54–55
Lymphatic system, 55
Lymph nodes, 55, 73
Lymphocytes, 53
Lymph vessels, 55
Lysosome, 36

M
Macrophages, 73
Mad cow disease, 72
Magnesium, 25
Magnifying power, 22
Malaria, 172–173
Male reproductive system, 89
Malfunction, 61, 75
Maltose, 25
Mammals, placental, 87
Marine biomes, 15
McClintock, Barbara, 110
Measles, mumps, rubella (MMR) vaccine, 74
Measurement instruments, using, 144–145
Medulla, 63
Meiosis, 84
    comparison of mitosis and, 85
Membrane, diffusion through, 148
Mendel, Gregor, 97, 98
Mendelian genetics, 97
Meningitis, 64
Meniscus, 145
Menopause, 89
Menstrual cycle, 89–90
    hormones of, 90
Menstruation, 90

Meristems, 94
Mesoderm, 87
Messenger RNA (mRNA), 109
Metabolism, 18–19
    wastes of, 43–44
Metastasis, 72
Metric ruler, 144–145
Microbes, 72
Microdissection instruments, 23
Micrometer, 23, 143
Micron, 143
Microscopes
    compound, 19–20, 22
    electron, 23
    phase-contrast, 23
    types of, 22–23
Microscopic specimens, determining size of, 143–144
Miller, Stanley, 119
Minerals, 49
Mitosis, 79–80
    comparison of meiosis and, 85
    events of, 79–80
Mixed nerves, 63
Molecules, 18
Monoploid, or 1n chromosome number, 84
Monosaccharides, 25, 50
Morgan, T. H., 97, 102
Motile organism, 46
Motor nerves, 63
Motor neurons, 62
Multicellular animals, 36
Muscles, 69
    cardiac, 69
    skeletal, 69
    smooth, 69
    striated, 69
Mutagenic agents, 104, 122
Mutations
    gene, 104, 110
    genetic, 103–104
    silent, 122
Mutualism, 3

N
Nasal cavity, 58
Natural selection, 120
    evolution by, 120–121
    genetic variation and, 122
    impact of humans on, 125
Negative feedback, 66
    mechanisms in, 71, 90
Nerve cells, 44, 62–63
    structure of, 44–45
Nerve control, 44
    adaptations for, 45
Nerve cord, 45
Nerve net, 45
Nerves, 63
    mixed, 63
    motor, 63
    peripheral, 45
    sensory, 63
Nervous system, 62–64
    autonomic, 63
    behavior and, 63
    central, 63
    disorders of, 64
    peripheral, 45, 63
    somatic, 63
Neurons, 44, 62
    motor, 62
    sensory, 62

Sample Examinations

The Living Environment/REVIEWING BIOLOGY
June 2015

Directions (1–30): For *each* statement or question, record on the separate answer sheet the *number* of the word or expression that, of those given, best completes the statement or answers the question.

1 Materials are transported within a single-celled organism by the

(1) nucleus   (3) mitochondrion
(2) cytoplasm   (4) ribosome

2 Which row in the chart below correctly pairs a food molecule with its building block?

Row	Food Molecule	Building Block
(1)	starch	amino acid
(2)	sugar	starch
(3)	protein	amino acid
(4)	amino acid	sugar

3 The flow of energy in an ecosystem is best described as energy moving in

(1) one direction from the Sun to the producers and then to the consumers
(2) one direction from a consumer to a producer and then to the Sun as heat and light
(3) two directions between the producers that are present
(4) two directions, back and forth, between the producers and the consumers

4 Occasionally, during pregnancy, the placenta can separate from the uterus. This causes a disruption in development and sometimes death of the fetus. Harm to the developing fetus might occur because the placenta

(1) transfers oxygen and nutrients to the fetal blood
(2) sends maternal blood into the fetus
(3) supplies milk for the fetus
(4) breaks down wastes of the fetus

5 Which process produces only identical offspring?

(1) meiotic cell division   (3) cloning
(2) selective breeding   (4) fertilization

6 A photograph of human cells as seen with a compound light microscope is shown below. A cell structure is labeled *A*.

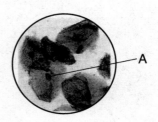

Structure *A* is most likely a

(1) mitochondrion that synthesizes food for the cell
(2) nucleus that is the site of food storage
(3) mitochondrion that absorbs energy from the Sun
(4) nucleus that is responsible for the storage of information

7 A land-dwelling organism, *A*, and an aquatic single-celled organism, *B*, are represented below.

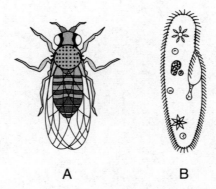

A   B

Which statement best explains how *A* and *B* are able to survive in their environments?

(1) The organelles in *B* perform similar functions to the organ systems in *A*.
(2) The transport system in *B* is more complex than the transport system in *A*.
(3) Both *A* and *B* take in oxygen from the water.
(4) Only *A* can pass on traits to offspring.

8 A man is exposed to large amounts of ultraviolet radiation while sunbathing at the beach. This exposure causes a genetic change in the DNA of a skin cell. In the future, this change can be passed on to

(1) his male and female children
(2) his male children, only
(3) all cells in his body
(4) his skin cells, only

9 Palm oil, produced from palm trees, is not only a biofuel, but is also used in food additives, cosmetics, and lubricants. Palm tree plantations are now cultivated in areas that were formerly natural forests. One ecological concern raised by this expansion is that

(1) the natural forest ecosystem may harm the palm trees
(2) the use of the land for agriculture will increase the biodiversity of the area
(3) humans are changing the basic processes of the palm trees
(4) planting large expanses of one crop reduces the biodiversity of the area

10 Fishermen have harvested certain fish to the point where the population of that fish is decreasing. This level of direct harvesting could cause

(1) ecosystems to be improved for future generations
(2) ecosystems to be severely damaged
(3) the restoration of environmental stability
(4) all other fish species to increase in number

11 Which phrase best describes a gene?

(1) a segment of a DNA molecule found only in the body cells of an organism
(2) a segment of a DNA molecule found only in the gametes of an organism
(3) a segment of a DNA molecule that contains the instructions for producing a trait in an organism
(4) a segment of a DNA molecule that contains the instructions for producing all the characteristics of an organism

12 The molecule DNA contains the four bases listed below.

A – adenine
C – cytosine
G – guanine
T – thymine

Which base pairings normally occur during DNA replication?

(1) Guanine pairs with cytosine. Thymine pairs with thymine.
(2) Adenine pairs with thymine. Cytosine pairs with guanine.
(3) Thymine pairs with guanine. Cytosine pairs with adenine.
(4) Cytosine pairs with cytosine. Thymine pairs with thymine.

13 Evolution of a species could occur as a result of changes in the

(1) DNA in muscle cells
(2) base sequences in liver cells
(3) genes in an egg cell
(4) number of chromosomes in a fetal bone cell

14 One positive impact that industrialization has had is that

(1) industrialization produces waste gases that pollute the air
(2) fossil fuels used by industries help reduce finite resources
(3) industrialization has been a source of many jobs for people
(4) new technologies have increased acid rain

15 When receiving x rays, individuals wear a lead shield over major organs in order to limit the body's exposure to radiation. One reason for this procedure is to

(1) protect the patient against broken bones
(2) prevent mutations in gametes
(3) improve circulation in the patient
(4) increase the chance of a change in DNA

16 When an ant in a colony dies, the live ants will throw the dead ant out of the anthill. If a live ant from the colony, ant X, is sprayed with a chemical characteristic of dead ants, the live ants will repeatedly throw this ant out of the anthill until they can no longer detect the chemical on ant X. What is the best explanation for this behavior?

(1) The ants are responding to a chromosomal mutation in ant X.
(2) The chemical is exhibiting a feedback mechanism.
(3) The live ants must continue this behavior until they have eliminated ant X.
(4) The chemical acts as a stimulus for a particular behavior.

17 Rabbits produce large numbers of offspring during each reproductive season, yet the number of rabbits within a given population changes very little from year to year. The stability of the population size is most likely the result of

(1) the development of mutations in young rabbits
(2) environmental factors that keep the population in check
(3) rabbits continuing to reproduce when the population is large
(4) the survival of more female rabbits than male rabbits

18 Genetic engineering has the potential to correct human genetic disorders. In gene therapy, a defective gene is replaced by using a virus to insert a normal gene into the cells of an individual. This treatment will be most successful if the virus is inserted into cells that

(1) lack a nucleus
(2) are recycled after death, rather than removed from the body
(3) carry out one specific function, rather than multiple functions
(4) continue to divide during the life of the patient

19 In one town, some people support a proposal to build a shopping mall on a large, undeveloped lot, because it would increase business and create new jobs. As a trade-off, the shopping mall would cause a decrease in the

(1) amount of air pollution
(2) volume of garbage and litter
(3) amount of wastewater entering the local sewage system
(4) variety of wildlife populations in the area

20 The human female reproductive system is represented below.

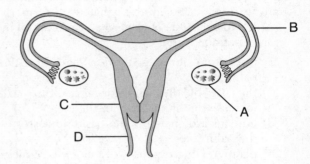

Which structure produces chemicals that regulate the reproductive cycle?

(1) A   (3) C
(2) B   (4) D

21 The diagram below represents a cell structure involved in converting energy stored in organic molecules into a form used by animal cells.

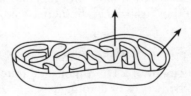

The arrows represent the movement of which substances?

(1) carbon dioxide and sugar
(2) oxygen and ATP
(3) ATP and carbon dioxide
(4) oxygen and sugar

22 The diagram below shows a concept map.

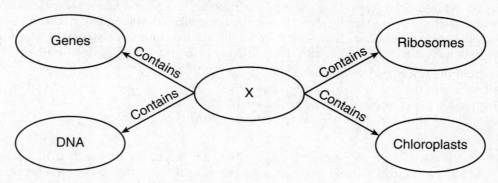

Which label correctly identifies what *X* represents in the concept map?

(1) nucleus

(2) chromosome

(3) autotrophic cell

(4) heterotrophic cell

23 The diagrams below represent two molecules that are involved in metabolic activities in some living cells.

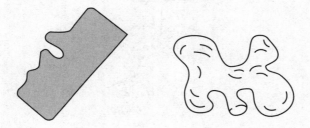

The shape of each of the molecules is important because

(1) molecules having different shapes are always found in different organisms

(2) the shape of a molecule determines how it functions in chemical reactions

(3) the shape of a molecule determines the age of an organism

(4) if the shape of any molecule in an organism changes, the DNA in that organism will also change

24 In the early 1900s, experiments were conducted on two caterpillar species. The members of the two species were each divided into two groups. One group of each species was placed under red light, while the other group of each species was kept in the dark. When the caterpillars developed into butterflies, their wings showed extreme color differences. Exposure to red light resulted in intensely colored wings, while those kept in the dark had paler wing colors. The color differences were most likely due to

(1) mutations in the color-producing genes
(2) the caterpillars in the red light producing more DNA
(3) gene expression being affected by the environment
(4) the caterpillars in the dark evolving less than those in the light

25 A student used a microscope to observe a single-celled organism. As he watched, it looked as if the organism split into two cells. He made drawings, shown below, of the organism over a short period of time.

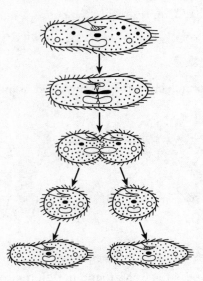

Which process did the student record in his drawings?

(1) genetic engineering
(2) asexual reproduction

(3) selective breeding
(4) gamete formation

26 Medical professionals are concerned with the increase in the number of bacterial species that are resistant to antibiotics. Once resistance appears in a bacterial population, it spreads rapidly. This is most likely because

(1) populations of resistant bacteria are small
(2) exposure to antibiotics increases the rate of reproduction in bacteria
(3) resistant bacteria are small when compared to non-resistant bacteria.
(4) resistant bacteria survive in greater numbers and pass the trait to their offspring

27 When getting a vaccination, which substance is injected into the body?

(1) bacteria to combat a pathogen
(2) white blood cells to engulf a pathogen
(3) a weakened form of a virus
(4) antibiotics to kill a virus

28 Many beverage companies are required to recycle bottles and cans because this activity directly reduces

(1) air pollution and destruction of the ozone shield
(2) overpopulation and soil erosion
(3) solid waste and depletion of resources
(4) thermal pollution and extinction of wildlife

29 The diagram below shows some of the DNA in a bacterium into which a human gene, X, has been successfully inserted.

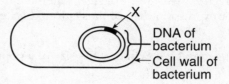

The bacteria that result from reproduction of this cell will most likely have the ability to

(1) replicate all of the genetic instructions found in humans
(2) produce vaccines to be used to immunize humans
(3) produce a human blood cell according to instructions in gene X
(4) produce the human protein coded for by gene X

30 The Eurasian water milfoil is a nonnative species, which was once commonly sold as an aquarium plant, and is now found growing in many lakes in New York State. It has few natural enemies, and grows rapidly, crowding out many native species. This plant ruins fishing areas and interferes with boating and other water sports. This is an example of

(1) human consumption of finite resources
(2) an unintended consequence of adding an organism to an ecosystem
(3) an abiotic factor having a negative effect on an ecosystem
(4) the introduction of a species that has increased the long-term biodiversity of an ecosystem

Part B–1

Answer all questions in this part. [13]

Directions (31–43): For *each* statement or question, record on the separate answer sheet the *number* of the word or expression that, of those given, best completes the statement or answers the question.

31 The graph below shows the size of a population of foxes over a period of years.

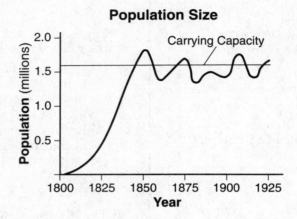

Population Size

If the line did not stay around the carrying capacity, but continued to rise, which concept would this graph best illustrate?

(1) environmental stability   (3) behavioral change

(2) genetic variety   (4) overproduction

32 A food web is represented below.

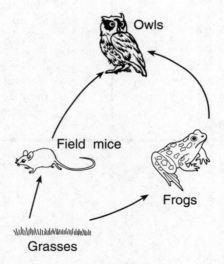

Which organism would receive the *least* amount of transferred solar energy?

(1) grasses   (3) frogs

(2) owls   (4) field mice

33 Birch bolete is a fungus that normally grows on the roots of birch trees in New York State. During the life of the fungus and the birch, each organism receives nutrients from the various biochemical processes of the other. According to this information, it can be inferred that these two species

(1) are both predators

(2) require the same amount of sunlight

(3) require a similar soil pH

(4) recycle the remains of dead organisms

34 The photographs below show different varieties of cattle and characteristics of each variety.

A
Good resistance to heat
but poor beef

B
Good beef but
poor resistance to heat

C
Good resistance to heat
and good beef

Which statement best explains the development of variety *C*?

(1) Nuclei from body cells taken from variety *A* were inserted into egg cells lacking nuclei taken from variety *B*.

(2) Selective breeding was used to combine desirable traits from both varieties *A* and *B*.

(3) The need to adapt to changes in the environment led to the selection of advantageous characteristics in the offspring of variety *B*.

(4) Mutations that occurred in the body cells of variety *A* were passed on to the offspring generation after generation.

35 The diagram below represents a remora fish attached to a shark.

A remora fish has an adhesive disk or sucker on its head, which it uses to attach itself to larger fishes, such as sharks. This attachment causes the shark no harm. The remora fish eat scraps of food that the sharks drop as they feed. This is an example of

(1) an adaptation to a specialized niche

(2) an adaptation of a successful parasite

(3) competition between two fish species for food

(4) competition for abiotic resources

36 Each row in the chart below represents a different population of the same species of insect. Which row shows the population with the greatest chance of survival in a changing environment?

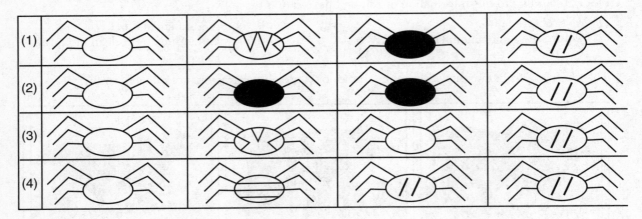

37 The development of nerve, muscle, and skin cells is represented in the diagram below.

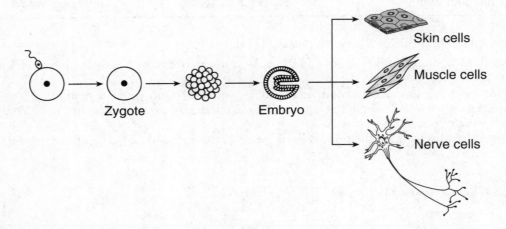

Which statement best explains how each of the different cell types can develop from the same embryo?

(1) The cells have identical genetic instructions, but different parts of these instructions are being expressed in each cell.
(2) The cells have identical genetic instructions, and all parts of these instructions are being expressed in each cell.
(3) The cells are produced by asexual reproduction and contain identical genetic instructions.
(4) The cells contain genetic instructions from two different parents and will express the instructions from one parent, only.

38 The graph below represents the effect of pH on three different enzymes at normal body temperature.

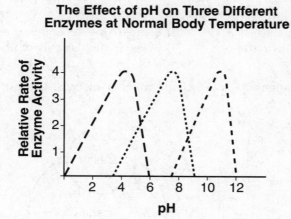

The graph illustrates that enzymes 1, 2, and 3

(1) are not affected by pH

(2) work best at different pH levels

(3) work best in an acidic environment

(4) work best in a basic environment

39 The human male reproductive system is represented below.

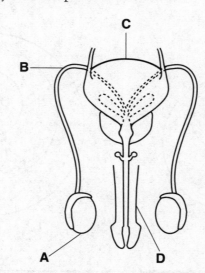

Which structure produces cells that have the potential to become gametes?

(1) A

(2) B

(3) C

(4) D

40 Some scientists have collected and stored seeds for many types of food-producing plants. The purpose of this is to

(1) increase the destruction of environments
(2) continue the deforestation of world ecosystems

(3) decrease the dependence on plants for food
(4) preserve the diversity of plant species

41 Which diagram best illustrates the relationship between the number of cells, tissues, and organs in a complex multicellular organism?

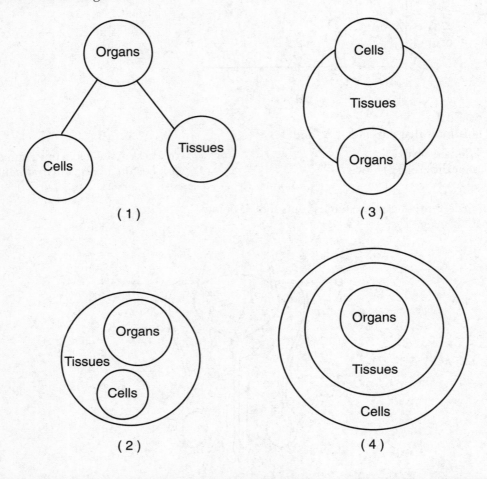

Base your answers to questions 42 and 43 on the diagram below, which represents an ameba engulfing bacteria, and on your knowledge of biology.

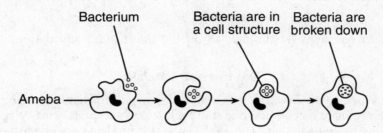

42 This ameba would most likely be classified as a

    (1) decomposer   (3) consumer

    (2) producer   (4) pathogen

43 The activity taking place is

    (1) photosynthesis   (3) autotrophic nutrition

    (2) differentiation   (4) heterotrophic nutrition

Part B–2

Answer all questions in this part. [12]

Directions (44–55): For those questions that are multiple choice, record on the separate answer sheet the *number* of the choice that, of those given, best completes each statement or answers each question. For all other questions in this part, follow the directions given and record your answers in the spaces provided in this examination booklet.

Base your answers to questions 44 through 48 on the information and data table below and on your knowledge of biology.

The Enzyme Catalase

Catalase is an enzyme found in nearly all living organisms that breathe or are exposed to oxygen. According to recent scientific studies, low levels of catalase may play a role in the graying process of human hair. The body naturally produces hydrogen peroxide, and catalase breaks it down into water and oxygen. If there is a dip in catalase levels, hydrogen peroxide cannot be broken down. This causes hydrogen peroxide to bleach hair from the inside out. Scientists believe this finding may someday be used in anti-graying treatments for hair.

A pharmaceutical company, investigating ways to prevent hair from turning gray, took tissue samples from two different individuals. Both individuals were the same age. Each of the samples was placed in a solution of hydrogen peroxide. The volume of oxygen gas produced was measured every 5 minutes for 25 minutes. The data the company collected are shown below.

Oxygen Production in the Breakdown of
Hydrogen Peroxide by Catalase

Time (min)	Sample from Person A (mL oxygen)	Sample from Person B (mL oxygen)
5	2.0	4.5
10	3.5	8.5
15	5.0	12.0
20	7.5	15.5
25	9.5	20.0

Directions (44–46): Using the information in the data table, construct a line graph on the grid on the next page, following the directions below.

44 Mark an appropriate scale, without any breaks in the data, on each labeled axis. [1]

45 Plot the data from the data table for the sample from person *A* on the grid. Connect the points and surround each point with a small circle. [1]

Example:

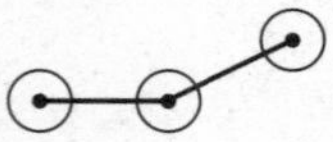

46 Plot the data from the data table for the sample from person *B* on the grid. Connect the points and surround each point with a small triangle. [1]

Example:

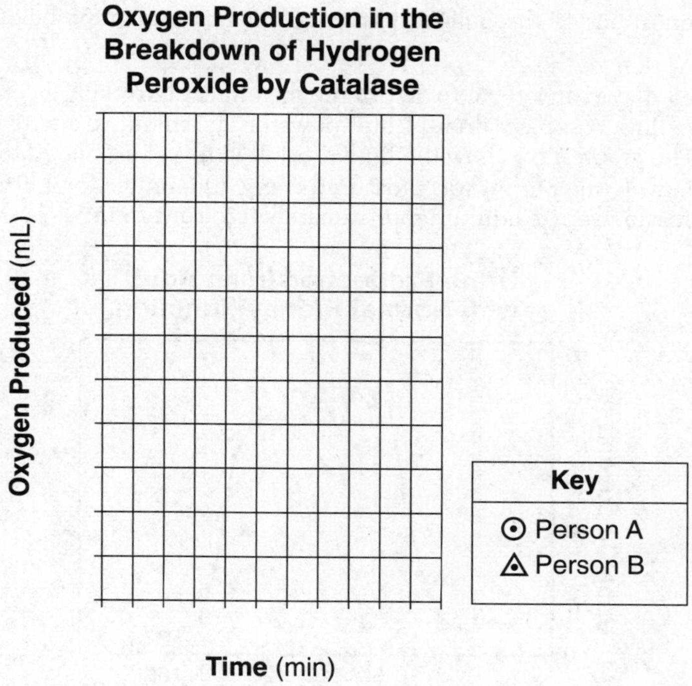

**Oxygen Production in the
Breakdown of Hydrogen
Peroxide by Catalase**

Oxygen Produced (mL)

Time (min)

Key
⊙ Person A
△ Person B

Note: The answer to question 47 should be recorded on your separate answer sheet.

47 If the temperature of the tissue samples used in the experiment had been raised from 37°C (body temperature) to 50°C, the results would have been different because

(1) more enzymes are produced at higher temperatures, increasing the amount of hydrogen peroxide
(2) more hydrogen peroxide is released at higher temperatures, increasing the activity of catalase
(3) increasing temperatures altered the structure of catalase, decreasing oxygen production
(4) increasing temperatures decreased the synthesis of amino acids, increasing levels of hydrogen peroxide

48 According to the data provided, which person, A or B, is more likely to be the first to have gray hair? Support your answer. [1]

Person: _____

_____

_____

Base your answers to questions 49 through 52 on the information and graph below and on your knowledge of biology.

An investigation was carried out to determine the effect of drinking an excessive amount of water on urine flow. A subject drank 1 liter of water in 5 minutes, and then urine output was measured. The graph shows how the human adult kidneys responded to regulate water balance in the body. Urine output was measured every 10 minutes for a little over 3 hours. Normal output for an average adult is approximately 0.5–1 mL/min.

**Urine Production in an Adult
with Normal Kidney Function**

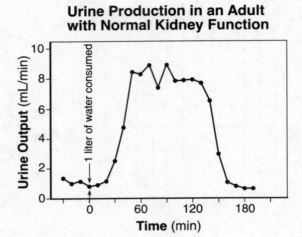

Note: The answer to question 49 should be recorded on your separate answer sheet.

49 One half-hour after the liter of water was consumed, the urine produced by the kidneys was

(1) between 2 and 3 mL/min
(2) between 4 and 5 mL/min
(3) eight times greater than normal
(4) below the normal range

Note: The answer to question 50 should be recorded on your separate answer sheet.

50 The change in urine production during this 3-hour period was most likely the result of

(1) antibody production
(2) homeostatic feedback
(3) enzymatic breakdown of the water consumed
(4) nerve cell malfunctions of the kidneys

51 Identify a structure, in organisms that do *not* have kidneys, that is adapted to regulate water balance.   [1]

_____

52 Approximately how long did it take, in minutes, for the body to return to normal after the intake of water? [1]

_____ **minutes**

Base your answers to questions 53 through 55 on the information and data table below and on your knowledge of biology.

The data table summarizes the changes that occurred to farmland in the years immediately following its abandonment. The land is located in a very stable ecosystem. It was abandoned after years of overuse and weathering, which resulted in the depletion of soil nutrients.

Common Types of Vegetation Present

Years Since Abandoned	Grasses and Weeds	Shrubs	Pine Forest	Hardwood Forest
1	X			
18	X	X	X	
30			X	
70			X	X
100				X
118 (present)				X

53 Which type of vegetation appears to have the lowest soil nutrient requirements? Support your answer with information from the data table. [1]

Lowest soil nutrient requirement vegetation: _____

_____

_____

54 Assuming the ecosystem remains undisturbed, which type of vegetation would you expect to be most common in this area 200 years after it was first abandoned? Support your answer. [1]

Most common vegetation: _____

_____

_____

55 Describe how the types of vegetation present on this farmland would change if a fire burned down all the trees 120 years after the land was abandoned. [1]

_____

_____

Part C

Answer all questions in this part.   [17]

Directions (56–72): Record your answers in the spaces provided in this examination booklet.

Base your answer to question 56–58 on the information and photograph below and on your knowledge of biology.

> The photograph below is part of an advertisement used by a company selling solar panels. The company claims that their panels, like plants, provide clean, renewable energy. They also claim that using solar panels will have a positive effect on the biosphere by reducing global warming.

Source:http://www.stockwatch.in/files/Energy.jpg

56–58 Explain why these claims are valid. In your answer, be sure to:
- explain why both plants and solar panels provide renewable energy, rather than nonrenewable energy [1]
- state how the widespread use of solar panels to generate electricity can help to reduce global warming [1]
- state how the energy-capturing process used by plants worldwide can help to reduce global warming [1]

_____

_____

_____

_____

_____

_____

_____

Base your answers to questions 59 and 60 on the information below and on your knowledge of biology

Fungi are interesting organisms that interact with humans in many ways. Yeasts are fungi used in the food industry to produce products such as bread and certain beverages. Some fungi are valuable in medicine. For example, the drug cyclosporine, which is capable of suppressing the response of the immune system to foreign antigens, and the antibiotic penicillin are both products from fungi. Other fungi are less welcomed by humans. The irritation of athlete's foot is caused by a fungus, and a number of allergies are caused by reproductive spores released by fungi.

59 Describe the role of a drug like cyclosporine when transplanting organs from one person to another person. [1]

_____

_____

60 Explain the difference between an infection caused by a fungus and an allergy caused by a fungus. [1]

_____

_____

_____

Base your answers to questions 61 and 62 on the information below and on your knowledge of biology.

Female mosquitoes need a meal of blood from a person or other animal in order to produce eggs. It has been discovered that mosquitoes have cells on their antennae that can detect the insect repellent known as DEET. The repellent is not harmful to mosquitoes, but when mosquitoes detect DEET, they will not land on the surface where the DEET has been applied. This protects people from being bitten by mosquitoes.

Recently, scientists found some mosquitoes that are resistant to DEET because they do not detect its presence. They bred these mosquitoes and eventually produced a population consisting of about 50% DEET-resistant insects.

61 Identify the process most likely responsible for a mosquito initially becoming resistant to DEET. [1]

_____

62 Mosquitoes with DEET resistance have been found in natural environments. Explain how the continued use of this repellent may cause the percentage of these resistant mosquitoes to increase in the future. [1]

_____

_____

Base your answers to questions 63 through 67 on the passage below and on your knowledge of biology.

Ocean-dwelling (marine) iguanas and land iguanas inhabit the Galapagos Islands. Some scientists believe that both types of iguanas diverged from a common ancestor. Marine iguanas eat algae. Land iguanas feed on cacti. Algae are more abundant in the ocean than cacti are on the islands. Both species lay their eggs in the sand.

Rats, cats, and goats have been introduced to the islands by humans. Rats feed on iguana eggs, cats eat baby iguanas, and goats eat cacti.

63 Identify the process by which ancestral iguanas developed into the present-day marine iguanas and land iguanas of the Galapagos Islands. [1]

Process: _____

64 Identify *one* organism in the Galapagos Islands that directly limits the population of both the marine iguanas and land iguanas. [1]

Organism: _____

65 Which population of iguanas, marine or land, would you expect to be larger? Support your answer. [1]

Population of iguana: _____

_____

_____

66 Would the introduction of goats have a greater effect on the population of the marine iguanas or the land iguanas? Support your answer. [1]

Population of iguana: _____

_____

_____

67 Identify *one* technique that can be used to support the conclusion that these two species of iguana developed from a common ancestor. [1]

Technique: _____

Base your answer to question 68–72 on the information and diagram below and on your knowledge of biology.

The presence of air is believed to be important for root growth in bean plants. The apparatus available to conduct an investigation is shown below. There are enough bottles and other materials to have multiple setups. Air (for aeration) can be bubbled into the bottle through the rubber tube.

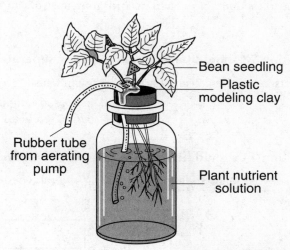

Bean seedling

Plastic modeling clay

Rubber tube from aerating pump

Plant nutrient solution

Source: Biology Handbook, SED 1960

68–72 Design an experiment to test the effect of aeration on the growth of roots of bean seedlings. In your answer, be sure to:

- state *one* hypothesis the experiment would test [1]
- describe how the control group will be treated differently from the experimental group [1]
- identify the dependent variable in the experiment [1]
- state *one* reason why many setups should be used in both the experimental and control groups [1]
- state *one* reason why several different kinds of seedlings were *not* tested in this experiment [1]

_____

_____

_____

_____

_____

_____

_____

_____

Part D

Answer all questions in this part. [13]

Directions (73–85): For those questions that are multiple choice, record on the separate answer sheet the *number* of the choice that, of those given, best completes the statement or answers the question. For all other questions in this part, follow the directions given and record your answers in the spaces provided in this examination booklet.

Note: The answer to question 73 should be recorded on your separate answer sheet.

73 The buildup of waste products in muscle cells that are active might cause

(1) digestion
(2) cellular respiration

(3) increased fatigue
(4) decreased heart rate

Note: The answer to question 74 should be recorded on your separate answer sheet.

74 The diagram below shows the evolutionary relationships among several types of mammals.

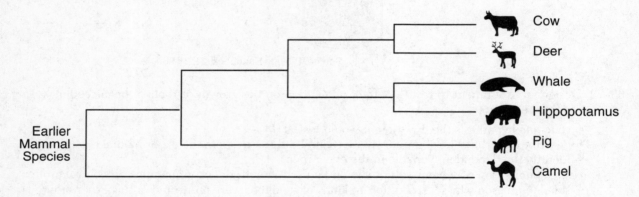

Which mammal would be most closely related to a hippopotamus?

(1) deer
(2) whale

(3) pig
(4) cow

Base your answers to questions 75 and 76 on the information and data table below and on your knowledge of biology.

A group of students obtained the following data while trying to determine the effect of exercise on pulse rate.

Effect of Exercise on Pulse Rate

Student	Resting Pulse Rate (beats per minute)	Pulse Rate After Exercising (beats per minute)
A	66	92
B	82	107
C	65	97
D	74	124
E	79	118
F	68	98
G	89	122

Note: The answer to question 75 should be recorded on your separate answer sheet.

75 Which statement is an example of an observation the students could have made?

(1) Pulse rates in beats per minute decrease for all people after exercise.
(2) Student A most likely exercises regularly.
(3) The pulse rate of student C was dangerously low.
(4) The pulse rate of student F increased by 30 beats per minute.

Note: The answer to question 76 should be recorded on your separate answer sheet.

76 Which two body systems were most actively involved in this experiment?

(1) respiratory and immune
(2) digestive and endocrine
(3) respiratory and circulatory
(4) immune and circulatory

77 The diagram below represents a green plant cell viewed with the high power of a compound light microscope before and after a particular substance was added.

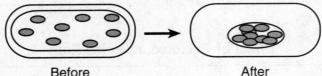

Before   After

Identify a substance that could have been added to the slide to bring about the change shown. [1]

_____

78 Using the DNA base sequences below, identify which *two* species are more closely related. Support your answer. [1]

        Species A: CAC GTG GAC AGA GGA CAC CTC

        Species B: CAT GTG GAC AGA GGA CAC CTC

        Species C: CAC GTA GAC TGA GGA CTT CTC

Species: _____ and _____

_____

_____

79 A student observing onion cells using a microscope was having difficulty seeing any detail in the cells. State *one* action the student could take to improve the detail. [1]

_____

Base your answers to questions 80 and 81 on the diagram below and on your knowledge of biology. The diagram represents the results of paper chromatography performed on extracts from five organisms.

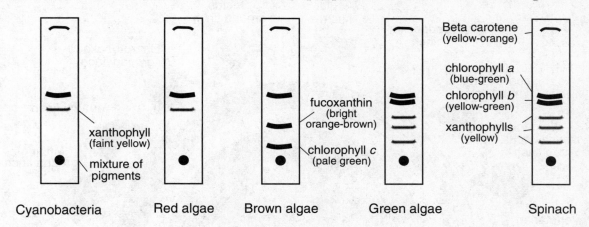

80 Identify *one* pigment molecule common to all five organisms.   [1]

_____

Note: The answer to question 81 should be recorded on your separate answer sheet.

81 Which two organisms are most closely related?

(1) cyanobacteria and green algae (3) brown algae and red algae
(2) red algae and spinach (4) red algae and cyanobacteria

Base your answers to questions 82 through 84 on the diagram below and on your knowledge of biology. The diagram shows variations in the beaks of finches in the Galapagos Islands.

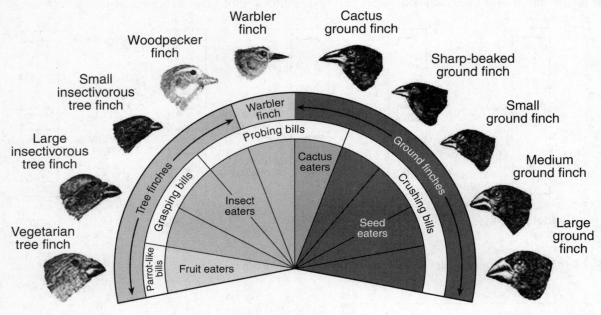

Source: www.pbs.org

Note: The answer to question 82 should be recorded on your separate answer sheet.

82 In this diagram, the variety of beak sizes and shapes are adaptations directly related to successful

(1) feeding

(2) camouflage

(3) defense

(4) singing

83 State *one* reason why the large ground finch and the woodpecker finch can live successfully on the same island. [1]

_____

_____

84 Identify *one* finch in the diagram that is *least* likely to compete with any of the other finches. Support your answer. [1]

_____

_____

85 State *one* reason why a molecule may *not* be able to pass into or out of a cell. [1]

_____

_____

THE LIVING ENVIRONMENT
JUNE 2015

ANSWER SHEET

Student . . . .

Teacher . . . .

School . . . . Grade . . . .

Part	Maximum Score	Student's Score
A	30	
B-1	13	
B-2	12	
C	17	
D	13	

Total Raw Score
(maximum Raw Score: 85)

Final Score
(from conversion chart)

Raters' Initials

Rater 1 . . . .   Rater 2 . . . .

Multiple Choice for Parts A, B–1, B–2, and D
Allow 1 credit for each correct response.

Part A

1	9	17	25 . . . .
2	10	18	26 . . . .
3	11	19	27 . . . .
4	12	20	28 . . . .
5	13	21	29 . . . .
6	14	22	30 . . . .
7	15	23	
8	16	24	

Part B–1

31	35	39	43 . . . .
32	36	40	
33	37	41	
34	38	42	

Part B–2

47	49	50 . . . .

Part D

73	75	81 . . . .
74	76	82 . . . .

The Living Environment/REVIEWING BIOLOGY
August 2015

Part A

Answer all questions in this part. [30]

Directions (1–30): For *each* statement or question, record on the separate answer sheet the *number* of the word or expression that, of those given, best completes the statement or answers the question.

1 Which statement describes a situation that would reduce the stability of a forest ecosystem?

(1) A fierce predator is removed from the ecosystem.

(2) The number of producers remains constant in the ecosystem.

(3) Organisms frequently interact within the ecosystem.

(4) The energy in the ecosystem flows from the Sun.

2 Although the digestive system is primarily responsible for the breakdown of food, this process can be disrupted if the circulatory system malfunctions. The best explanation for this disruption is that

(1) human body systems interact with each other to perform life functions

(2) the circulatory system is the control center of the body

(3) the digestive system and the circulatory system have many organs in common

(4) the circulatory system is responsible for the coordination of life functions, including the breakdown of food

3 When an organism reproduces asexually, it usually has

(1) only one parent, and half as much DNA as the parent

(2) only one parent, and the same chromosome number as the parent

(3) two parents, and twice as much DNA as either parent

(4) two parents, and the same chromosome number as each parent

4 The diagram below represents a food pyramid in an ecosystem.

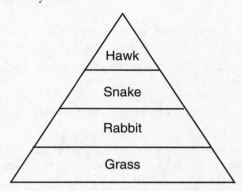

The best explanation for the decrease in the amount of energy transferred to each succeeding level is that much of the energy is

(1) consumed by predators

(2) released as heat

(3) stored within inorganic materials

(4) used in photosynthesis

5 The corn we eat today is larger and has more kernels than the corn people first grew thousands of years ago. Which process is most likely responsible for the changes that have occurred?

(1) mitosis   (3) direct harvesting

(2) succession   (4) selective breeding

6 Which statement is correct concerning hereditary information?

(1) A chromosome is composed of many genes.

(2) A gene is composed of many chromosomes.

(3) Each chromosome carries the same information.

(4) Each gene carries the same information.

7 Which process is most closely associated with the regulation of water loss from the leaves of trees?

(1) digestion of water within the cytoplasm in the leaf cells of the trees
(2) synthesis of protein by the chloroplasts in the leaf cells of the trees
(3) movement of water through leaf openings controlled by the guard cells
(4) absorption of nitrogen through leaf openings controlled by the guard cells

8 A mutation occurring in a human can be passed from parent to offspring when it occurs in a

(1) lung cell, due to exposure to a toxic gas
(2) gamete formed in the ovary
(3) body cell undergoing mitosis
(4) heart cell with chromosome damage

9 If the concentration of sodium is greater outside a cell than inside the cell, which process could move sodium out of the cell?

(1) diffusion
(2) carbohydrate synthesis
(3) active transport
(4) digestion

10 The basic building blocks of a protein are

(1) glucose molecules   (3) hormones
(2) amino acids   (4) fats

11 Over time, data that support the successful evolution of a species would include observations that describe

(1) an increase in the genetic changes occurring in body cells
(2) a decrease in the genetic variety carried in sex cells
(3) an increase in the proportion of offspring that have favorable characteristics
(4) a decrease in the proportion of the population that has beneficial traits

12 Caffeine is a compound found in the seeds of many different plants, such as coffee beans, cola nuts, and cacao beans (the source of chocolate). The presence of this chemical in all three types of plants suggests that these plants

(1) inherited identical mutations
(2) share a common ancestry
(3) were exposed to the same type of radiation in the past
(4) were cloned from a caffeine plant

13 Male turkeys are birds that naturally strut and display their large tail feathers, which attracts female turkeys. This display is an example of

(1) a behavioral adaptation
(2) selective breeding
(3) asexual reproduction
(4) a learned behavior

14 A scientist at a large natural history museum has a collection of fossils that were found throughout the world. Only a few of the fossils represent species that are still alive on Earth today. One reason for this is that

(1) most of the species that have ever lived on Earth are alive today
(2) most of the species that have ever lived on Earth are extinct
(3) fossils of only extinct species have been found
(4) species alive today will not form any fossils for future discovery by scientists

15 Which statement concerning sexual reproduction is correct?

(1) It is not necessary in order for the individual to survive.
(2) The offspring are identical to the parent.
(3) It is necessary in order for the individual to survive.
(4) The offspring are identical to each other.

16 When a paramecium, a single-celled organism, is living under stressful conditions, it sometimes switches from asexual to sexual reproduction. The main advantage when this switch occurs is that the paramecium is most likely to

(1) produce fewer offspring
(2) increase variation among its offspring
(3) avoid having to find a mate
(4) produce clones of itself

17 The diagram below represents some processes in the early development of a multicellular organism.

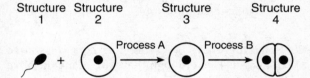

Structure 1   Structure 2   Structure 3   Structure 4

Process A   Process B

Which statement describing this diagram is correct?

(1) The cell represented by structure 3 has the same genetic content as structure 2.
(2) Process A represents the process of meiosis.
(3) Each cell in structure 4 has the same genetic content as that in structure 3.
(4) Processes A and B both occur in the placenta.

18 Which statement describes a function of the hormone estrogen?

(1) It regulates the secretion of digestive enzymes.
(2) It promotes sperm production in males.
(3) It influences the development of adult sex characteristics.
(4) It maintains blood sugar levels.

19 The primary function of the human male reproductive system is to

(1) provide a site for fertilization
(2) produce and transport gametes
(3) protect and nourish the embryo
(4) prevent urine from leaving the body

20 In an embryo, the formation of many types of tissues and organs occurs as a result of the process of

(1) fertilization
(2) genetic sorting
(3) differentiation
(4) gene recombination

21 Which activity would be an appropriate first step when designing an experiment?

(1) reporting a conclusion based on multiple experimental trials
(2) researching the problem, using information from a variety of sources
(3) creating a data table to organize experimental observations
(4) repeating the experiment with a different hypothesis

22 Every time a child visited a cousin who has two cats, the child's eyes turned red, itched, and began to water. Then, the child began to have trouble breathing. It is most likely that the child reacted this way because

(1) normally harmless cat antigens stimulated the immune system
(2) it is difficult for the respiratory system to filter cat antigens out of the inhaled air
(3) cat antigens are a health hazard, since they always cause disease
(4) cat antigens stop the immune system from making antibodies, so bacteria cause these responses

23 Shrimp that live in the cold waters off Alaska will die if introduced into warm water. One likely reason these shrimp do not survive is that enzymes in the shrimp

(1) start to replicate
(2) change shape
(3) are composed of fat molecules that melt
(4) break down into small starch molecules

24 A DNA segment removed from neurospora (a pink mold) contained the base sequence G-T-C-C-A-T-G-C-A. A similar segment of DNA removed from neurospora that had been exposed to radiation for several hours had the base sequence G-T-C-C-A-T. This change in the base sequence is an example of

(1) a deletion   (3) a substitution
(2) an insertion   (4) a replication

25 Farmers in India have increased the harvest yield of food crops like eggplant by growing them from seeds that have been modified to produce a bacterial toxin that is harmful to pest insects. This is an example of

(1) selective breeding of the insects
(2) spraying an insecticide on plants
(3) selective breeding of the eggplant
(4) an application of biotechnology

26 The graph below shows changes in human population numbers over time.

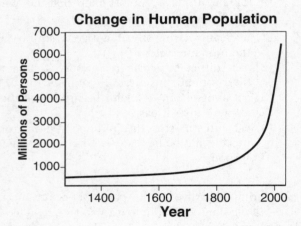

Change in Human Population

A consequence of these changes is

(1) an increase in the numbers and kinds of organisms worldwide
(2) a decrease in the availability of natural resources
(3) a decrease in deforestation due to technological improvements
(4) an increase in biosphere stability

27 In the fall, some farmers plow the remains of corn plants into the ground. This activity contributes most directly to the

(1) increase in the biodiversity of their fields
(2) depletion of nonrenewable resources
(3) destruction of natural habitats
(4) recycling of organic matter

28 A person usually experiences small variations in body temperature over a 24-hour period. These variations in temperature are an example of

(1) an immune response
(2) genetic differences between individuals
(3) an adaptation to global warming
(4) dynamic equilibrium

29 Fossil fuels have been used for years as a source of energy. Even though there are many negative issues associated with the use of fossil fuels, they continue to be used to a great extent. This is most likely because

(1) they have been commercially available as an energy source
(2) there are alternatives to these types of fuels
(3) they have had a positive effect on global temperatures
(4) fossil fuels can be burned to produce large quantities of carbon dioxide

30 Sometimes, a person is born with one or more extra chromosomes in each cell. This usually results in abnormalities because the affected person has

(1) a reduced number of genes in cell nuclei
(2) fewer cell mutations than a person with a normal chromosome number
(3) more genes in each cell than a person with a normal chromosome number
(4) less DNA in cell nuclei, but more proteins in cell mitochondria

Part B–1

Answer all questions in this part. [13]

Directions (31–43): For *each* statement or question, record on the separate answer sheet the *number* of the word or expression that, of those given, best completes the statement or answers the question.

Base your answers to questions 31 through 33 on the information and graph below and on your knowledge of biology.

A population composed of tan snails and black snails inhabits the same sandy beach. A nearby volcano erupted, and black lava particles washed down to the beach. The once tan beach was now black. The graph below shows the population of tan snails and black snails before and after the volcanic eruption.

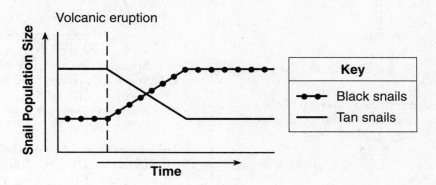

31 Which statement concerning the snails is correct?

(1) The lava particles turned the tan snails black.
(2) The tan snails will become extinct.
(3) The black snails had an adaptive advantage.
(4) The tan snails preyed on the black snails.

32 The increase in the number of black snails can best be explained by

(1) natural selection after an environmental change
(2) climatic change followed by ecological succession
(3) increased stability due to a decrease in variation
(4) an increase in mutation rate

33 Variation in snail color is an example of

(1) environmental stability
(2) a natural limitation
(3) equilibrium
(4) diversity

34 The diagram below represents relationships in a community. After a pathogen reduced the population of grasshoppers, the number of mice increased, while the numbers of toads and rabbits decreased.

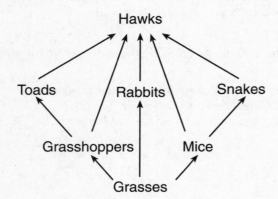

These changes in the community demonstrate that

(1) ecosystems are shaped by nonliving factors
(2) autotrophs convert solar energy into food
(3) grasshoppers are producers that are essential for ecosystem stability
(4) populations are linked with many others in the ecosystem

Base your answers to questions 35 and 36 on the diagram below, which represents a metabolic process, and on your knowledge of biology.

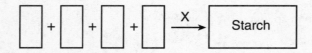

35 This process best represents

(1) the bonding of amino acids to form a starch molecule
(2) the digestion of amino acids to form a starch molecule
(3) the bonding of simple sugars to form a starch molecule
(4) the digestion of simple sugars to form a starch molecule

36 The letter X in the process represents

(1) an antibody   (3) a receptor
(2) a hormone   (4) an enzyme

37 The evolutionary pathways of ten different species are represented in the diagram below.

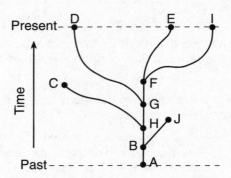

Which statement would most likely be correct, based on the information in the diagram?

(1) Species C had many variations and lived in a stable, unchanging environment.
(2) Species D, C, and J are extinct.
(3) Species F evolved from species D.
(4) Species J had little variation and lived in a changing environment.

38 Blockages caused by a condition known as Pelvic Inflammatory Disease (PID) are represented in the diagram of the female reproductive system below.

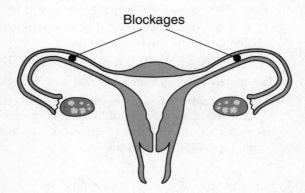

If blockages of this type occur, the most likely result would be that

(1) the egg would remain in the uterus and not travel upward
(2) the female gamete would not be able to unite with the male gamete
(3) hormones could not be produced by the ovaries
(4) the process of asexual reproduction would be prevented or interrupted

Base your answers to questions 39 and 40 on the information below and on your knowledge of biology. The graph below shows the growth of *Paramecium aurelia* in the same culture dish for 14 days.

Growth of *Paramecium aurelia*

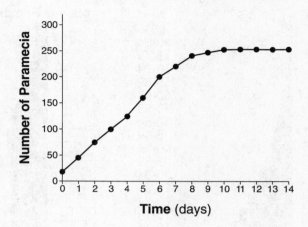

39 If no additional materials were added to the culture dish, after day 14, the paramecium population would most probably

(1) remain the same, since it has reached carrying capacity and has an unlimited food supply
(2) begin to increase as they continue to reproduce
(3) begin to increase, since they have not yet reached carrying capacity
(4) begin to decrease as finite resources are used up

40 In another experiment, a second species of paramecium was introduced into a culture dish with *Paramecium aurelia*. Which statement describes a possible result as the populations interact over the next 14 days?

(1) The population numbers of *Paramecium aurelia* would be lower than 250, since the new species is competing with it for resources.
(2) The population of *Paramecium aurelia* would increase above 250, since they would mate with the new species.
(3) The population of *Paramecium aurelia* would increase above 250, since the two species occupy the same niche.
(4) The population of *Paramecium aurelia* would remain at 250, since the species compete with each other for the same resources.

41 The chart below lists substances involved in the process of photosynthesis.

Substance

A	glucose
B	oxygen
C	carbon dioxide
D	water

Which statement best describes how these substances interact in photosynthesis?

(1) *A* and *B* combine to produce *C* and *D*.
(2) *B* and *C* combine to produce *A* and *D*.
(3) *C* and *D* combine to produce *A* and *B*.
(4) *A* and *C* combine to produce *B* and *D*.

Base your answers to questions 42 and 43 on the diagram below and on your knowledge of biology. The diagram represents the current percentage of each population by age and gender (male/female) for two countries.

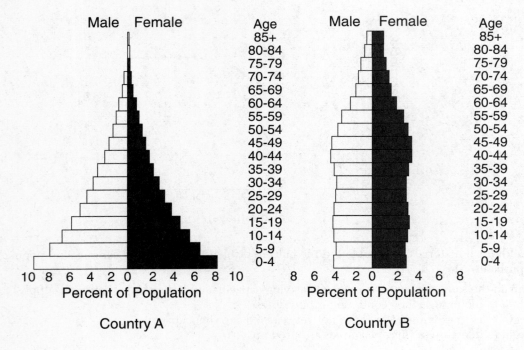

Adapted from: *Campbell Biology, 8th edition*

42 At the present time, both populations have the same number of individuals. In which of these countries will the population growth over the next 20 years place the greatest strain on the environment?

(1) Country *A*, since the larger percentage of young could result in rapid population growth
(2) Country *B*, since the smaller percentage of young could result in rapid population growth
(3) Country *A*, since the smaller percentage of people over 60 uses the most resources
(4) Country *B*, since the larger percentage of people over 60 uses the fewest resources

43 Approximately what percent of the population of Country *A* is less than 10 years old?

(1) 8%   (3) 32%
(2) 16%   (4) 64%

Part B–2

Answer all questions in this part. [12]

Directions (44–55): For those questions that are multiple choice, record on the separate answer sheet the *number* of the choice that, of those given, best completes each statement or answers each question. For all other questions in this part, follow the directions given and record your answers in the spaces provided in this examination booklet.

Base your answers to questions 44 through 47 on the information below and on your knowledge of biology.

An experiment was carried out to determine the effect of exposure to UV light on the growth of bacteria. Equal quantities of bacteria were spread on 5 petri dishes containing nutrient agar. Half of each petri dish was exposed to UV light for various amounts of time, and the other half was protected from the UV light with a UV screen. After the UV treatment, the bacteria were grown in an incubator for 24 hours, and the number of colonies was counted. The diagram below represents the initial set up.

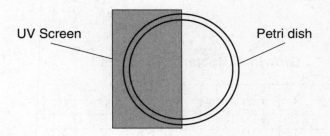

The table below contains the data collected by counting the number of bacterial colonies growing on both the screen-covered side and the unscreened side.

Growth of Bacterial Colonies

Petri Dish	Exposure Time to UV Light	Number of Bacterial Colonies on Screened Side	Number of Bacterial Colonies on Unscreened Side
1	No exposure (0.0 minutes)	17	18
2	1.0 minute	18	15
3	2.0 minutes	17	11
4	5.0 minutes	18	4
5	10.0 minutes	16	1

Directions (44–46): Using the information in the data table, construct a line graph on the grid below, following the directions below.

44 Mark an appropriate scale, without any breaks in the data, on each axis. [1]

45 Plot the data for the number of bacterial colonies on the screened side. Connect the points and surround each point with a small circle. [1]

Example: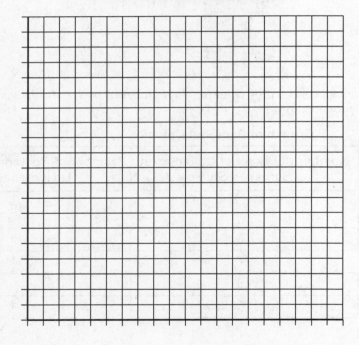

46 Plot the data for the number of bacterial colonies on the unscreened side. Connect the points and surround each point with a small triangle. [1]

Example:

Growth of Bacterial Colonies

Number of Bacterial Colonies

Key
⊙ Screened side
△ Unscreened side

Exposure Time to UV Light (minutes)

Note: The answer to question 47 should be recorded on your separate answer sheet.

47 The diagram below represents cellular growth that can occur in human skin after prolonged exposure to ultraviolet light.

Skin cells

Which statement provides a possible explanation for this growth pattern?

(1) Manipulation of genes caused the movement of embryonic skin cells.
(2) Exposure to light stimulated the development of cells containing ozone.
(3) Uncontrolled mitotic division occurred as a result of gene mutations.
(4) An immune reaction triggered the formation of excess blood cells.

Base your answers to questions 48 and 49 on the information and graphs below and on your knowledge of biology. The graphs show the relative enzymatic activity of four different enzymes in acidic (below pH 7) and basic (above pH 7) environments.

pH and Enzyme Activity

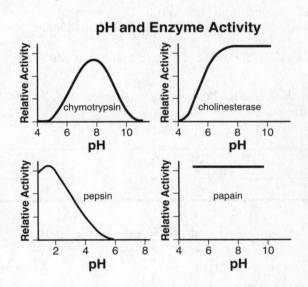

Part of Digestive System	pH Range
mouth	6.5 – 7.5
stomach	1.5 – 4.0
small intestine	4.0 – 7.0
large intestine	4.0 – 7.0

48 Which enzyme would most likely function in the stomach? Support your answer. [1]

Enzyme: _____

_____

_____

Note: The answer to question 49 should be recorded on your separate answer sheet.

49 The activity of which enzyme decreases in both acidic and basic environments?

(1) chymotrypsin
(2) pepsin

(3) cholinesterase
(4) papain

Base your answers to questions 50 and 51 on the information below and on your knowledge of biology.

Head Start for Hellbenders

The hellbenders (a species of large salamander) at the Bronx Zoo are now approximately seven inches in length and will grow to full size in about five years. Once they are about two-and-a-half years old, they will be returned to the wild in western New York State. Hellbender populations are declining due to several factors including over-collection for the pet trade, disease, pollution, and habitat destruction. Juvenile hellbenders in the wild currently face great difficulties in reaching adulthood, so the "head start" provided by the reintroduction of the 41 animals will help boost local populations.

Source: Wildlife Conservation Society, *Members News*
May/June 2011

Note: The answer to question 50 should be recorded on your separate answer sheet.

50 Which statement best explains the hellbender population decline in western New York State?

(1) Human activities had the unexpected consequence of decreasing the hellbender population to a dangerous level.

(2) Humans have purposefully removed the hellbender from its habitat due to its aggressive behavior.

(3) The decline of the hellbender population is due mainly to natural causes that humans cannot control.

(4) The hellbender population decreased because salamanders are very resistant to climate change.

51 Describe *one* potential ecological effect, other than the loss of the hellbender from western New York State, of the hellbender population continuing to decline.   [1]

_____

_____

_____

52–54 Animals eat and digest food to obtain the energy available for life activities. Discuss energy use in animals. In your discussion, be sure to:

• identify the type of protein molecules used to digest food   [1]

• identify the organelle where energy from nutrients is released   [1]

• state *one* inference that can be made concerning a cell that has many of these organelles   [1]

_____

_____

_____

_____

_____

_____

Base your answer to question 55 on the diagram below and on your knowledge of biology. The diagram represents four types of bacteria.

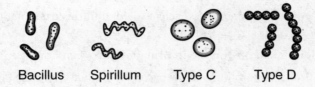

Bacillus   Spirillum   Type C   Type D

55 A dichotomous key to these bacterial types is shown below. Complete the missing information for sections 3a. and 3b. so that the key is complete for all four types. [1]

1a. Is rod shaped	bacillus
1b. Is not rod shaped	go to 2
2a. Is spiral shaped....................................	spirillum
2b. Is not spiral shaped..............................	go to 3
3a. _____	type C
3b. _____	type D

Part C

Answer all questions in this part. [17]

Directions (56–72): Record your answers in the spaces provided in this examination booklet.

Base your answers to questions 56 and 57 on the information below and on your knowledge of biology.

The fight-or-flight response in humans prepares the body to fight off or run away from a potential threat. This response results from a series of nerve and chemical signals that direct how cells function. This, in turn, determines the actions of organs in these situations. Some of the changes experienced by the individuals as part of this response include:

increased pulse rate
increased blood glucose levels
increased breathing rate

56 Select *one* of the listed changes experienced by the individual and write it on the line below. Explain how the change you chose allows the individual to effectively respond to a threat. [1]

Change: _____

_____

_____

57 Once the threat has passed, another series of changes returns the body to its original state. Why must this occur? [1]

_____

_____

Base your answers to questions 58 and 59 on the article below and on your knowledge of biology.

Bats Devastated by Deadly Fungus

The most common bat species in North America, the little brown bat, could be facing extinction because of a fungus. The fungus, called white-nose syndrome, grows on the exposed skin of bats as they hibernate in cool caves or mines. Infected bats develop lesions (sores) on their wings, which play important roles in water balance, circulation and heat regulation. These lesions on a bat's wings or on its nose cause the bat to wake up during hibernation. Waking up early forces the bat to use up the energy it has stored as fat for its long sleep, exhausting the animal and eventually killing it.

In some infected caves, 90 percent to 100 percent of bats die. On average, the disease takes out 73 percent of the bat population at a given hibernation site. If infection continues at current rates, the researchers predict that the little brown bat population will drop below 0.01 percent of its current numbers by 2026.

The loss of the little brown bat would be harmful for humans because bats eat their body weight in insects each night. Many of these bugs are agricultural pests or carriers of human disease.

One way to decrease the spread of the disease would be for the researchers who visit infected caves to decontaminate their clothes and gear with antiseptics. It has also been suggested that a small number of these bats could be placed in an artificial hibernating area and medicated to protect them.

58 Describe *one* way that an infection with the white-nose fungus can cause death in little brown bats. [1]

_____

_____

59 Describe *one* way that the little brown bats can be helped. [1]

_____

_____

60 Describe how a student could use a microscope to compare the size of frog skin cells to the size of human skin cells.   [1]

_____

_____

Base your answers to questions 61 through 63 on the information below and on your knowledge of biology.

    Chickenpox vaccine is the best way to prevent chickenpox. Vaccination not only protects vaccinated persons, it also reduces the risk for exposure in the community for persons unable to be vaccinated because of illness or other conditions, including those who may be at greater risk for severe disease. While no vaccine is 100% effective in preventing disease, the chickenpox vaccine is very effective: about 8 to 9 of every 10 people who are vaccinated are completely protected from chickenpox. In addition, the vaccine almost always prevents against severe disease. If a vaccinated person does get chickenpox, it is usually a very mild case lasting only a few days and involving fewer skin lesions (usually less than 50), mild or no fever, and few other symptoms.

Source: www.cdc.gov

61 Identify the component of a vaccine that makes it effective.   [1]

_____

_____

62 Describe how a vaccination prevents disease in the individual who receives a vaccination.   [1]

_____

_____

63 Describe how vaccinations help to prevent the spread of disease, even in people who have not received the vaccination.   [1]

_____

_____

Base your answer to question 64–66 on the diagram below and on your knowledge of biology. The diagram represents a food web typical of the Great Lakes area of New York State.

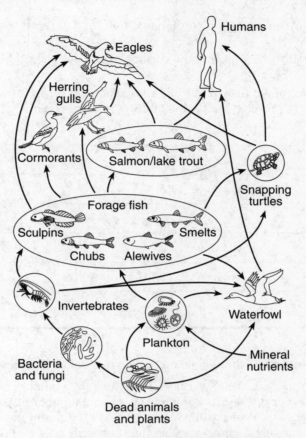

Adapted from: http://www.uwsp.edu/geo/ faculty/ritter/
geog101/textbook/title_page.html

64–66 Some people have argued for the removal of cormorants from the eastern shores of Lake Ontario because of their negative effects on the fishing industry. Describe the consequences of this action. In your answer, be sure to:

• state *one* reason why removing the cormorants from the food web could have a positive impact on the fishing industry   [1]

• state *one* possible effect of removing the cormorants on a species other than fish and support your answer   [1]

• describe *one* action, other than removing a population of organisms from the environment, that humans could take to preserve the fishing industry in Lake Ontario   [1]

_____

_____

_____

_____

_____

_____

Base your answers to questions 67 through 69 on the passage below and on your knowledge of biology.

   A field in New York State is mowed all summer long for a number of years. The field is sold, and the new owner decides to stop mowing. Over a number of years, the ecosystem begins to undergo ecological succession. After a series of different plant communities are present, the area eventually becomes a stable forest ecosystem.

67 Explain why *not* mowing the field allowed the ecosystem to undergo ecological succession.   [1]

_____

_____

68 Identify *one* specific human activity, other than mowing, that could alter this succession and explain how this activity affects biodiversity.   [1]

Human activity: _____

Effect on biodiversity: _____

_____

69 Describe how this forest ecosystem would respond to a natural disaster, such as a flood, that resulted in the destruction of the plant community.   [1]

_____

_____

70 In a laboratory, spinach leaves exposed to continuous fluorescent light increased in vitamin content by 50 to 100 percent. Spinach leaves kept in darkness for a similar period of time either lost vitamin content or produced no gain. Describe how these findings could influence the way in which spinach is displayed for sale in supermarkets.   [1]

_____

_____

Base your answers to questions 71 and 72 on the passage below and on your knowledge of biology.

On April 20, 2010, an explosion occurred at an oil well in the Gulf of Mexico, causing millions of gallons of oil to escape into the water over the next few months. Large areas of the Gulf were covered by oil. As the oil washed ashore, many areas along the coastline that were breeding grounds for various bird species were contaminated. By November 2010, researchers along the coast and in the Gulf had collected 6104 dead birds, 609 dead turtles, and 100 dead mammals. Although the oil well had provided oil for energy for a large number of people, the oil spill had a great effect on the ecosystems in and around the Gulf of Mexico.

71 Explain how the original decision to drill for oil in the Gulf of Mexico could be considered a trade-off. [1]

_____

_____

72 State *one* possible reason why it will most likely take the bird populations more time to recover from this oil spill than it will mammal populations.   [1]

_____

_____

Part D

Answer all questions in this part. [13]

Directions (73–85): For those questions that are multiple choice, record on the separate answer sheet the *number* of the choice that, of those given, best completes the statement or answers the question. For all other questions in this part, follow the directions given and record your answers in the spaces provided in this examination booklet.

73 A plant was discovered that contained a compound that was found to have potential medicinal value. However, the plant is rare, so it is important to see if a related plant might also produce the same compound. The chart shows some characteristics of the plant and four possible relatives.

Plant	Flower	Leaves	Amino Acid Sequence
Medicinal Plant	Red, 6 petals	simple, parallel veins	Ile–Ile–Try–Gly–Glu–Asp–Pro
A	Red, 9 petals	simple, parallel veins	Ile–Arg–Try–Gly-Glu-Asp–Ser
B	Yellow, 8 petals	compound, branched veins	Ile–Arg–Ala–Gly-Glu-Asp–Pro
C	Pink, 6 petals	simple, parallel veins	Ile–Ile–Try–Gly–Glu–Asp–Ser
D	Yellow, 6 petals	compound, parallel veins	Ile–Arg–Try–Gly–Glu–Asp–Pro

Note: The answer to question 73 should be recorded on your separate answer sheet.

Which plant in the chart would be selected as most similar to the medicinal plant?

(1) *A*
(2) *B*
(3) *C*
(4) *D*

Note: The answer to question 74 should be recorded on your separate answer sheet.

74 A drug company has discovered an endangered plant that produces a chemical that might be used to cure cancer. A first step in developing this cancer cure could be to

(1) preserve the habitat where the species is found
(2) introduce a new plant species that will share the habitat of the plant
(3) eliminate every species that eats this plant
(4) harvest all of the plants of this species and use them to treat cancer patients

Note: The answer to question 75 should be recorded on your separate answer sheet.

75 Students in a science class took their pulse rates before and after they ran in place for one minute. The class data showed that pulse rates increased with exercise. A graph of the data would look most like

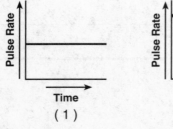
(1)

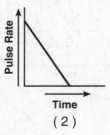
(2)

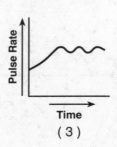
(3)

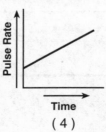
(4)

Base your answers to questions 76 and 77 on the information below and on your knowledge of biology.

Caretakers at a zoo are trying to determine which of two male tigers fathered the newest cub. They obtained DNA from the tiger cub, the mother tiger, and the two male tigers. The DNA was analyzed. The results of the analysis are shown below.

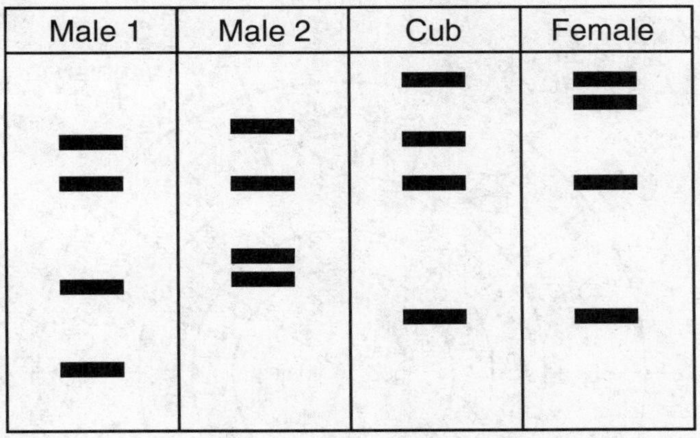

Male 1	Male 2	Cub	Female

Note: The answer to question 76 should be recorded on your separate answer sheet.

76 The technique used to separate the DNA for analysis is

(1) genetic engineering   (3) chromatography

(2) electrophoresis   (4) protein synthesis

77 Which male tiger is the father of the newborn cub? Support your answer. [1]

Male tiger: _____

_____

_____

78 Some roads are salted heavily in winter. Describe *one* way plants growing near these roads could be harmed by the salt. [1]

_____

_____

Base your answer to question 79 on the diagram below and on your knowledge of biology.

Variations in Beaks of Galapagos Islands Finches

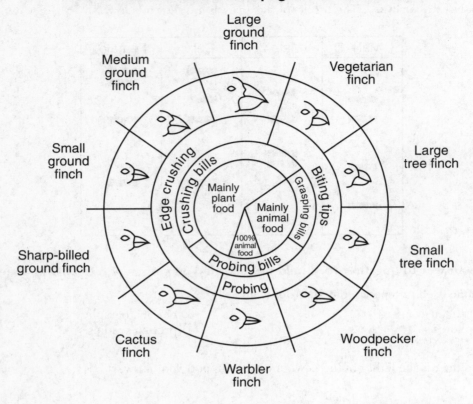

from: *Galapagos: A Natural History Guide*

79 Several populations of finches migrated to an island that had mostly large seeds with tough outer coverings. Identify a finch population that would most likely survive on the island. Support your answer.   [1]

_____

_____

80 The diagram below shows how a coverslip should be placed on a drop of pond water during the preparation of a wet mount.

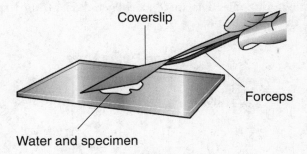

State *one* reason why this is the recommended procedure for placing a coverslip.   [1]

_____

_____

Base your answers to questions 81 through 83 on the information below and on your knowledge of biology.

There are two different species of finch that live on the same small island, species *A* and species *B*. Both species successfully feed and reproduce on the island. Species *A* nests in pine trees and eats large seeds. Species *B* nests in hollowed-out dead logs and eats small insects.

Note: The answer to question 81 should be recorded on your separate answer sheet.

81 Both bird species *A* and species *B* can most likely survive on the same small island because they
(1) use different resources and, therefore, they do not compete
(2) mate with each other, keeping both populations constant
(3) compete for food, but do not compete for shelter
(4) eat the same food, but feed at different times of the day

Note: The answer to question 82 should be recorded on your separate answer sheet.

82 The factor most often acting as a selecting agent for the survival of a species in a particular location is the
(1) strength of the organism
(2) new mutations within the individual
(3) speed of the organism
(4) environment they inhabit

83 A third species of finch, species *C*, migrates to the island. It nests in pine trees and eats small insects. Predict what most likely will happen to the populations of both species *A* and species *B* if species *C* successfully survives on the island. Support your answer.   [1]

_____

_____

Base your answers to question 84 on the information below and on your knowledge of biology.

Biology students conducted a preliminary survey to study the relationship between body height and resting pulse rate. The students collected data from 10 classmates and the results are shown in the graph below.

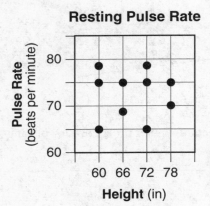

84 Is there a relationship between height and resting pulse rate? Support your answer.   [1]

_____

_____

85 The table below shows the number of individual molecules obtained when a DNA molecule from a bacterial species is broken down.

Molecules from Bacterial DNA

Molecule	Number
sugar	4.6 million
phosphate	4.6 million
adenine (A)	1.75 million
cytosine (C)	0.55 million
guanine (G)	0.55 million
thymine (T)	1.75 million

What data in the data table indicate that adenine pairs with thymine in a DNA molecule?   [1]

_____

_____

THE LIVING ENVIRONMENT
AUGUST 2015

Part	Maximum Score	Student's Score
A	30	
B-1	13	
B-2	12	
C	17	
D	13	

ANSWER SHEET

Student . . . .

Teacher . . . .

School . . . . Grade . . . .

Total Raw Score
(maximum Raw Score: 85)

Final Score
(from conversion chart)

Raters' Initials

Rater 1 . . . .   Rater 2 . . . .

Multiple Choice for Parts A, B–1, B–2, and D
Allow 1 credit for each correct response.

Part A

1	9	17	25 . . . .
2	10	18	26 . . . .
3	11	19	27 . . . .
4	12	20	28 . . . .
5	13	21	29 . . . .
6	14	22	30 . . . .
7	15	23	
8	16	24	

Part B–1

31	35	39	43 . . . .
32	36	40	
33	37	41	
34	38	42	

Part B–2

47	49	50 . . . .

Part D

73	75	81 . . . .
74	76	82 . . . .